Learn CAD with AutoSketch® for Windows™

Tom Boersma
Paul Moore

NRP
NEW RIDERS
PUBLISHING

New Riders Publishing, Carmel, Indiana

Learn CAD with AutoSketch for Windows

By Tom Boersma
Paul Moore

Published by:
New Riders Publishing
201 West 103rd Street
Indianapolis, IN 46290

Printed in the United States of America 1 2 3 4 5 6 7 8 9 0

Library of Congress Cataloging-in-Publication Data

```
Boersma, Tom, 1957-
     Learn CAD with AutoSketch for Windows / Tom Boersma, Paul
     Moore.
          p. cm.
     Includes index.
     ISBN 1-56205-161-X
     1. Computer graphics. 2. AutoSketch for Windows. 3. Com-
     puter-aided design. I. Moore, Paul, 1964- II. Title.
     T385.B64 1993                    006.6'869—dc20
     93-5436                          CIP
```

About the Authors

Tom Boersma learned CAD/CAM software applications while working as a tool-and-die maker and manufacturing engineer. His current position at Grand Rapids Community College involves business and industry training on leading CAD and CAM software packages. Boersma is co-author of *Inside AutoCAD Release 12* and *Inside AutoCAD for Windows*, available from New Riders Publishing. He has published magazine articles and worked as a consultant. Boersma has been an AutoSketch user since its first release, and has used AutoCAD since version 2.5.

Paul Moore is a graduate of the School of Architecture and Urban Planning at the University of Michigan. He currently uses Autodesk products as a computer-graphics consultant and is an instructor at Grand Rapids Community College.

Acknowledgments

New Riders Publishing expresses thanks to the following:

Kevin Coleman, for developing the project.

Gary Sobsczak, for his thorough technical review of the manuscript.

Nancy Sixsmith, for managing the project and steering it through the Production process.

Margaret Berson, Mary Ann Larguier, and Lisa Wagner, for their excellent and timely editing.

The Production Department of Prentice Hall Computer Publishing, for its expeditious handling and excellent layout of the book.

Trademark Acknowledgments

New Riders Publishing has made every attempt to supply trademark information about company names, products, and services mentioned in this book. Trademarks indicated below were derived from various sources. New Riders Publishing cannot attest to the accuracy of this information.

AutoCAD, AutoSketch, and AutoSketch for Windows are registered trademarks of Autodesk, Inc.

HP and LaserJet are registered trademarks of Hewlett-Packard Co.

IBM and OS/2 are registered trademarks of International Business Machines Corporation.

Macintosh is a registered trademark of Apple Computer, Incorporated.

Microsoft, MS-DOS, Windows, and Windows for Workgroups are registered trademarks of Microsoft Corporation.

UNIX is a registered trademark of Unix System Laboratories, Inc.

WordPerfect is a registered trademark of WordPerfect Corporation.

Trademarks of other products mentioned in this book are held by the companies producing them.

Warning and Disclaimer

This book is designed to provide information about the AutoSketch for Windows computer program. Every effort has been made to make this book as complete and as accurate as possible, but no warranty or fitness is implied.

The information is provided on an "as is" basis. The authors and New Riders Publishing shall have neither liability nor responsibility to any person or entity with respect to any loss or damages arising from the information contained in this book or from the use of the disks or programs that may accompany it.

Contents at a Glance

Contents

XX　　　　**Index**　　　　　　　　　　　　　**437**

Introduction

AutoSketch is a simple, powerful, computer-aided design (CAD) software package. Windows is a computer operating system that is gaining widespread popularity as the standard interface between the computer and the many software applications it supports. AutoSketch for Windows is an exciting CAD software application that combines the power and flexibility of CAD with the "user-friendliness" of Windows.

Learn CAD with AutoSketch for Windows (which includes a training version of AutoSketch for Windows) and a computer (to run the software) are all you need to learn computer-aided design.

The Goal of this Book

This book is intended to be a complete self-guided tour of computer-aided design. Because the only way to learn CAD is to actually work with the software, you should read most of the chapters while at the computer so that you can try out the tools and techniques as they are introduced.

Although you may feel that you are doing nothing but following a detailed set of instructions for the first few drawings, this procedure is the best way to actually experience CAD drafting. After your first several drawings have been completed, you will be ready to try some of your own simple drawings.

AutoSketch for Windows is an excellent tool for learning CAD. The main goal of *Learn CAD with AutoSketch for Windows* is for you to learn the general concepts of CAD so that you understand the process and the techniques. Because most CAD drafting packages share common tools and techniques, it will be easier for you to learn another specific CAD package once you master these CAD fundamentals.

About the AutoSketch Software Package

AutoSketch software is written and distributed by Autodesk, Inc., which is the leading worldwide producer of CAD software. Beginning in the early 1980s with AutoCAD, Autodesk now distributes a wide variety of CAD, multimedia, and educational software. AutoCAD has become the most popular CAD software in use today, and it has also grown to become a very large and complex software package.

AutoSketch was introduced when Autodesk recognized a need for a "light" CAD package. This package contained only the basic drawing and editing tools—those used most of the time on the more advanced software. (If you have ever used a software package such as a word processor or spreadsheet, you understand the concept of "using 20 percent of the commands 80 percent of the time.")

Another goal of this version of the CAD software was to ensure that the price and the learning curve would be a fraction of the full-featured CAD software applications.

AutoSketch met this criteria very well. Since its original DOS version, AutoSketch software has been enhanced with two major version updates. Separate versions have been written for Macintosh computers and for Windows. AutoSketch for Windows can exchange many types of data with other software packages through DXF files, text files, and the Windows Clipboard features.

Who Should Read This Book?

Learn CAD with AutoSketch for Windows is intended for a large cross-section of potential CAD users. Twenty years ago, CAD was a highly skilled discipline that required large amounts of training and practice. Even less than ten years ago, the idea of a complete CAD training book with software included seemed highly improbable. Today, CAD is becoming popular for a wide variety of applications, including the following:

- **Education.** *Learn CAD with AutoSketch for Windows*, with its bundled software, is an excellent educational resource. The complete book can be used as the basis for an introductory CAD class. Portions of the book can be integrated into other curricula that require some knowledge of CAD drafting. For less than the price of an average college textbook, a student can also legally obtain the software to use on a personal computer outside the classroom.

- **Professional applications.** For those who work with technical drawings or illustrations, *Learn CAD with AutoSketch for Windows* is a useful resource for learning CAD drafting and enabling experimentation with some applications. This type of book is especially helpful when time or budget constraints do not allow for formal CAD training classes. For the experienced CAD user, this book can be used as an accelerated training manual for AutoSketch for Windows.

- **Home use.** Home-computer users want the capability of industrial software at a fraction of the cost of software and training. *Learn CAD with AutoSketch for Windows* (and its included software) gives you an excellent way to begin using CAD in a home or small-business setting with a minimal cost investment.

How This Book Is Organized

Learn CAD with AutoSketch for Windows contains four major sections, and each part contains several chapters. Depending on your knowledge of Windows, CAD, and general drafting procedures, you may want to spend more or less time in certain areas of the book. Because the chapters build on each other in the use of the tools, the latter parts can be difficult if you have not learned the concepts presented in the earlier chapters.

Whenever possible, new terms are explained when they are first used. Although *Learn CAD with AutoSketch for Windows* follows standard mechanical-drafting procedures, you can disregard them if you understand the format of the drawings you want to create.

Part One: Getting Started

Part One introduces you to AutoSketch for Windows and gets you started working with the program.

Chapter 1, "A Sneak Preview of AutoSketch for Windows," emphasizes a hands-on approach to learning CAD. This chapter instructs you to load the software and immediately attempt your first drawing. Follow the instructions to create the drawing with the step-by-step illustrations.

Chapter 2, "Learning About CAD," explains many basic mechanical drawing terms and procedures. The chapter then outlines the history of CAD, and notes the similarities and differences between CAD and manual drafting.

Chapter 3, "Understanding Your Personal Computer," is a brief overview of computer hardware and CAD drafting equipment. The second half of the chapter deals with the Windows operating system. Although entire books are written on this subject alone, this information—along with some exploration of Windows on your own—should be adequate to proceed with the exercises in this book.

Part Two: Learning To Use AutoSketch for Windows

Part Two explains all the basic drawing and editing tools needed to create a drawing.

Chapter 4, "Beginning Your Drawing," explains the layout of the AutoSketch for Windows graphics screen. The drawing tutorial shows you how to use the basic tools to create a drawing.

Chapter 5, "Creating a Production Drawing," describes the steps involved in creating a complete mechanical drawing. CAD standards such as coordinate systems, units, layers, and object-snap tools are covered in this chapter.

Chapter 6, "Completing Your Drawing," explains how to finish your drawing by adding dimensions and notes. The concept of a drawing database that contains useful information about the entities is also explained, and the procedure to print the drawing is discussed.

Part Three: Advanced CAD Drafting Techniques

Part Three covers a variety of topics relating to productivity tools and advanced CAD drafting techniques.

Chapter 7, "Creating and Inserting," illustrates the use of *parts*, which are symbols or groups of entities that have been saved as files with specific names.

Chapter 8, "Using Pattern Fills, Polylines, Arrays, and Splines," demonstrates these advanced drawing techniques.

Chapter 9, "Creating Special Types of Drawings," shows you how to use the tools and techniques you have learned to draw special types of technical drawings.

Chapter 10, "Using AutoSketch with Other Applications," describes ways to use DXF and text files to share data with other applications. All the Windows tools, such as Copy and Paste, are also demonstrated, as entities are saved to the Windows Clipboard and then brought into other Windows programs.

Chapter 11, "Practicing with AutoSketch," provides two more drawing tutorials for you to work through. You are guided, step-by-step, through a three-view mechanical drawing and an architectural drawing.

Chapter 12 "Using Macros To Enhance AutoSketch Performance," introduces the macro-language capability of AutoSketch.

Part Four: Command Reference

Although all the AutoSketch tools or commands have been explained in the book, especially in the context of using them in the drawing tutorials, this chapter is an alphabetical list of these tools or commands.

About the AutoSketch Software Included with This Book

The disk in the back of this book contains a special training version of AutoSketch for Windows. It also contains drawing files for use with the book's exercises.

This training version of AutoSketch does not have all the features of the full commercial version of AutoSketch. If you want to purchase the complete version of AutoSketch for Windows, contact Autodesk Retail Products (1-800-228-3601).

Limitations of the Demo Training Version

The demo version of AutoSketch for Windows is limited, as follows:

- **Drawings are limited**. In this version, drawings are limited to 120 entities.

  When the maximum number of objects is reached, AutoSketch displays this alert message:

  ```
  You have reached the maximum drawing size for this
  demo version
  ```

  If the drawing has not been saved, an emergency save dialog box enables you to save your drawing. To add new objects to a drawing with 120 objects, you must erase some existing objects to lower the object count below 120.

- **File compatibility is limited.** The drawings you create with the training demo version of AutoSketch cannot be opened in other versions of AutoSketch. The option of saving the drawing to the DOS version of AutoSketch is not available.

- **Tools are limited.** The Import DXF, Export DXF, Game, Copy Metafile, Copy Objects, Paste Objects, and Show Clipboard tools are not available. If you choose one of these commands, this message appears:

  ```
  This feature is not available in this AutoSketch
  demo version
  ```

The following text appears on all drawings printed with the training version of AutoSketch:

```
Drawn with the training demo version of AutoSketch
for Windows
```

Conventions Used in This Book

Considerable time and effort has been spent on making this book easy to follow and understand. As much as possible, the wording and terminology follow the conventions used in the documentation for AutoSketch and in the Windows reference manual. The format also closely follows that of other New Riders Publishing books on similar CAD topics.

The contents of the chapters are presented in two basic formats. Much of the book is written in regular paragraph form, explaining concepts and ideas. Also included in most of the chapters are special drawing tutorials that specifically instruct you to perform operations on the computer. These chapters are best understood if you read them while you work at the computer.

AutoSketch commands are executed by selecting them with a pointing device from the menu or by using the function keys to specify a command. Although the tutorials in this book reference the menu selections, you can also use the function keys.

When you are instructed to *choose* a menu item, you must place the cursor over that item and click with the left button. If the word on the menu contains an underlined letter, this is referred to as a *hot key*, which is often used in Windows applications as a *shortcut key*. It is accessed by holding down the Alt key while typing that letter.

AutoSketch commands can be listed in a menu according to their names or represented by an *icon* (small picture). AutoSketch conventions refer to these groups of commands as *toolboxes*; the individual commands are known as *tools*.

Using the Tutorials

It is important to closely follow the drawing tutorials in the book so that your drawing resembles the one illustrated in the book. You may not always agree with the drawing techniques presented in the book, but they are designed to show you several different methods of using a tool. Figure I.1 shows a short sample illustration.

As many figures as possible are included to show the results of each step of the drawing tutorial. When appropriate, bubbles are used with arrows to show special locations that must be selected or designated in a drawing exercise.

The following sample exercise shows the format of the drawing tutorials in this book:

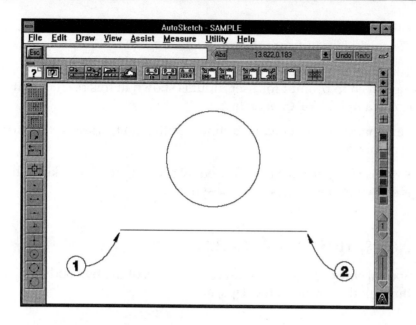

Figure I.1:
A sample
exercise
illustration.

A Sample Exercise

Begin a new drawing in AutoSketch and name it Sample.

Choose **D**raw, *then the Line tool*	Activates the Line tool
`Line Enter point:` *Pick near* ① *(see fig.I.1)*	Specifies the start point
`To point:` *Pick near* ②	Specifies the endpoint
Choose the Circle tool	
`Circle Center point:` **7,6** ↵	Shows the center point
`Point on circle:` **9,6** ↵	Shows the radius point

Except for short sentences that explain a concept, tutorials are
written in a two-column format. The left column tells you what to
do; the right column briefly explains the results of each action.

9

All instructions that tell you to perform an action (for example, *Choose the Line tool*), are shown in *italics*.

Text that AutoSketch displays in the prompt box near the top of the screen to prompt for user input is shown in this `special font` (for example, `Line Enter point`).

Text that must be typed in is shown in this `bold, special font` (for example, `9,6`).

Keyboard input must be followed by pressing the Enter key. This is shown in the exercises as a ↵ symbol.

Notes, Tips, and Warnings

Special emphasis is placed on certain parts of the text body through the use of Notes, Tips, and Warnings.

A Note contains additional information that clarifies or amplifies the topic under discussion.

A Tip provides you with "extra" information or suggestions that may apply to a certain situation. Although tips are not part of the official software documentation, they are based on the authors' experiences with using the software.

A Warning serves as a caution. It points to the careful use of a procedure or to an event that can cause a loss of data or work.

New Riders Publishing

The staff of New Riders Publishing is committed to bringing you the very best in computer reference material. Each New Riders book is the result of months of work by authors and staff, who research and refine the information contained within its covers.

As part of this commitment to you, the NRP reader, New Riders invites your input. Please let us know if you enjoy this book, if you have trouble with the information and examples presented, or if you have a suggestion for the next edition.

Please note, however, that the New Riders staff cannot serve as a technical resource for AutoSketch for Windows questions, including hardware- or software-related problems. Refer to the documentation that accompanies your AutoSketch for Windows package for help with specific problems.

If you have a question or comment about any New Riders book, please write to NRP at the following address. We will respond to as many readers as we can. Your name, address, or phone number will never become part of a mailing list or be used for any other purpose than to help us continue to bring you the best books possible.

New Riders Publishing
Paramount Publishing
Attn: Associate Publisher
201 W. 103rd Street
Indianapolis, IN 46290

If you prefer, you can FAX New Riders Publishing at the following number:

(317) 581-4670

We welcome your electronic mail to our CompuServe ID:

70031,2231

Thank you for selecting *Learn CAD with AutoSketch for Windows*!

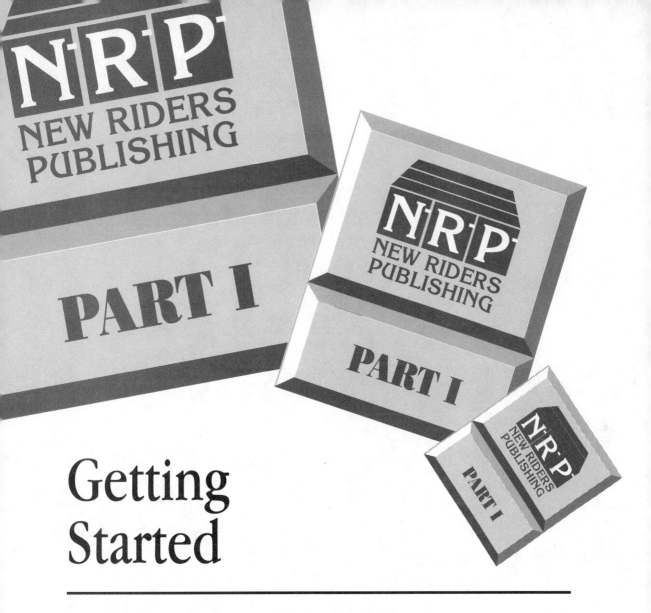

Getting Started

A Sneak Preview of AutoSketch for Windows
Learning About CAD
Understanding Your Personal Computer

A Sneak Preview
of AutoSketch for
Windows

T he best way to be introduced to computer-aided design
(CAD) is to begin using the software. AutoSketch for Windows is
the software you use with this book. Although each CAD software
package has its own unique features, most of these packages use
the same general procedures to create a drawing.

This chapter begins with the software-installation procedure, and
it ends by having you experiment with your first AutoSketch for
Windows drawing. If you have previous experience installing
software on a computer, especially in the Windows environment,
you will find the installation quite simple. If you have had very
little experience with computer software, do not panic—the
installation should still work well for you. Chapters 2 and 3
explain many of the terms and concepts from this chapter in
greater detail.

Installing the Software

When you purchased this book, you received a disk containing all of the files referenced in this book. The files include:

- A limited edition of AutoSketch for Windows software

- An installation routine

- Sample files for use with this book's exercises

Make a backup copy of these disks before starting the installation procedure.

 For detailed instructions on copying disks, refer to your DOS or Windows manual (or see Chapter 3 for more information on the Windows File Manager).

Checking the Hardware and Software for Minimum Requirements

Computer software has limitations regarding the types of computer hardware and operating-system software with which it is compatible. AutoSketch for Windows is no exception. Common practice is to specify the minimum requirements to run the software. As computer hardware becomes more powerful, software is written to take advantage of the additional power. This may exclude the software from running on the earlier computer platforms or operating systems.

 Whenever you attempt to upgrade software, first determine whether your existing computer hardware will fully support the upgrade.

The minimum requirements to run AutoSketch for Windows are as follows:

- An IBM or true compatible computer, based on a 386SX or greater CPU. The type of computer includes a 386- or 486-based computer, but excludes the 286 class of computers. A math co-processor chip is not required, but it is recommended for increased performance.

- A minimum of 2M (megabytes) of RAM (random-access memory). The recommended amount of RAM is 4M.

- A hard disk, containing at least 4M of free disk space. An additional 1M is necessary for the drawings created in this book.

- A graphics adaptor and monitor with VGA (video graphics array) or better resolution.

- A Windows-compatible mouse or pointing device.

- DOS version 3.3 or later.

- Microsoft Windows 3.0 or later.

The Windows software should be installed on your computer and configured for the proper input and output devices before you try to load AutoSketch for Windows.

Booting Up Your Computer

Begin the installation process by turning on your computer. This is also known as *booting* the computer, which is the process of letting the computer perform the internal system and memory checks, and then prompting you to enter information. Your computer is probably configured to start up in one of the following three ways:

- If your computer displays the DOS prompt (shown as a >), you can enter any valid DOS command.

- If your computer has a special opening menu, you can select a certain task or software application.

- If your computer is configured to start up and load the Windows software, you see Window's Program Manager and application groups (see fig. 1.1).

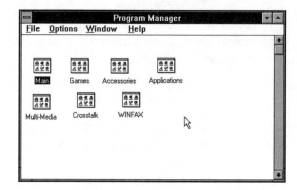

Figure 1.1:

The Windows Program Manager.

Running Windows

AutoSketch for Windows is normally loaded and run from within the Windows operating environment. This means that Windows must be running before you go any further in this chapter.

If Windows has been properly installed on your computer, you can enter **WIN** at the DOS prompt to start up the Windows software.

Windows should also be properly configured for the peripherals you will use with AutoSketch for Windows. These peripherals can include a pointing device, VGA-graphics compatibility, and an output device such as a printer.

If Windows does not run properly, consult your *Microsoft Windows Reference Manual*, or a book such as *Inside Windows 3.1* or *Maximizing Windows 3.1*, available from New Riders Publishing.

18

Loading AutoSketch for Windows

You are now ready to load the AutoSketch for Windows software and the other sample files used in this book. The file named SETUP.EXE creates the necessary directories on your hard disk drive and copies the appropriate files into them. The \WSKDEMO\LC subdirectory contains the drawing and sample files for this book. The directory structure is as follows:

```
\ (Root directory)
        \WSKETCH
                \PARTS
                \SUPPORT
                \TOOLBOX
        \LAW
```

The following exercise shows you how to load the AutoSketch for Windows software. Be sure that you have Windows running and that Program Manager is visible on your screen. If you are using a floppy disk drive other than A:, substitute that drive letter where appropriate.

Installing AutoSketch for Windows

Start up Windows, and place AutoSketch disk #1 in your floppy disk drive.

Double-click on the Main icon	Opens the Main Group
Double-click on the File Manager icon	Opens the File Manager
Click on the A: drive icon near ① *(see fig. 1.2)*	Reads the disk and displays its files
Double-click on the SETUP.EXE *file shown near* ②	

The installation program creates the directories, copies the files into the proper location, and creates the AutoSketch application group in Windows, as shown in figure 1.3.

When installation is complete, choose **F**ile, *then* E**x**it	Leaves the File Manager

---

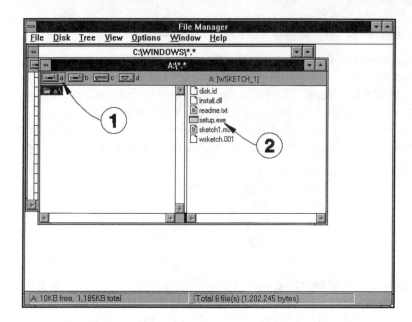

Figure 1.2:
The File Manager window.

Figure 1.3:
The Windows AutoSketch application group, with the AutoSketch icon.

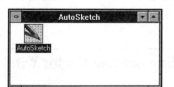

An alternate way to load the software involves choosing the **R**un option from the **F**ile menu in the Program Manager.

Enter **A:SETUP** in the Command Line text box, and the installation proceeds. It is assumed that disk #1 is in the A: drive—otherwise, substitute the letter of your current drive.

Now that AutoSketch has been successfully installed, you are probably anxious to run it. One of the helpful features of application software that run in the Windows environment is that there is usually no need to configure the software. It should be ready to run at this point. The rest of this chapter shows you how to begin working in AutoSketch for Windows.

Drawing with AutoSketch for Windows

AutoSketch for Windows can be run by double-clicking on the AutoSketch icon, shown in figure 1.3. The following exercise shows you how to run AutoSketch from the Windows Program Manager.

Starting AutoSketch

Double-click on the AutoSketch Program Group icon

Opens the AutoSketch Program Group window

Double-click on the AutoSketch icon

Starts AutoSketch

The AutoSketch emblem appears briefly while the software is loading.

Welcome to AutoSketch for Windows! Move your pointing device to see if it is functioning properly. Your graphics window should appear, similar to the one shown in figure 1.4, with the small cursor arrow following the movement of your pointing device.

Becoming Familiar with the Graphics Window

The AutoSketch graphics window may not look very user-friendly at first glance. Part of what you are seeing is a very standard *window*, which all application software running in the Windows environment must conform to. If you are familiar with other Windows applications, you will recognize several common features of AutoSketch for Windows. If you are not familiar with Windows, concentrate on the computer-aided design capabilities of the software for now.

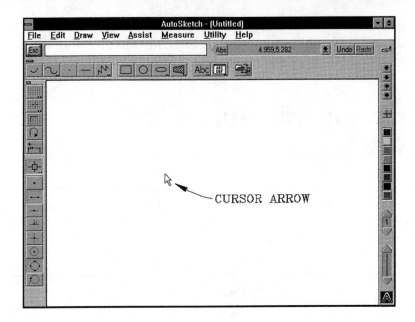

Figure 1.4:

The AutoSketch graphics window and the cursor arrow.

Chapter 3 explains the Windows features in greater detail.

Begin your exploration of AutoSketch for Windows by browsing around the graphics window and experimenting with the various tools and accessories that are available to you. Figure 1.5 identifies the main areas of the graphics window.

Just as a drafter must have a drafting table organized with all appropriate tools within reach, you need a variety of CAD drawing tools surrounding your drawing area. Different draftspersons may prefer a variety of work-area layouts.

Chapter 12 describes how the AutoSketch work area can be arranged to fit your specific needs.

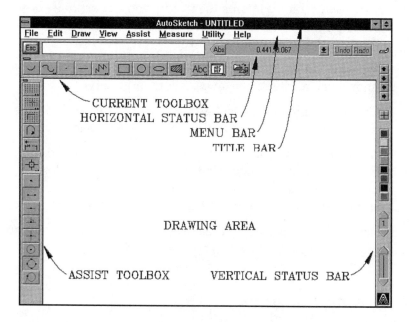

Figure 1.5:

The main parts of the AutoSketch graphics window.

The illustrations in this book are based on the graphics window layout you see when you first run AutoSketch. The following parts of the graphics window will assist you in your work:

- **Drawing Area.** The center portion of the graphics window is the *drawing area,* which is where the graphic entities are drawn and edited. The drawing area's size can vary from .001" in width to 1,000 miles or more, depending on the way your viewing parameters are set. If the graphics window is resized, the drawing area adjusts accordingly.

- **Title Bar.** At the top of the AutoSketch graphics window is the *title bar,* which shows the name of the current drawing. If the drawing has not been assigned a name, the display indicates that the current drawing has not yet been named. This area is sometimes used to display help messages, as explained in Chapter 4.

- **Menu Bar.** Directly under the title bar is the *menu bar*, which enables you to select a particular group of tools.

- **Horizontal Status Bar.** Under the menu bar is the *horizontal status bar*, which contains the prompt box, coordinate box, and several other buttons. (These tools and settings are further explained in Chapter 4.)

- **Vertical Status Bar.** The *vertical status bar* shows other settings, such as the active layer, color, and linetype.

- **Current Toolbox.** The last group of tools selected from the menu bar are displayed in the *correct toolbox* as icons.

- **Assist Toolbox.** The *assist toolbox* is used so frequently during drawing sessions that it is usually displayed at all times for fast access of the tools. In figure 1.5, you see the assist toolbox along the left side of the drawing area.

Now that you have a general idea of the graphics-window layout, it is time to start using the software to draw a picture.

Accessing the Tools

All AutoSketch functions that are used for drawing, editing, measuring, and so on are called *tools*. These tools are arranged in the eight *toolboxes* listed on the menu bar. When a toolbox is opened, the tools are displayed in the current toolbox area.

 AutoSketch can display tools as icons or as tool names. Unless you have changed the toolbox-display features, the File and Help toolboxes are shown as Windows-style pull-down menus with tool names, and the rest of the toolboxes display as icons. Later, you will learn how to change the display of toolboxes and pull-down menus.

There are three ways to activate an AutoSketch tool:

- Click on the toolbox name on the menu bar, then click on the tool name in the current toolbox.

- Open the toolbox, and choose a tool by using its hot key. A *hot key* is shown in this book as a special character that is underlined on the screen (as in the File menu). Hold the Alt key down while typing hot keys. Although hot keys always appear on the toolboxes, only choose a tool in a pull-down menu.

- Use function keys to activate many of the common tools. A list of the function keys and the tools they access is found in the Command Reference.

Using the AutoSketch Tools To Draw

You can now try CAD drafting by using AutoSketch for Windows. In this example, the drawing is a sketch of a general layout of a campground. Do not be concerned about dimensions or scale factors. Try to use a little imagination—your sketch might even look better than the one shown in figure 1.6.

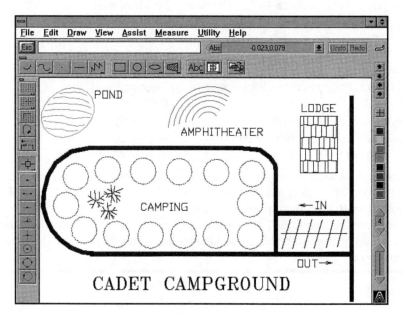

Figure 1.6:

The completed campground sketch.

A short explanation of each part of the drawing is followed by step-by-step instructions for completing the sketch. This drawing is only an exercise that enables you to experiment with the software. Detailed instructions for using tools and creating scaled drawings come in later chapters.

To proceed with the following exercise, you should already have AutoSketch running from the last exercise. If not, double-click on the AutoSketch icon in Windows to run the program.

The first step is to draw in the roads, as shown in figure 1.7. The Polyline tool works well because it can draw connected lines with a specified width, and then shows them filled in as a wide line.

Drawing the Roads with Polylines

Choose the **D**raw *menu, then double-click on the Polyline tool*	Activates the Polyline tool, and displays the current polyline settings
Type **.15** *in the polyline* Width *text box, and choose* OK	Specifies width of polyline
`Polyline First point:` *Pick a point near* ① *(see fig. 1.7)*	Specifies start point of the polyline
`To Point:` *Pick twice near* ②	Locates next point and ends polyline
`Polyline First point:` *Pick a point near* ③	Begins second polyline
`To point:` *Pick twice near* ④	Ends polyline
Polyline First point: *Pick a point near* ⑤, *then* ④	Begins loop around campground

Continue picking points all the way around the loop until you reach the main road at ⑥. Because these are straight-line segments, pick the points closer together on the curves. Be sure to pick the last point twice to terminate the polyline. If you are not happy with your polyline, click on the Undo button in the horizontal status line, then click on the Polyline tool and try again.

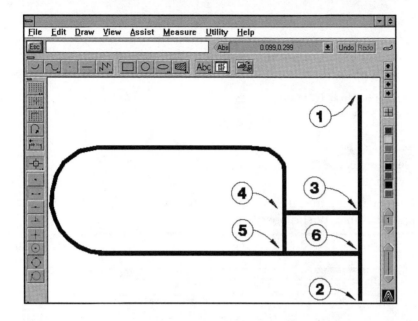

Figure 1.7:
Polylines used to draw the roads.

Most of the drawing commands enable you to pick points on the screen to indicate entity locations and sizes. In Chapter 4, you learn to control point locations with coordinates.

In the following exercise, you use the Line tool, which is one of the most commonly used entities in CAD. Use the Line tool to draw in some parking spaces near the entrance, as shown in figure 1.8. First, pick start and endpoints for the line.

Become a little more creative and draw a few trees over in the camping area (see fig. 1.9). Clicking on the green color button on the vertical status bar changes your current color to green before you start to draw the trees.

Using the Line Tool To Draw the Parking Spaces and Trees

From the **D**raw *toolbox, choose the Line tool*

Activates the Line tool

`Line Enter point:` *Pick near* ① *(see fig 1.8), then near* ②

Draws the first line

continues

Line Enter point: *Pick near* ③, *then near* ④	Draws the second line

Continue using the Line tool to draw in the rest of the lines for the parking places.

Click on the green color button in the vertical status bar near ① *(see fig. 1.9)*	Changes current color to green

Choose the Line tool

Line Enter point: *Pick near* ②, *then near* ③	

Continue using the Line tool to draw the rest of the tree, along with a few other trees or shrubbery.

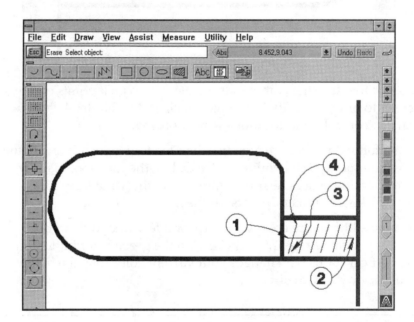

Figure 1.8:

Creating the parking spaces.

By now, you see how AutoSketch works. The drawing toolbox shows the available drawing tools. Choose the one you want to use, and follow the prompt in the text box of the horizontal status bar.

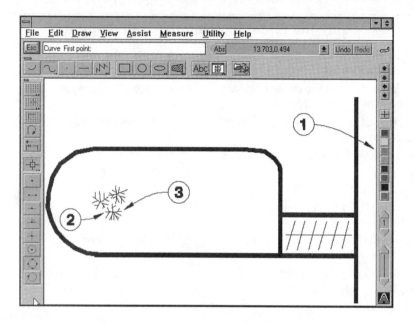

Figure 1.9:
Adding the trees.

When you have completed a graphic entity, the tool usually remains active, assuming you want to continue using that tool. If you choose a different drawing tool, it replaces the current tool.

The Circle tool will be used to show the campsites. A dashed linetype indicates that these are general locations only. Use the red color for the circles to help them stand out.

After drawing the first circle by picking a center point and a point on the circle, use the Multi-copy tool from the Edit toolbox to quickly place the remaining circles in position.

 As you work through the exercises, remember to keep your eye on the prompt box in the horizontal status bar. This box shows the current AutoSketch tool, and prompts you to pick points or enter information that AutoSketch needs.

29

Using the Circle Tool and the Multi-copy Tool

Click on the red color button in the vertical status bar	Changes the color to red
Click on the up arrow on the linetype control near ① *(see fig. 1.10)*	Changes the linetype
From the **D**raw *toolbox, choose the Circle tool*	Activates the Circle tool
`Circle Center point:` *Pick near* ②	Shows the center and edge of circle
`Point on circle:` *Pick near* ③	
Choose the **E**dit *menu, then the Multi-copy tool*	
`Multiple Copy Select object:` *Select the edge of the circle with the cursor*	Specifies the entity to copy
`From point:` *Pick a point near* ②	Locates the base point
`To point:` *Pick a point near* ④, *then near* ⑤	Shows the new locations

Continue to pick points to place another circle until all campsites have been located.

You begin to see the advantage of using CAD for repetitive features that only have to be drawn once and then are copied into place.

The next step is to draw the pond. After changing the color to light blue and the linetype back to solid, use the Ellipse drawing tool to show the pond. Then use the Curve drawing tool to show some ripples on the pond. AutoSketch draws a curve by fitting a *spline* (variable curve) between a series of points.

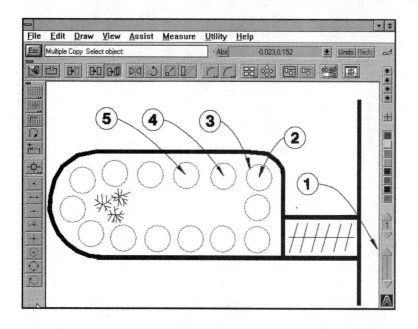

Figure 1.10:
The completed campsites.

Drawing the Pond with the Ellipse and Curve tools

Click on the light blue color button on the vertical status bar to change the current color, and click on the down arrow on the linetype control to change back to a solid linetype.

Choose **D**raw, *then the Ellipse tool*

`Ellipse Center of Ellipse:` *Pick near* ① *(see fig 1.11)* — Specifies the center of the ellipse

`Axis endpoint:` *Pick near* ② — Shows the axis endpoint

`Other axis distance:` *Pick near* ③ — Shows the second axis endpoint

Choose the Curve *tool* — Begins the curve

`Curve First point:` *Pick near* ④

Pick three or four more points along the curve, picking the last point twice to end the curve. The curve appears as straight-line segments until the last point is picked twice. Continue using the Curve tool to draw several more curves across the pond.

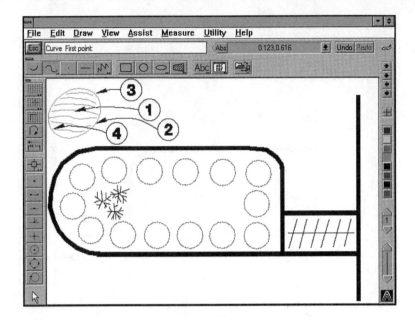

Figure 1.11:
Drawing the
pond.

Drawing an ellipse is as easy as picking the center point and the ends of the two axes.

Curves are explained in detail in Chapter 8.

Continue your campground drawing by using the Arc tool to show an outdoor amphitheater. The Arc tool requires three points: the start point of the arc, a second point on the arc, and the end-point of the arc. The following exercise shows you how to use the Arc tool.

Using the Arc Tool

Begin by choosing a color of your choice from the vertical status bar for the amphitheater.

Choose **D**raw, *then the Arc tool*   Activates the Arc tool

32

Arc Start point: *Pick near* ①   Specifies the start
(see fig 1.12)   point

Point on arc: *Pick near* ②   Specifies a second
                                        point on the arc

End point: *Pick near* ③   Specifies the
                                        endpoint

Draw several more arcs until you have a suitable amphitheater drawn.

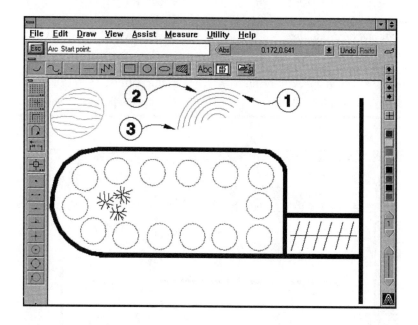

Figure 1.12:
The amphi-
theater, drawn
with arcs.

Your drawing is really starting to take shape. It is surprising how
much you can accomplish with the small number of drawing tools
available.

Two more tools are used to create the lodge. The Box tool draws
the rectangular shape; the Pattern tool enables you to select a fill
pattern to show the roof material. For the rest of this drawing, feel
free to choose whatever colors you wish to use.

Drawing the Lodge

Choose **D**raw, *then the Box tool*	Activates the Box tool
`Box first corner:` *Pick near* ① *(see fig. 1.13)*	Identifies the first corner of the box
`Second corner:` *Pick near* ③	Shows the other corner
Double-click on the Pattern Fill *tool*	Shows the dialog box for the pattern settings
Click on the AR-RSHKE *pattern*	Selects the pattern
Double-click in the Scale *text box and type* `.03`, *then click on the* OK *button*	Enables the scale to be specified
Pick the corner near ①, *then pick near* ②, ③, ④, *and pick* ① *again*	Shows the perimeter of the pattern
Click on **A**ccept *in the dialog box*	Accepts the pattern as shown

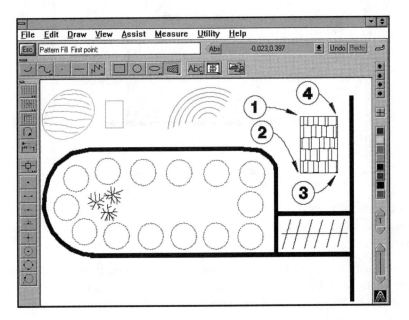

Figure 1.13:
Drawing the
lodge.

Now the drawing is complete, except for the text. AutoSketch has
a very easy-to-use Quick Text tool for placing text on your drawing. Many options are also available for text enhancement. After

placing the text labels on your drawing, use the Leader tool for the in and out labels, then finally change the text font and size for the drawing name.

Completing Your Drawing with Text

Choose **D***raw, then the* Quick Text *tool*

`Quick text Enter point:` *Pick near* ① *(see fig. 1.14)*

Indicates the text location

`Enter text:` **POND** ø

Repeat this sequence to label the AMPHITHEATER, LODGE, and CAMPING areas.

Choose **M***easure, then the* Leader *tool*   Activates the Leader tool

`Leader Start point:` *Pick near* ②   Shows the start and end of leader

`To point:` *Pick twice near* ③
Type **IN** *, then choose* **OK**   Adds text to the leader

Create another leader for the OUT arrow by repeating the same steps.

Choose **D***raw, then the* Quick Text *tool*   Opens the text settings dialog box

Choose the RomanT *font, then double-click on the* Height *text box, type* **.5,** *and choose* **OK**

Selects the ROMANT font with a .5 height

`Quick Text Enter point:` *Pick near the start of the text (*④*), and type* **CADET CAMPGROUND** ø

Congratulations! You have completed your first CAD drawing using AutoSketch! If this sketch is not the type of drawing you intend to use AutoSketch for, or if you do not completely understand all of the tools used in this exercise, don't worry. The rest of this book will fully explain all the techniques and tools you need to fully utilize this software.

You may want to save the drawing and print it out on the printer or plotter with which your Windows software is currently configured. The following exercise shows you how.

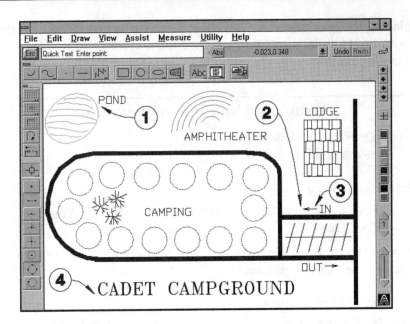

Figure 1.14:
The completed drawing with text.

If the attempt to output your drawing is not successful, make sure that your Windows software is properly configured for your output device. Chapter 6 explains the AutoSketch printing settings and procedures.

Saving and Printing Your Drawing

Choose the **File** *menu, then* **Save**, *enter* **CAD-CAMP** ↵ *in the text box*	Saves the drawing as CAD-CAMP.SKD
Choose **Print** *from the* **File** *menu*	Sends the drawing to the printer
Choose Ex**it** *from the* **File** *menu*	Closes the AutoSketch window

Depending on the type of output device you have, the drawing may take a few minutes to print.

Summary

This chapter introduced you to CAD drafting and the AutoSketch CAD software. You began by booting up your computer, running Windows, and making sure that your computer was ready to run AutoSketch. The software was loaded by selecting the SETUP file from the Windows File Manager. After a brief explanation of how the software is organized on your hard drive, you were ready to begin drawing with it.

If you have run other Windows applications, the AutoSketch graphics window probably looked somewhat familiar. You need to understand the organization of the various tools and menu areas in the graphics window. Finally, a short drawing exercise introduced you to the capabilities of the software.

Chapters 2 and 3 explain more of the concepts behind CAD drafting standards, personal computer hardware and software, and the Windows operating environment. Turn to Chapter 2 to learn more of the basic concepts of technical drawings, as well as the relationship between manual drafting and CAD.

Learning About CAD

Learning about CAD requires that you have a basic understanding of a *drawing*, which is a graphical representation of a real or imagined object. Drawings actually preceded written communication, and represent a very important form of communication. Two primary types of drawings exist: technical and artistic. Although AutoSketch can be used for both, this book focuses on technical drawings.

Artistic drawings can be created only with creative and artistic talents. *Technical* drawings, on the other hand, can be created by anyone who takes the time to learn the proper procedures and follow rules that conform to industry standards. Some CAD software is now capable of *rendering*, which requires adding artistic features to technical drawings to make them appear more realistic. (These capabilities are beyond the scope of this book.)

Your comfort level with the concepts presented in Chapter 1 probably related to your level of experience in using personal computers and CAD software. Your comfort level with the rest of the drawing tutorials in this book will depend on how well you understand the meaning of the lines, arcs, and other graphic entities that represent the drawing.

This chapter provides a brief overview of the basic parts of a CAD drawing. Because the introduction of CAD as a drafting tool has not changed basic drawing and sketching conventions, the first part of the chapter emphasizes the similarities between manual drafting and CAD. The second part of Chapter 2 points out some of the differences between artistic and technical drawings.

Observing Standard Drafting Conventions

One of the first things a student learns in a technical writing class is how to properly format documents such as business letters, memoranda, resumes, and so on. In a technical drafting class, students must begin by learning standard drafting formats and layouts, which make drawings more uniform and easier to interpret.

Perhaps you are already an experienced architect or mechanical drafter. Or maybe you plan to use AutoSketch for graphics in desktop publishing or technical illustrating. You may already understand exactly how your finished product should appear. Some industries or disciplines have unique drawing formats that are generally accepted as standards for that type of drawing.

National and international agencies, such as ANSI (American National Standards Institute) and ISO (International Standards Organization), have spelled out many specific drawing-format requirements. These agencies are typical of many trade associations that promote standards within the industry. Many CAD systems have tried to conform to these standards in areas such as dimensioning, tolerancing, and standard view layout.

Identifying Types of Technical Drawings

Most technical drawings convey graphic information that shows the size, shape, and features of a particular object. This object falls into one of the following classifications:

- **Architecture.** Buildings must be shown in the plan and elevation views, as well as at different scale factors to show certain levels of detail.

- **Civil engineering.** Maps and plots of land must be drawn to show lot lines, utilities, roads, and other features that are included in surveys. Contour lines are also important to represent different elevations.

- **Mechanical design.** An important part of any new product-development cycle is to first sketch the part, then create full working drawings to assist in manufacturing the part.

- **Plant layout and interior design.** Placement of industrial equipment, office furnishings, landscaping, and many other items are first done on paper to evaluate alternatives.

- **Electrical schematics.** Everything from printed circuit boards to home and automotive electrical diagrams must be drawn in a technical format. In some cases, these schematics are not drawn to scale, but emphasize the labeling of the components and the relationships between them.

- **Technical illustations.** Many newsletters and technical bulletins require graphics to help convey information.

Components of a Typical Drawing

When creating a technical drawing, you must have a general idea of what needs to be done and what steps are required to complete the project. Figure 2.1 shows a typical drawing with features that are used in many drawing applications.

The following sections describe these drawing components in detail.

Border

Most drawings have a *border* that provides a margin, between the edge of the paper and the edge of the drawing itself, between .5" and 1.0". A border makes the drawing look cleaner, and allows for the fact that it is difficult to draw manually or on a plotter or printer right up to the edge of the paper.

With CAD drafting, it is helpful to have a border to keep the drawing entities within the size of the paper. A border is often a good place to start when creating a drawing. Standard border sizes can be stored and recalled on a CAD system, in the way that different sizes of drawing sheets are available for manual drawings.

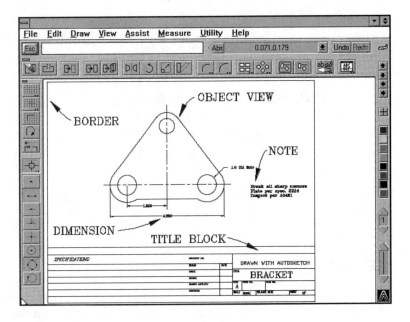

Figure 2.1:
Components of a typical drawing.

Title Block

The *title block*, a standard part of most technical drawings, contains verbal specifications of the drawing. Many companies have developed standard title blocks that are pasted or pre-printed on all of their drawing sheets. They can also be easily recalled on a CAD system. The following information can usually be found in a title block:

- Drawing title or part name
- Dates of the original drawing and revisions
- Names of the draftspersons involved in the project
- Customer name and project number
- Sheet and detail numbers
- Additional information about the materials used, standard tolerances, and manufacturing methods

Notes

Some technical drawings require text in the form of *notes* and special instructions. AutoSketch has a convenient text editor to create and edit notes; it also has the capability to import notes and text strings from word processors. This capability makes the often tedious job of adding annotations to drawings very fast and efficient.

Object

The center of attention in most technical drawings is the *object* itself, which is centrally placed within the borders of the drawing and is often drawn to a specific scale factor. Figure 2.1 shows the object from the front side only; showing the object from several sides is sometimes required to fully describe the part.

Dimensions

Dimensioning fully describes the object's features. A *dimension* shows the actual location and size values of the objects on the drawing. The dimensions in figure 2.1 show the length of the part and the location of the hole.

Dimensions fall into two categories: dimensions of *size* and dimensions of *location*. These categories are both important for the complete interpretation of a drawing. Although dimensioning can be another tedious process of technical drawing, AutoSketch has some very useful dimensioning tools that are accurate and easy to use.

Conforming to the Alphabet of Lines

Perhaps the phrase *alphabet of lines* is new to you. Different line representations on a technical drawing help to distinguish between various features on a drawing. Linetypes can be set apart from each other by using a special pattern of dots, dashes, and spaces. The thickness of a line is also used to set it apart from other lines. Figure 2.2 shows a typical part drawing that displays several different linetypes.

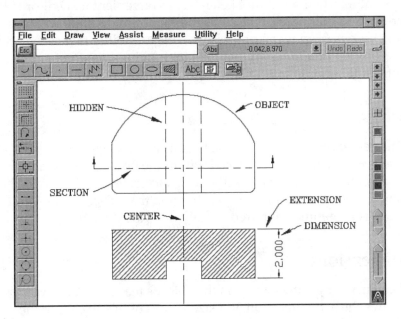

Figure 2.2:

Several different linetypes in a drawing.

The following linetypes are often used in a technical drawing:

- **Object.** Most of the visible features of a part are shown with object lines. An *object line* is drawn with a continuous linetype, which also may be wider than the other lines. This helps the outline of the part stand out.

- **Hidden.** A *hidden line* is shown as a dashed line. It represents features of the part that are hidden behind other features. In figure 2.2, the groove is shown with hidden lines because it is not visible from the top.

- **Center.** A *center line* is shown using long and short dashes, alternatively. It shows that an object is symmetrical about a line, and indicates the center of an arc or circle. Sometimes it is shown as thinner than an object line.

- **Extension.** An *extension line* is shown as a solid line. It indicates the points on the object referenced by the dimension lines. There is a slight gap between the object and the extension line to help clarify that the extension lines are not really part of the object.

- **Dimension.** A *dimension line* specifies locations and sizes. AutoSketch can automatically produce several types of dimension lines, depending on the drafting standards to which you must conform. A dimension line often has arrows on both ends and a numerical value in the middle.

- **Section.** A *section line* is represented with a pattern of one long dash, then two short dashes (also by thick dashed lines). It shows the location at which a section view is taken from another view.

Depending on the type of drawings you produce, other linetypes may be required for clarity or special emphasis. Figure 2.3 shows the standard linetypes that are available in AutoSketch.

In manual drafting, various lead weights and sizes are employed to produce lines of varying width and density. In CAD drafting, plotters are often equipped with pens of different widths. Some entities, such as AutoSketch polylines, can have widths assigned to them, so that lines that are wider than a plotter pen can be drawn.

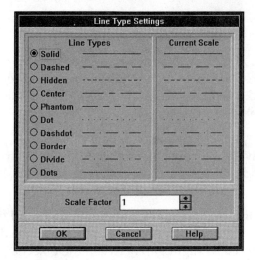

Figure 2.3:

AutoSketch standard linetypes.

Using Standard View Layouts

When you first view a technical drawing, it is important to visualize what that object would actually look like. Standard linetypes help to clarify drawings. Standard view layouts are also used to make sure that all drawings appear uniform in the way the views are arranged. Figure 2.4 shows four types of views, which are normally used in an architectural application.

- **Plan view.** A *plan view* is a view looking directly down from above a building. Plan views show room layouts; length and width dimensions; and locations of buildings, lot lines, and other such features.

- **Elevation view.** An *elevation view* shows a building as you approach it from one of the sides. The height of a building, and features such as windows and doors are best shown in this view. Several different elevation views may be required, depending on the complexity of the building.

- **Detail view.** A *detail view* is often required to show the small part of an object in an enlarged view. This view helps to fully show the components or features of a critical area. Detail views are especially important in a *working drawing*, which is the drawing that is used to actually construct a building.

- **Pictorial view.** A *pictorial view* helps to visualize the way an object would actually appear. It can be a rather challenging view to draw.

Chapter 9 explains several methods of creating pictorial views in AutoSketch.

Using standard views with proper layouts is important for using technical drawings as a clear and concise way to convey graphic information.

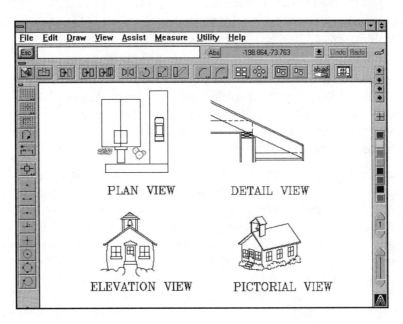

Figure 2.4:

Four types of architectural views.

Comparing CAD Drafting to Manual Drafting

Many similarities exist between CAD-generated drawings and manual drawings. When given a choice, most employers are more concerned with an employee's ability to create a technically correct drawing than with the employee's specific CAD skills. (It takes five years of college, plus years of experience, to become a competent architect—it takes only a fraction of that time to develop sufficient CAD skills.)

Exploring the History of CAD

The integration of computer-aided design into drafting and engineering operations has taken place over the past four decades, and has closely followed the development and use of computers in industry.

The 1960s saw experimentation with computer graphics develop into a useable system that could perform complex operations which are difficult to duplicate manually. Companies with large research budgets and the technical capacity to operate and maintain the systems were finding innovative ways to use CAD.

The development of this CAD-drafting technology led to an impressive selection of mainframe-based CAD systems in the 1970s. Advances in minicomputers and workstations gave the graphics systems much more power. CAD software was also being written for specific applications, including facilities management, product design, computer-aided engineering, and electronics design. Although these systems were still very expensive, they became much easier to use and maintain. Because of the cost, many companies used highly skilled "CAD operators" who spent most of their shifts working on the CAD system.

Computer-aided design grew most rapidly during the 1980s because of the introduction of the IBM personal computer.

Throughout the decade, as computers came down in price and increased in performance, CAD software for the PC was developed. Instead of buying an expensive turnkey system dedicated to CAD, companies could purchase PCs to run a variety of applications. Employees who could operate a personal computer and who had knowlege of technical drawings could learn CAD to enhance their jobs.

In the 1990s, computer-aided design continues to integrate into ordinary drafting and sketching applications. Many people now have a computer at home that can run Windows applications, and the price of software packages such as AutoSketch for Windows is very reasonable compared to other software applications.

AutoSketch may be used as one component of a multimedia system that combines computer graphics with rendering, animation, and sound to produce very effective presentations. The only certainty about the remainder of this decade is that the performance of computers will be greatly increased, prices will decrease, and software will continue to exploit all of the capabilities of the new technology.

Applying Techniques of Manual Drafting to CAD

There has been much debate about whether students should be taught basic drafting skills on the computer versus the drawing board. Without argument, the basic drafting skills mentioned in this chapter need to be learned. The proper use of standard views, linetypes, title blocks, notes, and other drafting conventions can be learned by using a wide variety of instructional techniques. Whether these skills are learned on a manual drawing board or on a computer should depend on the equipment on which the student will work.

Manual Drafting Tools

One of the differences between manual and CAD drafting is the choice of tools used to create the drawing. Figure 2.5 shows some of the tools used in manual drafting, including a drafting table, T-square, compass, protractor, and circle template. A good selection of lead helps to create proper line widths. In addition to using the proper drafting tools, lettering techniques must be developed for professional-looking drawings. The proper use of these manual drafting tools requires a great deal of practice, and it may not be beneficial for those preparing to work on a CAD system.

Figure 2.5:
Conventional drafting tools.

CAD Drafting Tools

Computer-aided design requires the introduction of many new tools to the draftsperson. Figure 2.6 shows some of the computer hardware tools that are used in CAD. The drafting table is re-placed with a desk, pencils for lettering are replaced with a key-board, and other hand-held tools are replaced with a mouse or graphics tablet. The drawing paper becomes a computer graphics screen, which is printed with a printer or plotter.

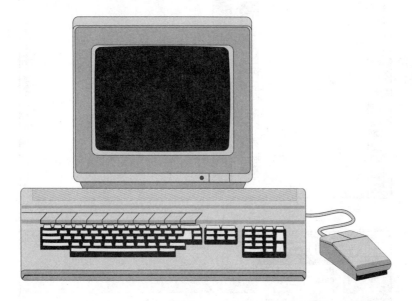

Figure 2.6:
CAD drafting tools.

Computer-aided design tools involve computer hardware similar to other software applications. Perhaps a better comparison of manual drafting tools to CAD tools is found in the design tools provided by AutoSketch. Figures 2.7 and 2.8 show some common drawing and editing tools, shown as icons and a pull-down menu, that are used in CAD drafting.

Notice the drawing tools in the Draw menu: Line, Circle, and Arc. These tools, when used with the proper coordinate input, replace tools such as rulers, compasses, and protractors.

Other drawing tools can easily create more complex graphic entities. The Quick Text tool enables text to be placed at the cursor position and entered with the keyboard. The Erase tool, found on the Edit menu, is much easier to use than a manual eraser.

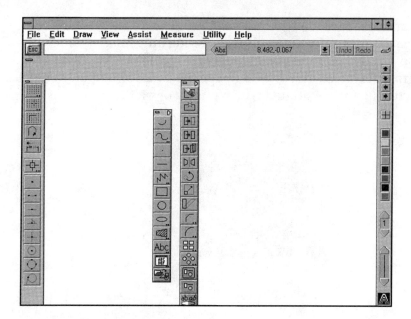

Figure 2.7:

AutoSketch icons.

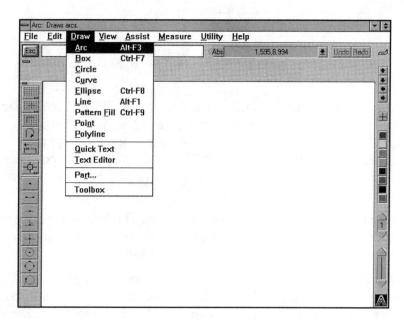

Figure 2.8:

AutoSketch pull-down menu.

Other useful editing tools include **M**ove, **C**opy, **R**otate, and **S**tretch. These tools have no equivalents in manual drafting; they open up many new possibilities of editing and changing drawings that previously would have to be redrawn.

The greatest difference between CAD drafting and manual drafting lies in the end product. In manual drafting, the final product is the original sheet of paper that contains the technical drawing. If any engineering changes are made, the original drawing is carefully modified, and copies (called *blueprints*) are taken from the original.

In CAD drafting, the end product is the computer database of the drawing. Printed sheets (called *hard copies*, *plots*, or *prints*) can be created from the database at any time. If a drawing is changed, the database is modified, and new hard copies are created.

CAD drawings are often stamped with the following message: NO MANUAL CHANGES. This message means that it is not proper to change dimensions or part features by using manual drawing techniques. The original CAD database should be retrieved and properly modified.

Determining the Proper Drawing Scale

One common misunderstanding between CAD and manual drafting involves the scale of the objects in the drawing. There are several points that you should know about scaling.

Scaling is discussed in detail in Chapter 6.

First, you must understand the importance of properly proportioned and scaled drawings. In manual drafting, your objects must be scaled unless they are a size that can be drawn at full-scale on a given sheet size. In a technical drawing, it is very important to properly proportion objects so that the relationships between the objects can be visually confirmed before the object is produced. Imagine the confusion on a map or a plant-layout drawing in which objects are not properly proportioned to each other.

Second, you should know that the standard scale factors are used on a given drawing (for example, 10 to 1 or 1/4"=1'). These standard scale factors make it easier to visualize the objects. Architectural scales and templates are often produced to such scales. For some applications, measurements are taken directly from a drawing.

Manual drawings require all entities to be scaled as they are drawn on the paper. CAD drawing entities are normally drawn full-scale—whether they are one millimeter or one mile in length—and then scaled as they are plotted to fit the sheet size that is required for that drawing.

Utilizing the Special Capabilities of CAD

There are many similarities between manual drafting and CAD. The first step in learning how to create a technical drawing with a CAD software package is to learn the individual tools. The second step is to learn the proper techniques of CAD drafting. Your most productive CAD drafting techniques will vary, depending on the type of work you do and your comfort level with the software.

Much of the productivity gain that is attributed to CAD is not its capability to quickly draw single entities. Drawing speed is greatly enhanced when these entities can be quickly copied, rotated, or arrayed into multiple positions. A general rule in CAD design is to draw an object once and use it many times.

Another great productivity advantage of CAD is its capability to create parts. *Parts* are objects, or groups of entities, that can be set aside (similar to a manual drafting template) and used again by placing them into the drawing in the proper position. Figure 2.9 shows a typical library of landscaping parts that are ready to be placed in a drawing.

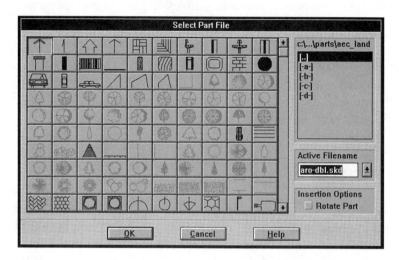

Figure 2.9:

A parts library of landscape symbols.

Because of exceptional editing capabilities, CAD drawings can often be modified instead of redrawn. For example, a builder may have a standard floor plan for a house drawn in CAD. While sitting down with a customer in front of a CAD workstation, some walls can be moved, doors and windows relocated, and closets resized. It can be faster to recall an old product design and modify it than to redraw it from scratch. Because of constant design and engineering changes, many companies insist on CAD to meet the demands of their customers.

Another capability of a CAD-generated technical drawing is the usefulness of the CAD database throughout the design and building stages of a product. For a building design, the CAD database can obtain sizes and quantities of raw materials, such as flooring, roofing, or siding. The CAD graphics can be imported into desktop publishing for pamphlets or sales literature. Interior designers can use the floor plans to complete their own designs.

Product designs are often directly used in computer-aided manufacturing software to generate the shapes for computer numerically controlled machining. The product-design data is used by the quality-control department for inspection data. It may also be used to design manufacturing fixtures or packaging components.

Instead of being used as an innovative drafting tool, computer-aided design is being viewed as the basis for creating and maintaining a great deal of critical product information. As computers are used in many more design and manufacturing functions, software is becoming more powerful in its capability to share data with other software applications.

Summary

To use CAD for your applications, it is important that you understand the type of drawing you are trying to create. Be sure that you are aware of the drawing standards and layouts that are acceptable in your field. Having a good understanding of technical drawings benefits you in your ability to express yourself and understand others by using this very important form of communication.

Although there are many parallels between manual drafting and CAD, CAD goes much further and requires many different skills that are not used in manual drafting. CAD drafting has already exceeded the projections of ten years ago regarding its popularity and the number of disciplines that benefit from it.

Chapter 3 discusses the CAD workstation, and explains the way individual components are used in CAD applications. The Windows operating environment, which is a key part of AutoSketch for Windows, is also explained. Several short tutorials are included to help you learn some tasks that are important to maintaining your CAD software and databases.

Understanding Your Personal Computer

Chapter 2 mentioned some of the computer hardware used in a typical CAD workstation. In the first part of this chapter, you learn the basic functions of the hardware components used in computer-aided drafting. The basic operating characteristics of your computer are important for you to understand so that you can maximize your use of the equipment.

The second part of Chapter 3 explains the Windows operating environment. Because Windows is the basis for running AutoSketch for Windows, as well as all other Windows application software, it is important that you experiment with Windows. The brief tutorials in this chapter are meant to build your confidence in your ability to set up Windows to conform to your personal and computing requirements. Several common disk- and file-maintenance procedures are explained so that you do not lose track of your drawings after you create them.

Identifying CAD Hardware Components

Most activities performed on a computer can be classified into three categories:

- **Input.** Computers must have software loaded into RAM (random-access memory). Commands are then issued, or more data loaded, which can be analyzed by the computer. *Input devices* enable you to feed data into the computer.

- **Processing.** The main board in a personal computer—called the *motherboard*—contains all the chips and circuits necessary to evaluate and process the information.

- **Output.** After the data is processed, it must be sent back to the user or to a permanent storage area. The information returned by the computer is referred to as *output*.

Central Processing Unit

When you purchase a personal computer, it is usually a complete system that includes the keyboard, monitor, and whatever else is necessary to make a functional system. The computer processing unit resides in a case, such as those shown in figure 3.1.

Computer cases come in a variety of shapes and sizes. For a desktop application, standard or slim-line cases are available. A tower model is a vertical cabinet that sits on the floor. Very compact and lightweight models are good for portability. The size of the case has no direct bearing on the capacity of the computer; however, it can limit the number of additional circuit boards and auxiliary devices that can be added.

Inside the computer case is the motherboard, which determines the processing capability of the computer.

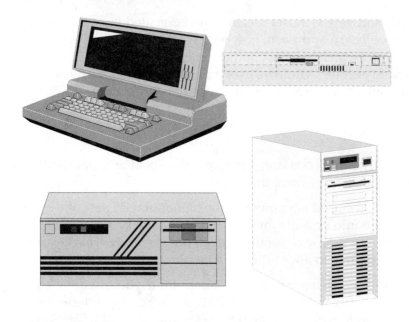

Figure 3.1:
Typical computer cases.

Memory is another term that is important for understanding the capacity of a computer. The basic memory unit is a *byte*, which is the amount of space needed to represent one alphanumeric character. A computer file containing your first and last name is about 20 bytes in size, depending on the length of your name. The minimum amount of disk space required to load AutoSketch for Windows is about four megabytes (two million bytes).

Other items in the computer case include a power supply, disk drives, and other optional accessories. Like the purchase price of a new automobile, the total sale price of a computer depends on how many extras are added to the base unit.

Input Devices

Several methods of data input are available on personal computers. As more people learn to use computers, both hardware and software vendors are trying to make communication with computers as easy and efficient as possible. For example, sometimes

CAD software is most efficient when executed from the keyboard. The keyboard approach, however, relies on users who can type well and who have most of the commands memorized. AutoSketch for Windows uses a much more graphical user interface, which requires less practice and memorization.

Keyboard

The keyboard is certainly the most prominent and standardized input device on a computer.

If you have used a typewriter, the alphanumeric part of the keyboard should be quite familiar. What used to be the carriage return key is now commonly called the *Enter* key. This key must often be pressed after typing a command.

Several keys that are unique to computer keyboards are the *Control* (Ctrl) and the *Alternate* (Alt) keys. You hold these keys down while typing another character, much like the *Shift* key. Later in this chapter, you learn to use the Alt key to access some of the Windows commands.

The function keys are also used with many software packages as *shortcut* keys for popular commands. The key pad on the right side of the keyboard makes it convenient to type numbers.

The *cursor* keys, which are arrows pointing in four different directions, are used to move the cursor around in text strings, and can sometimes be used to move the cursor on the graphics screen if a pointing device is not available.

Note the difference between the cursor left arrow and the *destructive backspace* key, which deletes text as it is moved backwards. The cursor keys are grouped together; the destructive backspace key is located near the upper right corner of the alphanumeric keys.

Pointing Devices

Instead of using the keyboard to issue instructions, many software packages support the use of a pointing device to move the cursor around on the graphics screen and select items from menus. Figure 3.2 shows several pointing devices used with personal computers.

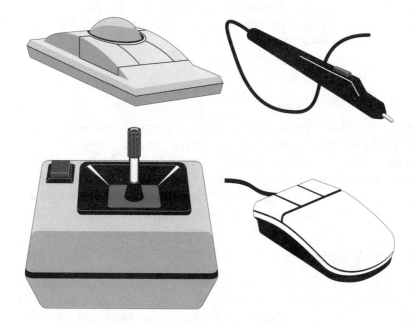

Figure 3.2:
Common pointing devices.

A *mouse* is the most common pointing device; it is shipped with most computers as a standard part of the workstation. At least one button, called the *pick* button in CAD, is needed to select items from the screen. Often two or more buttons are included on a pointing device, and they function according to the software application with which they are used.

A *digitizer* is a more sophisticated pointing device, which provides cursor movement based on an absolute grid located on the tablet. This technique enables tracing of existing drawings or the use of a digitizer-overlay tablet if the software package supports those features. Some digitizers have a *stylus*, which is held like a pen for tracing or selecting points. A digitizer is sometimes called a *graphics tablet*.

Trackballs and *joysticks* may be used as input devices when rapid cursor control is needed for applications such as video games.

If your input device works with Windows, it probably functions well with AutoSketch.

Disk Drives

Most computers are equipped with two types of disk drives—floppy disk drives and hard disk drives. A *disk drive* is considered an input or output device. Data can be read into the computer memory from the disk or stored from the computer memory to the disk. Figure 3.3 shows a hard disk drive and a floppy disk drive, as well as several types of removeable disks.

Floppy Disk Drives

Floppy disk drives were some of the first media used on personal computers to store and retrieve data. Although eight-inch disks were sometimes used when personal computers were first introduced, today the two standard sizes are 5-1/4 inch disks and 3-1/2 inch disks. At least one of these sizes is standard on a computer, with a second disk drive optional. A typical floppy disk can store over 1M (megabyte) of data. Floppy disk drives are useful because disks can easily be removed for backup data storage or transferred to another computer.

Hard Disk Drives

A *hard disk drive* is another very important part of a computer workstation. You do not usually see the inside of a hard disk drive (see fig. 3.3) because it is a sealed unit inside your computer. It is often called a *fixed disk* because it is not normally removed from the computer case. The advantage of a hard disk drive over a floppy disk disk drive is that a hard disk drive reads and writes data much more quickly, and can store much more data. A typical hard disk drive on a personal computer holds between 50M and 200M of data.

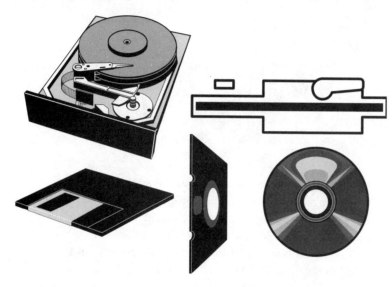

Figure 3.3:
Disk drives and removable disks.

NOTE Standard naming conventions for disk drives are used on most personal computers. The main floppy disk drive is called A, the secondary floppy disk drive is designated B, and the hard disk drive is named C. Additional disk drives can be designated as D (or any other letter name).

Input and Output Ports

Personal computers also come standardized with several ports to communicate with other devices. Printers, plotters, mice, monitors, networks, and other devices must be connected to the computer through these connections. Figure 3.4 shows a 25-pin connector, 9-pin connector, and coaxial cable end, which are commonly used on personal computers.

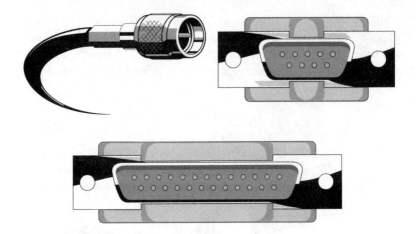

 Just because a given socket accepts a cable with a compatible plug, do not assume that the computer and the peripheral are automatically compatible. Cable configurations, communication parameters, and software configurations must be properly set up.

Output Devices

After the software is loaded into the computer, and additional commands have instructed the computer to perform certain operations, the resulting data must be output from the computer. In addition to disk drives, several other important *output devices* are used. The following sections describe these devices.

Graphics Display

The *graphics display* is one of the primary output devices. Some-times referred to as a *monitor*, or *cathode ray tube (CRT)*, it is available in either monochrome or color. The diagonal size of the screen (usually between 14" and 21") is measured much the same way as a television screen.

Another important feature of the graphics display is its *resolution*. The more *pixels,* or individual dots, on the screen, the better is the clarity and character definition. The AutoSketch screen shots in this book are shown at the standard VGA resolution of 640×480 pixels. Higher resolutions of 800×600 or 1024×768 pixels are supported on some systems.

Although your monitor is the most obvious component of your graphics display, the *graphics adapter card* in your computer must be compatible with your monitor. It contains most of the high-performance graphics capabilities, and it controls the way computer output is translated into graphic entities on the screen.

On a typical personal computer, adding a large monitor and high-performance graphics card can sometimes double the base cost of the workstation.

Printers

Printers are necessary to provide printed copies of text or graphics. Sometimes called *hard copies,* printed copies are still the most common form of computer output. Although the term *paperless office* has been associated with computers, it sometimes seems that computers produce more paper instead of less. Figure 3.5 shows two popular computer printers.

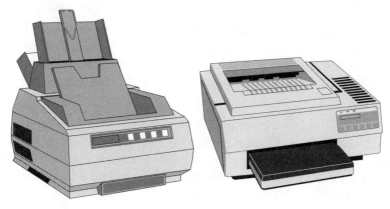

Figure 3.5:
A dot-matrix printer and a laser printer.

Computer printers vary greatly, depending on the type of applications for which they are used. Some of the most common characteristics are the following:

- Paper size and paper-feed capacity
- Multiple-color capability
- Graphics resolution
- Printing speed
- Purchase and operating cost
- Amount of noise generated
- Memory size

It is important that the printer is supported by Windows so that it processes output from Windows application software. As a general rule, dot-matrix printers are the least expensive printers; laser printers are more costly.

Although *dot-matrix printers* can quickly produce check plots or text-file printouts, they do not always scale entities very accurately.

A *laser printer* uses a much higher resolution to produce very clear final drawings. Because a drum and toner are used (similar to a copier), multiple copies can be quickly produced.

Plotters

Although some printers are capable of providing high-quality hard copies of CAD drawing files, *plotters* are generally recognized as being better suited to producing large sheet-size technical drawings. Plotters are rated on many of the same features as printers.

Plotters often have the capability of using pens with different widths and colors. Plotters must also be capable of accurately reproducing drawings to a specified scale factor. Figure 3.6 shows a desktop plotter for A- and B-size drawings, and a freestanding model capable of larger sheet sizes.

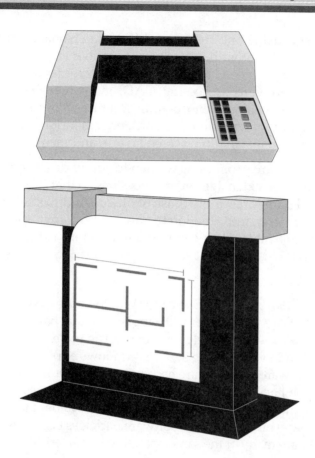

Figure 3.6:

A desktop plotter and a freestanding plotter.

Because computers are used in more applications, it is important for you to know the basic parts of a computer workstation and to understand the function of these components. In the next part of this chapter, you learn more about how to use your computer and configure it to make all the components communicate with each other.

Getting into Windows

As the personal computer evolved, standard models were cloned by other manufacturers. For this reason, you are probably comfortable using one of several different personal computers. Software, on the other hand, was moving in many different directions with screen layout and general command usage. You may have had word processing, CAD, and spreadsheet software that were not at all in their operating features. Those same three software packages, modified to run under Windows, now appear very similar in installation, screen layout, and menu organization.

When a software program is written to run under Windows, it must follow an extensive set of guidelines so that its menu-command names resemble those of other Windows software. For the average user, introduction to another Windows application becomes enjoyable when compared to previous experiences (like having to learn a different screen layout and command structure).

 AutoSketch for Windows is based on a former DOS application that has been entirely rewritten to run under the Windows operating system. Windows-application software packages are becoming very popular—once you have learned how to run software packages in the Windows environment, you can quickly adapt to many other Windows software packages because they share many of the same operating characteristics.

Understanding Operating Systems

When you first start your computer, an operating system is loaded into RAM. An *operating system* is necessary for you to be able to communicate with your computer. Functions such as formatting disks, copying files, and setting up directories are controlled by the operating system.

MS-DOS (Microsoft Disk Operating System) is the standard operating system for most personal computers. Although this operating system has many limitations, DOS has been greatly improved in the more recent upgrades, and it is still shipped with most new computers.

 Today's PCs are generally divided into two categories: those running on a version of DOS, and Macintosh computers, which have their own operating system.

Because of the popularity of these two types of computers, many software packages are available in both the DOS and Macintosh versions. AutoSketch is actually available in three platforms: DOS, Macintosh, and Windows.

Other operating systems, such as UNIX, are more common on workstation platforms and mainframe computers. Some large computers still use *proprietary operating systems* (those that are unique to that type of computer).

The Windows operating system is not meant to replace DOS. In fact, it requires DOS to be running before it is loaded. Windows is intended to be an enhancement to DOS by providing a graphical user interface and an array of tools to assist in running application software.

Starting Up Windows

Many computers purchased in the last several years have come with the Windows software already loaded. If you do not have the Windows software, or if you want to upgrade to a newer version, you can purchase the software at most computer-software outlets.

 Before installing or upgrading your Windows software, be sure that you have the proper version of DOS and the minimum amount of RAM needed to run the Windows software.

Begin your exploration of Windows by booting your computer. The computer is programmed to perform memory checks, load the operating system software into RAM, and prepare to run your application software.

Two files are automatically read by your computer during start-up. The CONFIG.SYS and AUTOEXEC.BAT files contain special instructions for your computer: loading various utility software, allocating memory, and configuring various hardware peripherals.

 Many software packages, including Windows, automatically modify the CONFIG.SYS and AUTOEXEC.BAT files to optimize your computer to run that particular software. This modification normally occurs during software installation. Follow the procedures described later in this chapter to make backup copies of these two files, in case they are lost or corrupted.

If your computer leaves you at the DOS prompt, enter **WIN** to load the Windows operating system. Some computers have this command at the end of the AUTOEXEC.BAT file so that the computer automatically runs Windows when it boots. The Windows logo displays briefly while the software is being loaded, and then you see the Windows Program Manager, as shown in figure 3.7.

Configuring Windows

When the Windows software is installed, it asks several questions about the hardware on which it is running. It also performs a complete system check while it is loading to determine the amount of RAM memory available, the type of input device being used, and the type of graphics card in your computer. If your peripherals are supported by Windows, no further configuration is necessary.

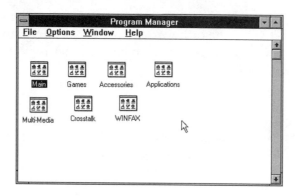

Figure 3.7:

The Windows Program Manager.

If you are using special peripherals, or if you want to customize your hardware configuration, choose Windows Setup (see fig. 3.8) or Print Manager from the Main program group (see fig. 3.9).

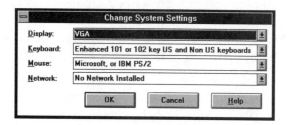

Figure 3.8:

Dialog box used by Windows Setup.

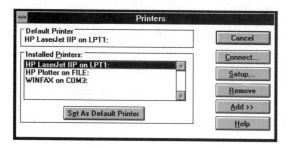

Figure 3.9:

Dialog box used by Print Manager.

You may need to insert floppy disks that contain special driver files for some peripherals. These disks can often be obtained from the manufacturer of the peripheral. The beauty of this configuration process is that once you have Windows properly configured for your computer hardware and peripherals, all application software that you run use this interface to communicate with your peripherals. This is a major improvement to the alternative DOS applications, in which each software package has to be separately configured for your hardware.

Consult your Windows reference guide for more detailed information on configuring Windows.

Working in the Windows Environment

The Windows environment is a graphical user interface that uses *icons*, or small pictures, to represent commands and functions. Icons sometimes also have text labels to reinforce the meaning of the icon. One or more windows can be opened simultaneously, each one containing a different software application.

A mouse or other pointing device is essential in Windows—using the keyboard to manipulate the cursor can be inefficient. Try moving your cursor around on the screen to be sure it is working. If it is not responding, refer to the previous section on hardware configuration.

From the Program Manager, try opening up a *program group*, which is a window containing a selection of icons. A single *click* of the left button on your mouse (press and release the button) highlights a program group icon and displays a menu of options for that icon. Clicking on the **R**estore command opens up the program group window containing the icons for those applications.

A quicker method of opening a window is to *double-click* (press the button twice in rapid succession) on the icon, which immediately opens up the program-group window. After some practice, double-clicking on an icon or selection will come naturally.

The following exercise shows you how to start Windows from the DOS prompt and how to open a program group window.

Starting Windows and Running a Windows Application

Boot your computer and begin this exercise at the DOS prompt. If your computer automatically runs Windows after booting, skip the first step.

C:\> **WIN** ↵   Starts Windows

Double-click on the Accessories   Opens the
program-group icon   Accessories window

Double-click on the Notepad *icon*   Opens the Notebook
(see fig. 3.10)   window

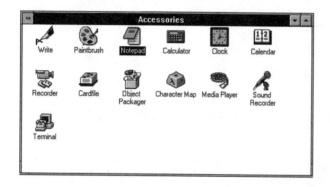

Figure 3.10:

The Notepad icon in the Accessories program group.

Given the many capabilities of Windows accessories such as Write, Paint, and Notepad, you can perform many functions without having to run third-party Windows application software.

Learning the Windows Control Features

Now that you are working in a standard window, you should become familiar with the layout of this window and learn the functions of its features. These features are consistent with all other Windows applications. Figure 3.11 identifies many of the standard Windows features.

The *title bar* shows the name of the application and the file name, if one has been assigned. If you want to reposition the entire window on your screen, you can drag the title bar to a new location.

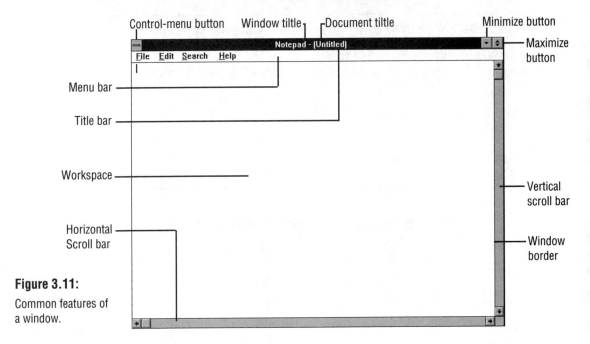

Control-menu button   Window tiltle   Document tiltle   Minimize button

Menu bar

Title bar

Workspace

Horizontal
Scroll bar

Maximize
button

Vertical
scroll bar

Window
border

Figure 3.11:

Common features of
a window.

To *drag* an item, place the cursor over the
item, press and hold the left button, move
the cursor to a new position, then release
the button.

Three important buttons are located on the title bar. The *Control-
menu button*, located at the left side of the title bar, controls the
display of the window. Clicking on the Control-menu button
displays a pull-down menu that contains several options, including **C**lose; double-clicking on it closes the window.

The two buttons on the right side of the title bar also control the
display of the window. The *Minimize* button reduces the window
to an icon. This button does not close the window—it reduces it to
an icon to make room on the screen for another application. Double-
clicking on the icon opens up the window again.

The *Maximize* button resizes the window to fill up the entire screen,
which gives you the maximum amount of working area in a window.

If you minimize a window, be sure to return to that window by double-clicking on that minimized icon. If you go to the program group in Program Manager and double-click on that icon, you run a second instance, or *session*, of that same application.

Figure 3.12 shows an active window with several minimized icons.

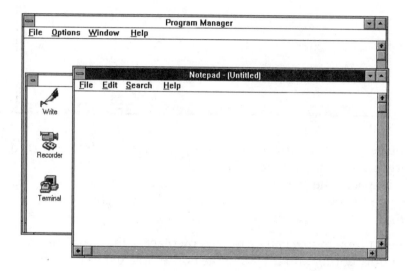

Figure 3.12:
Three minimized icons.

The *menu bar* is also common to all Windows software. Clicking on a menu item such as File shows the pull-down menu list of all the common file commands, such as those that open new files or save existing ones. Many items in the menus are assigned *hot keys*, which are underlined characters in the menu item. Hot keys can be activated from the keyboard by depressing the Alt key while pressing the hot key. Figure 3.13 shows a typical pull-down menu.

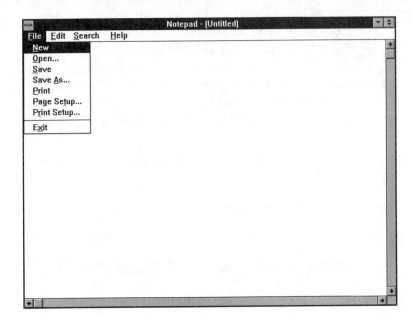

Figure 3.13:

A typical Windows
pull-down menu.

The vertical and horizontal *scroll bars* are used to display parts of
large lists or bodies of text that do not fit into the existing
workspace. The elevator box can be dragged across the scroll bar,
or you can click on the arrow buttons to move across the work
area.

The entire window can be resized by placing the cursor on the
window border and dragging the border to create a larger or
smaller workspace. By dragging the corners of a window in a
diagonal direction, the length and width are resized together.

Using Dialog Boxes

Windows software often uses *dialog boxes* to enable the selection of
settings or text input. A typical dialog box, as shown in figure
3.14, is the Open dialog box.

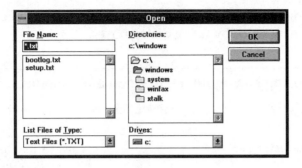

Figure 3.14:
The Open dialog box.

This dialog box contains two *list boxes*. The list box in the center displays the current level of file directories, and the list box on the left displays file names. Double-clicking on a selection from one of these list boxes activates that selection. If the list is very long, the up and down arrows enable you to scroll through the list. Below the directory list box is a drop-down list box. By clicking on the arrow button of the Drives drop-down list box, a list of disk drives appear, and you can choose a different one.

The text box shown under File **N**ame shows the current default, and enables you to enter your own text. When the vertical text cursor is flashing, you can modify the existing text string. By double-clicking on the text box so that the text is highlighted, you can enter a new text string in place of the existing one.

Notice the OK and Cancel buttons in the upper right corner of the dialog box. Choosing one of these buttons is the only way to close the dialog box. Choosing Cancel ignores any changes you may have made; choosing OK executes the changes.

 You can use the Tab key on the keyboard to move the cursor to the various parts of the dialog box; use the Enter key to execute the highlighted button. Hot keys can also be used, if they are indicated by the underlined character.

The following exercise shows you how to retrieve and save a file under a new name by using dialog boxes.

Using Dialog Boxes To Open and Rename a File

Continue working in the Notepad window you opened in the previous exercise.

Choose **F**ile, *then* **O**pen	Activates the Open dialog box (see fig. 3.14)
Double-click on C:\ *in the directories list box*	Makes the root directory of C current
Click on the List Files of **T**ype *drop-down box arrow, and choose* All Files *.*	Changes the file extension in the list box
Double-click on the file AUTOEXEC.BAT	Opens the file

At this point, you can make any required changes to the file.

Choose **F**ile, *then* Save **A**s	Activates the Save As dialog box (see fig. 3.15)
Click on the File **N**ame *text box at the end of the text string*	Places the cursor at the end of the text string

Use the backspace key to remove the t. Type **K** so that the file name becomes AUTOEXEC.BAK.

Click on the OK *button*	Saves the file with a new name
Double-click on the control button at the left side of the title bar	Closes the Notepad application

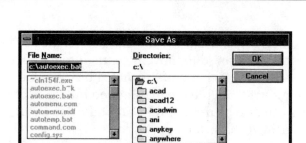

Figure 3.15:

The modified Save As dialog box.

You may wonder why this exercise uses the Notepad application of Windows. It does not matter in which application you work— the File dialog boxes appear similar in all the packages. If all you want to do is rename or make a backup copy of the file without editing it, you can use the Windows File Manager, which is described in the following section.

Working with the Windows File Manager

An important part of learning to use a personal computer for any application involves working with data files and disks, which is necessary to properly save files, back up files, and move files from one location to another. The previous exercise used the process of opening a file and then saving it under a new name to make a backup copy. If you are familiar with DOS, you know how to type these file commands at the DOS prompt. Windows provides a graphical interface to perform these functions.

The next exercise shows you how to copy a file from your hard disk drive (C) to a floppy disk (A). (If your disk drives have different names, substitute the corresponding drive names in the exercise.)

Using File Manager To Copy a File

You should be running the Windows Program Manager to start the exercise. Place a formatted floppy disk in your A drive.

Double-click on the Main *icon from Program Manager*	Opens the Main program group
Double-click on the File Manager *icon*	Opens the File Manager
Double-click on the LAW *directory (see fig. 3.16)*	Displays the files in that directory
Click on the file CHAP5.SKD	Highlights the file
Choose File, *then* Copy	Opens the Copy dialog box

continues

Type **A:** *in the text box, then choose* OK *(see fig. 3.17)*	Specifies where to copy the file
Double-click on the Control-menu button	Returns to the Main program group
Double-click on the Control-menu button	Returns to the Program Manager

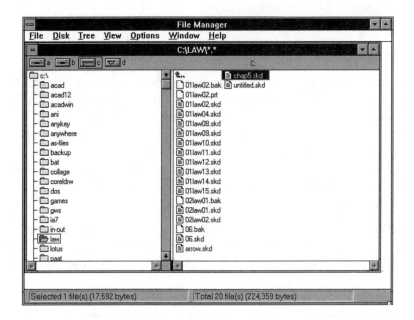

Figure 3.16:

The Windows File Manager.

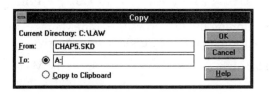

Figure 3.17:

The File Manager Copy dialog box.

If you want to copy several files, hold down the Shift key while you select the files.

The File menu in Program Manager has several other choices for file maintenance, such as Move, Delete, and Rename. These commands have dialog boxes that are similar to the Copy dialog box.

 You can also try several of the commands from the Disk menu. In Chapter 1, the software-installation instructions suggested making copies of the original software disks before using them. This is easily done with the Copy command under the Disk menu. If you need to format disks, use the Format command; the dialog box prompts you through the rest of the procedure.

Running Multiple Windows Applications

One of the advantages of Windows is its capability to run several different applications at once (or several sessions of one application can be opened concurrently). It requires more memory and computing power to keep several applications running at once. Also, your window sizes are smaller if you want to see several applications on the screen. Remember that an open Windows application can be visible in three ways—in a full screen, as a partial screen, or as an icon. These modes are controlled by the Minimize and Maximize buttons.

The last exercise in this chapter shows you how to open several Windows applications simultaneously. Be as creative as you like in this next exercise. You probably want to try several different screen arrangements to see which ones best suit your needs.

Running Multiple Windows Applications

Double-click on the Accessories *icon*   Opens the
from the Program Manager   Accessories Group

Double-click on the Clock *icon*   Opens the clock window

Drag the title bar of the clock window to reposition the window in the upper right corner of the screen (see fig. 3.18).

Double-click on the Calculator *icon*   Opens the calculator window

Drag the title bar of the calculator window to move the window to the lower right corner of the screen.

Double-click on the Write *icon*   Opens the Write window

Drag the Write window to the upper left corner of the screen, then drag the right and bottom window border until your screen looks like figure 3.18. Clicking on an open window makes it active, and it lays over the other open windows. When you are finished experimenting with the windows, close each of the windows. You can now exit the Program Manager by double-clicking on the Control button.

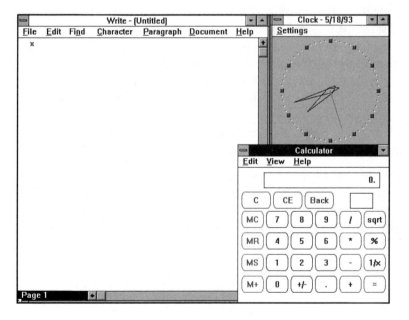

Figure 3.18:

Three Windows applications, running concurrently.

Windows settings and configurations are stored in two files in the Windows directory: WIN.INI and SYSTEM.INI. Whenever you leave Windows, these files are automatically updated to your most recent settings.

You may want to save copies of the SYSTEM.INI and WIN.INI files so that your original settings can be retrieved if the files are lost or corrupted.

The Windows operating system is powerful, and it contains many useful features that are beyond the scope of this book. Refer to your Windows reference guide or to one of several books by New Riders Publishing that are dedicated to the topic of Windows.

Summary

You now have some basic information about the way your personal computer workstation operates. A general understanding of the computer hardware is important for utilizing your computer to its fullest extent. When making decisions on computer repair, purchasing, or upgrading, be sure you know what equipment is available and how the equipment can best meet your needs. Price, performance, and features must be re-evaluated, at least on an annual basis, because of the rapidly changing technology of computer hardware.

Every computer must have *software*, or *programs*, which become the interface between you and the computer. The two most important software packages are the operating-system software and the application software. This chapter introduced you to the Windows operating system. The rest of this book shows you how to use a specific application software—AutoSketch for Windows.

Because of its graphical user interface and wide array of powerful features, Windows is becoming the operating system of choice for many personal computer users. The Windows software is constantly being upgraded to take advantage of the improved performance of the newer computers. After you learn the Windows user interface, you will be able to navigate through the many applications written for Windows.

Part 2 of this book teaches you the basics of computer-aided design using the AutoSketch for Windows software. Spend a little more time experimenting with Windows; then turn to Chapter 4 to begin your next CAD drawing.

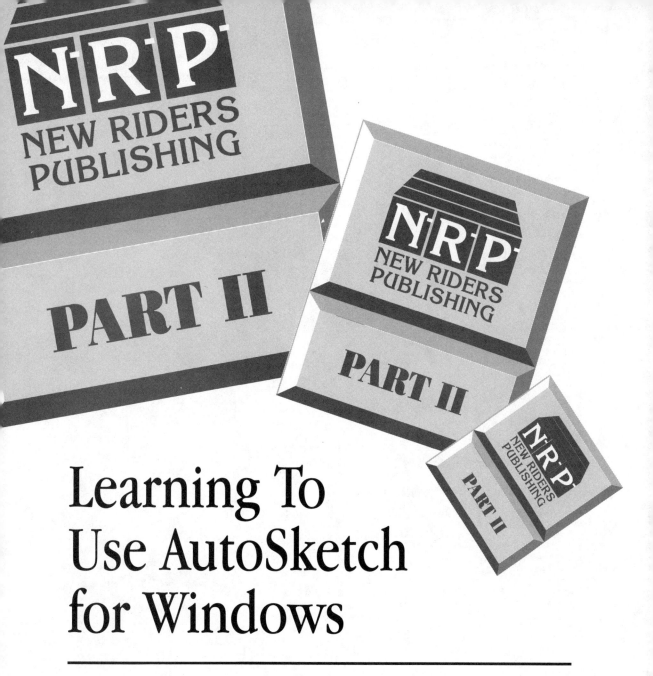

Learning To Use AutoSketch for Windows

Beginning Your Drawing
Creating a Production Drawing
Completing Your Drawing

Beginning Your First Drawing

In this chapter, you will learn how to use the basic tools needed to draw, edit, and save your work. Although this book was written for AutoSketch for Windows, most CAD packages, including Generic CADD and AutoCAD, use similar conventions and operations. Becoming familiar with the terms and language of CAD is an important first step toward learning CAD drafting.

If you are new to the CAD environment, there are some fundamental differences between drawing manually and creating drawings on the computer. The object you create in AutoSketch is called an *entity*. An entity can be a line, circle, arc, or any other mark on the screen. Entities contain information that AutoSketch uses to interpret color, linetype, location, and layer. (Many of these concepts will be addressed in the following chapters.)

Another difference is that you create a *drawing file*, which can be considered the piece of paper on which you are creating the drawing.

Beginning and Naming a New Drawing

As you produce and edit entities in this chapter, the drawing slowly begins to form. The following sections of the chapter discuss the methods used to begin the drawing process.

Assigning File Names

In the following exercise, you go through the steps used to name and save a new drawing. These actions save the drawing as CHAPTER4.SKD to the hard drive.

Naming and Saving a Drawing

Start up AutoSketch for Windows.

Choose **F**ile, *then* Save **A**s   Opens the Save As File dialog
                                                          box

In the File**n**ame *text box, type*
CHAPTER4, *then click on the*
Save *button*

The next section shows the location of your saved SKD files, and discusses how to negotiate the directories AutoSketch uses to store important information.

Using Directories

In the Save as File dialog box, directly under File**n**ame, is the *path*, which shows you the directory on the hard drive into which the file will be saved. When you load AutoSketch for Windows, it automatically sets up the directories in which AutoSketch files are located.

Consult your DOS or Windows
reference guide for more information
on using directories.

In the Save As File dialog box, the path indicates the current
directory. In the Files list box, the files with an SKD extension are
shown; in the Directories list box, the subdirectories of the current
path are shown.

At the top of the list are two dots in brackets [..]. If you double-
click on this pair of dots, you are backed up one level in the
directory tree. You can also choose any of the drives that are
available on your system, including the floppy disk drives. When
you double-click on any of the directories under the Directories
list box, your path changes to that directory.

Exploring the AutoSketch Graphics Window

Now that you have saved a drawing, the following sections
describe other important aspects of the drawing environment.
With any new software package, it is natural to feel overwhelmed
by the amount of information that is being presented. Ask any
veteran CAD user about the first time he sat down with a program—you are likely to hear anecdotes that range from exhilara-
tion to frustration.

Using the Windows Features in the AutoSketch Graphics Windows

Microsoft Windows has become the platform of choice for many software developers. Its ease of use and the graphic interface make it a popular choice for both the novice and the experienced user. AutoSketch for Windows was designed to provide Windows users with the ability to maximize the best features of Windows with all the benefits of a great CAD package.

If you are new to the Windows platform, you will immediately see the difference between Windows-based and DOS-based programs. The icons that are organized around the border enable you to see the tools that are available while drawing and editing.

Identifying the Parts of the Graphics Window

The drawing that you create is being generated in the *drawing area*, which is where entities are displayed.

- **Assist toolbox.** The *Assist toolbox* contains the Grid, Snap, and Ortho tools, which enable you to draw as if you are drafting with a straight edge on graph paper. The Attach tools give you the ability to grab entities at specific points.

 The Assist toolbox is explained more thoroughly in Chapter 5.

- **Vertical status bar.** The *vertical status bar* contains a number of tools that adjust an entity's characteristics. These tools include the following:

Aerial view. When you click on the small airplane icon in the upper right corner, AutoSketch displays the whole drawing in a small window. The current drawing displays in a full-color *view box.* This feature enables you to see the current view in relation to the entire drawing. The current view can be adjusted by moving the view box in the aerial-view window or by adjusting the view in the drawing area.

Aerial view is described in further detail in Chapter 5.

Scroll buttons. Enable you to view other parts of the drawing that are outside the current view.

See Chapter 5 for more information on the view tools.

Crosshair-display button. Turns the display of crosshairs on and off.

Color-palette buttons. Sets the current colors of the entities being created. A double-click on any of the colors brings up the entire AutoSketch palette.

Chapter 5 provides a full description of the color options.

Current layer scroll box. The current layer (numbers 1 through 10) is shown and can be changed by clicking on the up or down arrows.

The current-layer settings are described in Chapter 5.

Current linetype scroll box. Contains a graphic representation of the current linetype.

See Chapter 5 for more information on linetype adjustment.

Autodesk logo. Doubles as a Redraw tool. When you click on the logo any time during the drawing sessions, the screen redraws itself and refreshes the display.

- **Main toolbox.** The icons in this toolbox change according to the menu that is currently active. This only changes if the main menu item is set to display icons.

- **Menu bar.** The File, Edit, and Help pull-down menus are consistent throughout almost all Windows programs. Although the rest of the menus are different in each program, the menu-bar format is followed by all Windows software developers as a way to maintain a consistent look and feel to Windows-compatible programs. Each of the menu-bar items has a unique set of toolbox icons, which is displayed in the main toolbox window. You can set each of the menu-bar items to display either toolbox icons or a pull-down menu.

- **Horizontal status bar.** The area between the menu bar and the main toolbox window. It is divided into the following four sections:

Esc button. Cancels you out of any tool operation. The Esc key on the keyboard performs the same function.

Prompt box. Shows the current tool or command, and prompts you for the user input to execute that command. CAD users commonly make the mistake of not reading prompts. When a tool is not responding correctly, look at the prompt box for instruction.

Coordinate display. Shows the current cursor location, which can be described in four ways (Absolute, Polar, Relative and Last Point), or it can be turned off.

The coordinate display is fully examined in Chapter 5.

Undo/Redo. Enables you to remove an entity that was just created or reverse the effects of a change made with an editing tool. Redo reverses the effects of the Undo tool.

You can only undo/redo one step while drawing or editing. You cannot undo a File Save.

These tools are used in the exercises throughout the book.

Learning the Menu Locations

The File item is displayed as a pull-down menu, as shown in figure 4.1.

All menu-bar items activate either toolbox icons or conventional Windows pull-down menus. The AutoSketch for Windows package installs with the File and Help menu items as pull-down menus; the other menu items default to toolbox icons. For simplicity, this book assumes that the menu-bar defaults have not been changed.

When a toolbox is active, there is a small minus sign in the upper left corner of the toolbox window. This symbol is called the *Control-menu button*. If you click on this button, a *Control-menu box* displays (see fig. 4.2), which contains commands that control the way the menu is displayed in the AutoSketch window. The last item on the list changes the menu from a toolbox to a conventional Windows pull-down menu.

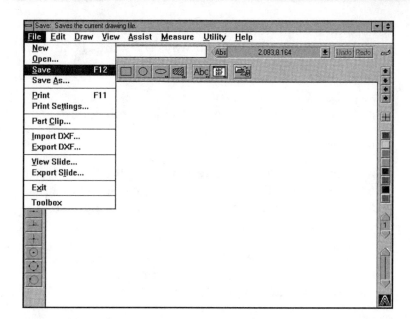

Figure 4.1:

File pull-down menu.

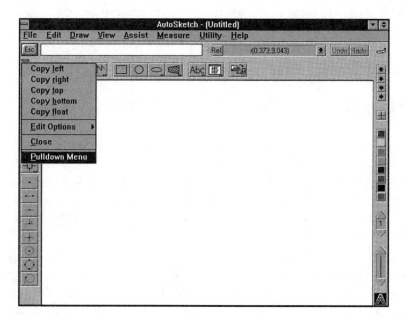

Figure 4.2:

The Control-menu box.

Converting Between Pull-Down Menus and Toolboxes

Choose **D**raw, *then click on the Control-menu button*	Displays the Control-menu box
Choose the last item from the list, **P**ulldown	The toolbox disappears and causes the pull-down menu to appear
Choose **D**raw, *then* **T**oolbox *from the bottom of the menu*	Changes the **D**raw menu back to a toolbox

The order of the tools in the pull-down menu may differ from the order of the icons displayed in the corresponding toolbox.

The **E**dit, **D**raw, **V**iew, **A**ssist, **M**easure, and **U**tility toolbox menus contain tools that relate to each toolbox name. As you perform the exercises, the menu-bar items and the tools they contain will become more familiar.

Using the Function Keys

Another way to access AutoSketch commands is to use the function keys. Commands that can be used from the function keys have the key combination next to the corresponding command in the pull-down menus. All 12 function keys have assignments in their normal state. Additional commands can be invoked by holding down the Alt or Ctrl keys, in combination with function keys F1 through F10. For example:

Alt-F1 starts the **L**ine tool
Ctrl-F7 starts the **B**ox tool
F2 is the Undo button

Creating and Editing Graphic Entities

Today's marketplace reflects a shift toward a computer-aided workplace. In the 1980s, many skeptics in the drafting and engineering fields regarded CAD as a fad that would pass. Thus, many firms are now playing catch up with those who saw the new technology as a way to save time, energy, and resources.

Companies that continue to work "on the board" remain competitive only to a point. The problem is that these firms cannot share information like CAD-based companies can. The capability to make improvements and adjust to unforeseen changes makes CAD the optimal choice.

The biggest difference between CAD and manual drafting is the medium of the project in the drawing process. A manual drawing uses a piece of paper; a CAD drawing is stored as a database until you print a hard copy.

The *database* consists of numbers and codes that define a drawing's *entities* (lines, circles, shapes) that are drawn and edited with the tools available in the software package.

Now that you are familiar with the AutoSketch graphics window, the best way to learn these concepts is through completing the exercises. In the following exercise, the AutoSketch drawing tools are used to begin a simple drawing. Figure 4.3 shows the front view of the bus.

Figure 4.3:
The completed bus drawing.

Using the Drawing Tools

The following tools are used to create entities that are the foundation of the drawing:

- Line
- Circle
- Arc
- Box
- Polyline

All CAD programs use the Cartesian-coordinate system to specify the location of points. The *Cartesian-coordinate system*, used in algebra, describes a point in two-dimensional space. The vertical axis is called the *Y axis*; the horizontal axis is called the *X axis*. The axes intersect at the *origin*, which is the 0,0 point. *Absolute coordinates* define a location as being a given distance in the X and Y directions from the datum point.

To enter the absolute coordinates of a point, use the following format:

(4,5). Specifies a point four units to the right of the lower left corner, and five units up.

All the methods used for coordinate input are reviewed entirely in Chapter 5. Using the absolute coordinates as a method of entering points, you construct the outline of the bus (see fig. 4.4). The first step of the exercise begins with the Line tool.

The Line Tool

Using the Line Tool

Choose **F**ile, *then* **N**ew	Begins a new drawing
Choose **F**ile, *then* Save **A**s	Names the drawing
In the Filename: *text box, type* **MY-4**, *and choose the* Save *button*	
Choose **D**raw, *then select the* Line *tool*	
Line Enter point: **4,2** ↵	Specifies the start point
To point: **9,2** ↵	
Line Enter point: **4,2** ↵	Tool stays active
To point: **4,4.5** ↵	

```
Line Enter point: 9,2 ↵
To point: 9,4.5 ↵
Line Enter point: 4,4.5 ↵
To point: 4.5,7.5 ↵
Line Enter point: 9,4.5 ↵
To point: 8.5,7.5 ↵
```

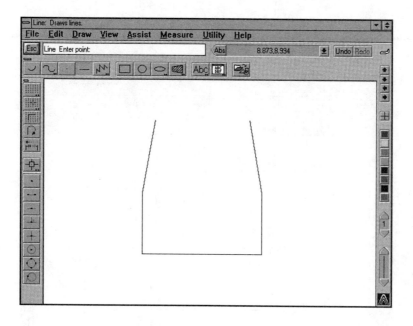

Figure 4.4:
Beginning the
bus drawing.

The Circle Tool

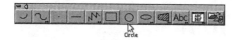

Another tool that is fundamental to most CAD programs is found
in the Draw toolbox: the *Circle* tool. When you invoke this tool, the
first prompt asks you to pick a center point. After selecting a
center point on the screen, the next prompt asks for a point on the
circle. (This is another way of asking for the *radius* of the circle.)

The point on the circle can be picked with the cursor or typed from the keyboard as coordinates.

Using the Circle Tool

From the Draw *toolbox, choose the* Circle *tool*

Circle Center point: **5,3** ↵   Locates the circle center (see fig. 4.5)

Point on circle: **5.4,3** ↵   Creates a radius of .4 units

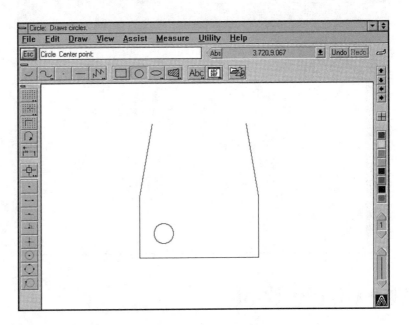

Figure 4.5:

The bus headlight.

The Arc Tool

An *arc* is a segment of a circle. It is defined by picking three points: a start point, a point on the arc, and an endpoint.

Try using the Arc tool to form the top of the bus.

Using the Arc Tool

Choose the Arc *tool*

Arc Start point: **4.5,7.5** ↵	Specifies the start point (see fig. 4.6)
Point on the arc: **6.5,8** ↵	Specifies the middle point of the arc
End point: **8.5,7.5** ↵	Specifies the endpoint

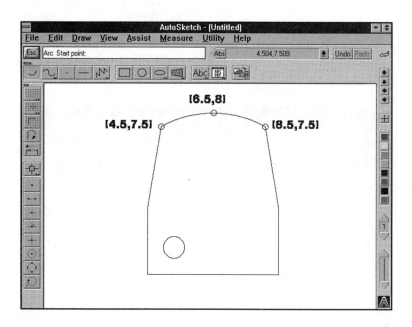

Figure 4.6:
The arc forms the top of the bus.

The Box Tool

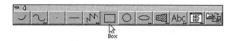

The Box tool enables you to specify opposite diagonal corners to create a rectangle. Like the other drawing tools, the corner points can be entered as coordinates or picked with the cursor.

Continue with the bus drawing by producing a destination sign for the bus by using the Box tool (see fig. 4.7).

Using the Box Tool

From the Draw *toolbox, choose the* Box *tool*

```
Box First Corner: 5.5,7 ↵
Second corner: 7.5,7.5 ↵
```
Places the second corner 2 units to the right and .5 units up from the first corner point

---

Your drawing should now resemble figure 4.7.

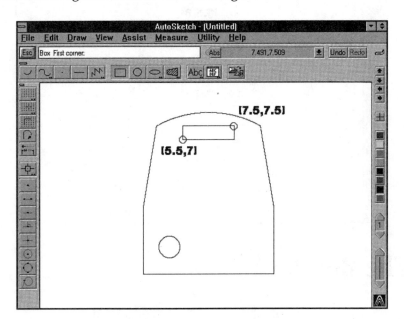

Figure 4.7:

The destination sign, drawn as a box.

The Polyline Tool

A *polyline* is composed of a series of lines and arcs that form a single, continuous entity. The lines and arcs that form the polyline have different lengths and bearing angles, but they are all one entity.

Although you pick points for the polyline, you assign control points for the whole polyline. *Control points* are used by AutoSketch in the database to define the shapes that appear on the screen. Each entity has at least two control points (except Point). A rectangle has four control points; a triangle has three control points; a polyline has as many control points as you pick while using the tool.

 Polylines are discussed in Chapter 8.

Notice that the Polyline tool icon has two small dots in the lower right corner. Any tool-icon box that displays these dots can be double-clicked on with the mouse. If you double-click on a tool-icon box, a dialog box appears that controls the settings for that tool.

 If the pull-down menus are used exclusively, the double-click option does not apply. You have to use the **D**rawing Settings tool in the **U**tility menu to adjust all tool settings.

Many of the current display boxes (coordinates, color, linetypes, and so on) in the graphics screen can also be double-clicked on. After you double-click on the Polyline tool button, a dialog box displays. The dialog box in figure 4.8 shows the current settings for the Polyline tool.

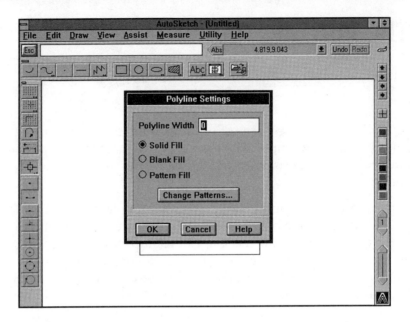

Figure 4.8:

The Polyline
Settings
dialog box.

The text box displays the current width setting. The width setting defaults to 0 and is drawn to the scale of your drawing. The Polyline tool stays active until you select the first point again, select the last point twice, or choose another tool.

In the following exercise, you change the polyline width and create a windshield for the bus.

Using the Polyline Tool

Double-click on the Polyline *tool*	Displays the Polyline Settings dialog box
In the Polyline Width *text box, type* **0**, *and choose* OK	Sets the width to 0
Polyline First point: **4.5,4.5** ↵	Specifies the first control point of the polyline
To point: **8.5,4.5** ↵	
To point: **8.1,6.6** ↵	
To point: **4.9,6.6** ↵	
To point: **4.5,4.5** ↵	Specifies the first point assigned, and ends the polyline (see fig 4.9)

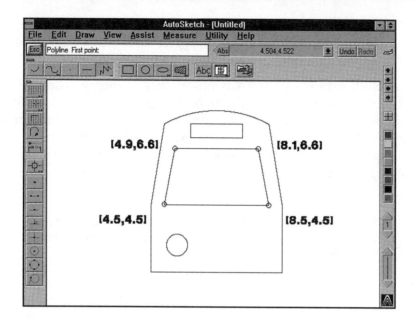

Figure 4.9:
The bus windshield.

Entity-Selection Techniques

Now that the drawing contains information, the next step in the process is *editing* the drawing. To edit the entities, they must first be selected. This is done by placing the cursor on the object and clicking.

 While using the editing tools, the cursor changes from an arrow into a pointing finger, indicating that you are in the entity-selection process.

To select several entities, use a window. A *window* enables you to select entities by using the cursor to form a box around the entities to be edited. A window box displays on the screen as a solid-line rectangle. When you select entities with a window box, only the entities that are fully surrounded by the box are selected.

A *crosses box* grabs all the entities that are crossed by the box, as well as those surrounded by the box. The crosses box displays on the screen as a dashed-line rectangle.

The selection boxes are formed automatically when you are prompted to select objects. By choosing a point and moving to the right, a window box is formed; by moving to the left after the first point is chosen, a crosses box is created. Objects selected for editing are temporarily displayed as hidden lines until after the tool completes its task.

 When you use boxes to select entities, pick the first point in an open area of the screen. Otherwise, AutoSketch thinks you are selecting single entities.

Editing Graphic Entities

The following section clarifies one of the most important aspects of CAD drafting—the capability to change a drawing. The entities that appear in the drawing area are easily deleted, scaled, stretched, copied, or moved. Entities can be modified and stored in separate files to test different ideas and designs without having to start a drawing from scratch. Once the basic ideas and outlines of a drawing are established, anyone can work on it during the process to completion.

AutoSketch for Windows has many of the editing tools that are associated with more expensive CAD packages. The capability to move, copy, resize, and erase individual entities or whole portions of a drawing make CAD drafting desirable in a market that has time constraints and constant changes. Mastering the editing techniques in a CAD package can reduce the amount of time it takes to complete a project from design through production. The following editing tools are discussed:

- Erase
- Break
- Copy
- Move
- Mirror
- Fillet

In the following sections, these tools are used to continue drawing the bus.

The Erase Tool

The Erase tool, the most commonly used editing tool, gives you the ability to remove entities from the drawing. While the Erase tool is active, all selected entities are erased.

 The Undo button (or F2) reverses the effects of the Erase tool.

Using the Erase Tool

Choose **E***dit,* *then select the* Erase *tool*

`Erase Select object:` *Pick any of the entities in the drawing area*

Selected entities disappear

`Erase Select object:` *Pick in the drawing area away from any entities, and move the mouse to the right or left to form a crosses or window box*

continues

Pick the Undo *button in the horizontal status bar, or press the F2 key repeatedly until all erased entities return*	Undoes the Erase tool

The Copy Tool

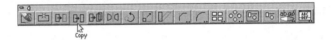

The Copy tool can duplicate, or copy, an entity or group of entities to another place in the drawing. The copied objects have the same properties as the originals. You are asked to select an object(s), then to specify a base point in the drawing area. This base point can be specified by picking with the cursor or by entering coordinates from the keyboard.

You are then prompted for a To point (which specifies where to move the selected objects). The selected objects are moved in relation to the second point specified.

In the following exercise, the headlight is copied to form the base of the tire.

Using the Copy Tool

Choose **E**dit, *then select the* Copy *tool, or press* F6	
Copy Select objects: *Pick the headlight at* ① *(see fig. 4.10)*	Highlights the circle
From point: **5,3** ↵	Defines the base point
To point: **5,1.4** ↵	Defines the destination point

108

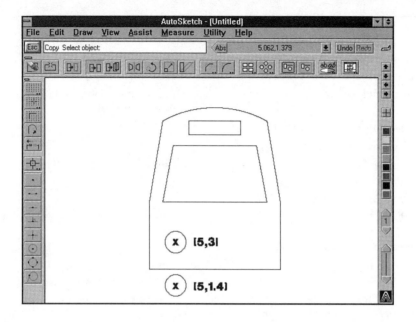

Figure 4.10:
The bus'
headlight
forms the
tire base.

The Break Tool

The Break tool enables you to split or remove a section of an entity. After the gap is created, the entities that are produced can be erased or edited with other tools. The prompt asks you to select the object to break, and you then pick two points on the entity that will define the portion to be removed. If the two points are the same, the entity is split at that location.

The following exercise is divided into two parts. Figure 4.11 shows the lines that will be created in the first half; figure 4.12 shows the results of using the Break tool during the second half of the exercise.

Using the Break Tool

*Choose **D**raw, then select the* Line *tool*

```
Line Enter point: 5.4,1.4 ↵
```
Picks the first point on the circle

```
To point: 5.4,2 ↵
```
Picks the second point on the bottom of the bus

```
Line Enter point: 4.6,2 ↵
```

```
To point: 4.6,1.4 ↵
```

*Choose **E**dit, then the* Break *tool, or press the F4 key*
Lines are drawn (see fig.4.11)

```
Break Select object:
```
Pick the tire (see fig. 4.12)
Highlights the circle as the entity to break

```
First break point: 5.4,1.4 ↵
```

```
Second break: 4.6,1.4 ↵
```
Removes the top half of the circle to form the tire

Choose the Redraw button, the Autodesk logo in the lower right corner of the graphics window
Refreshes the drawing area

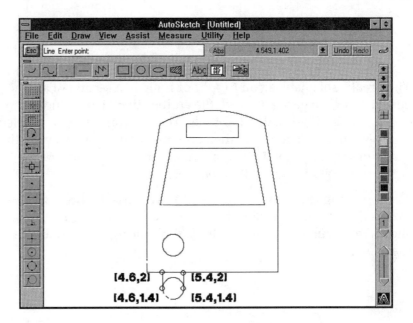

Figure 4.11:

Using lines to form the sides of the tire.

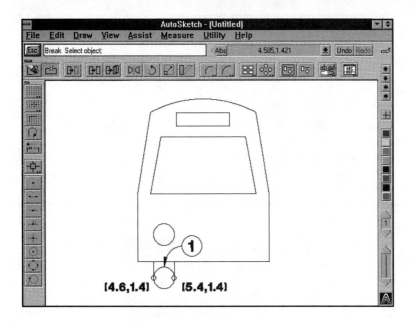

Figure 4.12:
The completed tire.

The Fillet Tool

The Fillet tool enables you to draw an arc as a blend between two entities. You can create fillets between lines, arcs, and circles. Fillet can also be applied to the corners of a polyline. There are two ways to perform a fillet: by selecting the two lines separately or by forming a crosses/window box around the entities to be filleted.

In the following exercise, you use a crosses box to select the windshield polyline for filleting.

Using the Fillet Tool

Double-click on the Fillet *tool*

Brings up the Fillet Setting dialog box

Type **0.2** *in the* Fillet Radius *text box, and choose* **OK** *(see fig. 4.13)*

`Fillet Select object(s):` *Pick at* ②
(see fig. 4.14)

Forms a crosses box

`Crosses/window corner:` *Pick at* ①

Creates a .2-radius fillet

Repeat the preceding action three times to form fillets on all four corners of the windshield.

Figure 4.13:

The Fillet Setting dialog box.

Figure 4.14:

The bus windshield with filleted corners.

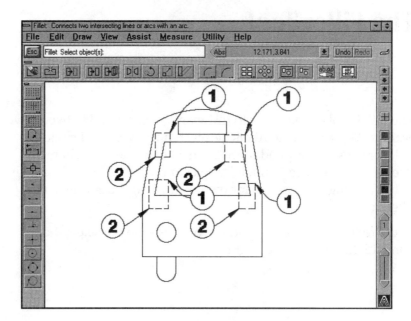

The Move Tool

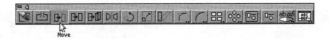

The Move tool moves an entity or group of entities from one point on the screen to another. *Moving* an object is similar to copying one—after selecting the entities to be moved, you specify a base point, and then specify a new position relative to the base point.

In the next exercise, you use the Move tool to move the destination sign down to the grill on the front of the bus.

Using the Move Tool

Choose the Move *tool*

`Move Select object:` *Pick the destination sign at* ① *(see fig. 4.15)*	Highlights the destination sign
`From point:` **5.5,7** ↵	Defines the base point
`To point:` **5.5,3.5** ↵	Completes the move

The Mirror Tool

The *Mirror tool* enables you to create a mirrored image of an entity or group of entities. This tool is similar to the Copy tool, but the resulting entities are copied as a mirrored image. The objects are mirrored across a *mirror line,* which is defined as two points.

- If the mirror line is *vertical*, the object mirrors right or left.

- If the mirror line is *horizontal*, the object mirrors up or down.

- If the mirror line is *angular*, the objects mirror perpendicular to the mirror line.

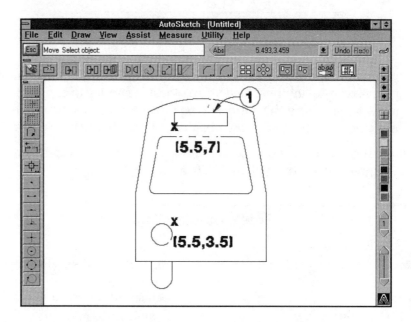

Figure 4.15:

Creating the bus grill.

You can also mirror text, but AutoSketch does not reverse the characters. Mirrored text always reads left to right.

In the following exercise, you mirror the bus tire and headlight to the right side of the bus.

Using the Mirror Tool

Choose the Mirror *tool*

Mirror Select object: *Pick at* ①, then ② NO FIGURE TO SHOW POINTS   Forms a selection box

Base point: **6.5,3.5** ↵   Specifies the first point on the mirror line

Second point: **6.5,0** ↵   Specifies the second point on the mirror line

---

The Multi-copy Tool

The Multi-copy tool is the same as the Copy tool, with one exception: it enables you to continue copying the selected objects until you have completed the task.

When you use the Multi-copy tool, the base point changes with each copied object. After the first base point and "To point" are established, the next "To point" is set in relation to the last point specified.

In the following exercise, you use the Multi-copy tool to create the rest of the bus grill and complete the drawing.

Using the Multi-copy Tool

Choose the Multi-copy *tool*

```
Muliple Copy Select object:            Highlights the box
```
Pick grill at ① WHAT FIGURE

```
From point: 5.5,3.5 ↵                  Defines the base point
To point: 5.5,2.9 ↵
To point: 5.5,2.3 ↵
To point: 5.5,7 ↵
To point: TURN OFF MULTI-COPY         Saves the file
```
Choose **F**ile, *then* Save **A**s

The next section demonstrates AutoSketch's capability to provide built-in help features.

115

Using the Help Features of AutoSketch

Like most Windows programs, AutoSketch provides you with an on-screen help menu that gives you access to information about using the program. *Help menus* contain commands that can answer questions you have about any of the tools, commands, words, or phrases used in AutoSketch. Like the File menu, the Help menu defaults to a pull-down menu. The menu lists several commands that are discussed in the following sections.

Activating the SmartCursor

The *SmartCursor* is listed under the Help menu. As you pass over the different tools, the SmartCursor displays each name. A small checkmark in front of the SmartCursor item in the Help menu tells you it is on (by default, it is always on). When the SmartCursor is on, a label appears next to the cursor, identifying the icon near the cursor point.

Turning on Quick Help

Quick Help is also available under the Help menu. This utility displays a brief comment about each of the tools as you pass the cursor over the icon. The information displays over the title bar, at the top of the screen. For example, if you place the cursor over the airplane in the upper right corner, AutoSketch displays this information over the title bar:

```
Aerial View: Displays the drawing in a small window to help
you navigate.
```

While you are becoming familiar with AutoSketch for Windows, Quick Help can be invaluable.

Accessing Help with the Contents Tool

Another way to access help is to use the Contents tool in the **Help** menu. After you choose it, you see a dialog box with an alphabetical list of reference topics that pertain to AutoSketch. The list contains all the toolboxes, tools, dialog boxes, buttons, and other features of AutoSketch. It also gives detailed descriptions of topics—for example, "File Naming Conventions" and "Sample Drawings."

The scroll bar and the up/down arrows on the right of the dialog box enable you to move up and down through the list. The following four buttons at the top of the window have specific functions:

- The **C**ontents button displays the contents of the current help file. Clicking on this button always takes you back to the original list of the current help file.

- The **S**earch button enables you to search for a specific topic.

- The **B**ack button returns you to the previous screen. As long as the button is highlighted, you can continue to move back through the screens.

- The His**t**ory button shows a list of help topics that you have been using. This is an easier method of accessing past information.

The following menu pull-downs in the Help menu bar are similar to the AutoSketch menu-bar options:

- The **F**ile menu enables you to open any existing help files on your hard drive, to set up and print the current help document, and to exit Help.

- The **E**dit menu enables you to place parts of the help document in the Clipboard, and to annotate or create notes that are attached to the help topics. If an annotation is linked to a help file, a small green paper clip appears in the first sentence of the topic.

- The Book**m**ark menu enables you to mark topics for easy reference. The bookmarks that are created appear in a list under the menu.

- The **H**elp function in the AutoSketch menu bar explains how to use help features.

Using the Search Tool

Using the Search Tool is similar to using an index of a book. It enables you to choose topics from a list or to specify search criteria.

When you specify search criteria in the Search window, you are given a list of topics that are related. By using the **w**ord option, you can enter a word or phrase. Observe the list as it tries to anticipate the word that you are trying to search.

You use the Search command in the following exercise.

Using Search

Choose **H**elp, *then* **S**earch	Displays the Search window
Type `control` *in the text box*	Alphabetical list follows the text string
Pick `control` menu *in the list, and click on the* **S**how Topics *button*	Displays a list of topics that relate to Control menus

continues

Click on the Toolbox Control-Menu Button, *and choose* **G**o To

Scroll down the information until you see Open toolbox *in green lettering*

Click on the Open toolbox *lettering*

Opens the help information on opening toolboxes

Select the **B**ack *button*

Returns to the toolbox Control-Menu button help information

Choose **F**ile, *then* E**x**it

You can close the Search command at any time by double-clicking on the Control-menu box in the upper left corner of the dialog box.

Ending Your Drawing Session

After you work hard on your CAD drawing, the most important step is to be sure that it is saved on the hard drive. As you work on the drawing, the graphics database is stored in a place called RAM. *RAM*, random access memory, is easily accessed by the computer, but is used as a temporary work space in which AutoSketch stores data. By performing a save, the computer takes the information out of RAM and stores it on the hard drive in the form of an SKD file.

When you turn off the computer, the data in RAM is lost. Save your drawing often!

Saving Your Work with the Save and Save As Tools

At the beginning of the chapter, you used the Save **A**s command to name the drawing. The **S**ave and Save **A**s commands both save information to the hard drive as a drawing file with an SKD extension. After you have given the drawing a name, and saved it the first time, any subsequent saves that you perform automatically overwrite the existing file. The Save **A**s command enables you to rename the file or to respecify the directory into which the SKD file is saved.

 The Save **A**s command always brings up the Save As File dialog box, which enables you to modify the name of the file or to redirect the path.

Another way to quickly save your work is to intermittently press the F12 key. As long as the file has a name, the F12 key saves the drawing. If you have given the file a name and used Save **A**s, the file name displays in the Filename text box. Any preset name or variable within any tool is often described as the *default* value. In this case, the name of the existing file is the default—you can rename the file at this point if you want.

Replacing Your Existing Drawing with Another Drawing

The **O**pen command, located in the **F**ile menu, enables you to open existing SKD files. By using the path features and keeping track of the location of your saved files, you can jump from drawing to drawing with the click of the mouse.

At the bottom of the File menu, there is a list of the last five files that have been opened in AutoSketch. Choosing one of these drawing files is a shortcut to using the Open command.

The New command, under the File menu, enables you to create a new file from scratch. Although you can only edit one file at a time, the capability to jump between the drawings is one of Windows' most powerful features. In the exercise that follows, you open a series of files, and jump back and forth between them.

Opening Files

Choose File, then Open

Double-click on the TRY-1 *icon box in the LAW directory*   Ic   Loads the TRY-1 file

Choose File, then Open

Double-click on the TRY-2 *icon box in the LAW directory*   Loads the TRY-2 file

Choose File, then Open

Double-click the TRY-3 *icon box in the LAW directory*   Loads the TRY-3 file

Choose File, then select any of the five files at the bottom of the menu   Loads any of the files listed

---

Exiting AutoSketch

Exit, located in the File menu, enables you to quit the AutoSketch program. If you have made changes to the drawing since the last save, a dialog box appears and asks if you want to save the changes, discard the changes, or cancel the command and return to AutoSketch.

If you have not performed a save during the drawing session, AutoSketch does not allow you to exit without prompting you to save your work. If you enter a file name that already exists in the current path, another dialog box appears to ask if you want to overwrite the existing file. Make a habit of organizing your work when saving files—it is easy to make modifications to a file and give it a new name, but this practice quickly fills up your hard drive.

 Exit can be invoked by pressing Alt-F4.

Summary

This chapter showed you how to use some basic drawing and editing tools. Although only a few of the editing and drawing tools were used, these tools provide you with a solid base for your work. Many of the drawing and editing tools work in a similar fashion. Remember to read the prompt box to see what information AutoSketch requires.

You were introduced to the graphics window. You learned the difference between a toolbox and a pull-down menu. The function keys were introduced as another method of invoking the various tools.

The **H**elp menu was examined as a method of accessing information during a drawing session. Remember to use the help functions to learn more about the capabilities of AutoSketch. Finally, the methods used to save, end, and exit the drawing were shown.

In the next chapter, you will create a production drawing that includes using many other CAD techniques available in AutoSketch.

Creating a Production Drawing

This chapter shows you how to use CAD as a tool in the real world. So far, you have been experimenting with CAD to learn some of its basic tools, but have not used CAD for its real purpose—to efficiently produce drawings that can be used for production purposes.

In this chapter, you will learn new skills and tools to make a production drawing for adding a bathroom to an existing structure. The skills you develop in this chapter include drawing-setup capability, coordinate-entry methods, entity organization, and accurate drawing capability.

Setting Up for a Production Drawing

One of the most important skills to learn is how to set up a drawing to provide the foundation for efficient and accurate drafting.

Many of the same setup considerations you make in manual drafting also apply to CAD drafting. These considerations include the drawing's sheet size, object size, scale, and unit of measure.

The process for determining the drawing's setup parameters in CAD is different from manual drafting. In CAD, once these parameters have been set up for a particular drawing type, they can be saved and later retrieved to start another drawing.

Understanding Scale in CAD Drawings

In CAD, all objects are drawn in their real-world sizes. It does not matter if you are drawing in feet and inches or in light-years— everything is drawn in actual size.

This is the opposite of the way things are done in manual drafting. In manual drafting, objects are usually scaled down to fit on a sheet of paper. In CAD, the electronic paper is large enough to draw anything.

 Drawing in real-world units lessens the likelihood of making size-related errors because you do not have to think about the scale of the object.

In CAD, the only time you have to think about scale is when you set up or plot the drawing. You must think about scale when you set up a drawing to have a visual representation of your electronic sheet, and to know how to size text and symbols. When you plot the drawing, you have to make the objects fit on paper. Between setting up and plotting the drawing, you do not have to worry about scale.

To set up a CAD drawing, you first determine the drawing's scale factor and limits.

Determining a Scale Factor

A *scale factor* is a number that you use to determine your drawing limits, text size, symbol size, line width, linetype scale, and plot scale.

To determine the scale factor, you need the unit of measure for the drawing (this chapter's example uses feet as the unit of measure). You also need the scale of the drawing when it is plotted to paper. (In this chapter, the traditional architectural scale of 1/4"=1' is the plot scale of the bathroom addition.)

To calculate a scale factor, take the plot scale and convert it to a ratio in the form of 1:x, in which x is the scale factor. The steps for converting this chapter's plot scale to a ratio are the same for any scale.

First, make both sides of the scale equation share the same units, and show the equation as a ratio. For this chapter's scale, both sides of the equation are converted to inches. The feet and inches marks can be dropped when both sides share the same units:

> 1/4"=1' becomes 1/4:12

Next, the ratio needs to be expressed in the form 1:x. Using algebra, you can multiply both sides of the ratio by the same factor and still maintain the ratio. In this example, multiplying both sides of the ratio by 4 yields the desired form:

> 1/4 (4) : 12 (4) becomes 1:48

Thus, the scale factor for this chapter is 48, which you can use to calculate the drawing limits.

Calculating Drawing Limits

The *limits* of a CAD drawing are the same as sheet size in manual drafting. In CAD, the electronic sheet is scaled up, based on the scale factor, to fit around the full-size object.

The bathroom addition you draw in this chapter is approximately 12'×21', which translates into 144"×252". It is easier to calculate the limits if you work with one unit type (in this chapter, you work in inches when calculating the limits).

Test a sheet size to see if the bathroom addition will fit. First, try a C-size sheet of 22"×17". Multiply each dimension of the sheet by the scale factor to see the size of the electronic sheet:

> 22 (48)×17 (48) becomes 1056×816

A C-size sheet with a 48-scale factor makes an electronic sheet of 1056"×816"—too big!

Now try an A-size sheet:

> 11 (48)×8.5 (48) becomes 528×408

An A-size sheet scaled up by a factor of 48 gives an electronic sheet of 528"×408", which fits around the 144"×252" bathroom addition.

Setting the Drawing Limits in AutoSketch

In AutoSketch, a drawing's limits are set in the Grid/Snap/Limits Settings dialog box, which is accessed with the Drawing Settings tool (located in the Utility toolbox).

The Drawing Settings tool also provides access to many other settings, discussed in this chapter and following chapters.

The Drawing Settings tool brings up the Drawing Settings dialog box (see fig 5.1). The Grid/Snap/Limits option of the Drawing Settings dialog box accesses the Grid/Snap/Limits Settings Dialog box.

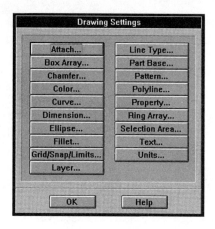

Figure 5.1:
The Drawing Settings dialog box.

When you start a new drawing, the default lower left corner of the limits is the coordinate 0,0. The default upper right corner of the limits is 12,9. In the first exercise, you set the limits to the calculated limits size of 528"×408".

Setting the Limits

Start AutoSketch from Windows. If AutoSketch is already running, begin a new drawing.

Choose **U**tility, *then select the Drawing Settings tool*	Displays the Drawing Settings dialog box
Choose the Grid/Snap/Limits button (see fig. 5.1)	
Double-click on the Drawing Limits Right *text box*	Highlights 12
Type **528**	Sets the X coordinate of the upper right corner
Double-click on the Drawing Limits Top *text box*	Highlights 9
Type **408**	Sets the Y coordinate of the upper right corner
Click on OK	Closes the Drawing Settings dialog box

Now the limits are set for an 11"×8.5" sheet at a scale factor of 48. Although the limits frame the drawing, you can draw, move, and edit objects outside the limits, which are used by other tools to give you a visual frame of reference in which you can draw.

The next step in setting up a drawing is to determine what type of units to use for distances, and to let AutoSketch know what type of units you want to use and how much precision to display.

Selecting Your Drawing Units

You determine a drawing's units based on the type of drawing you want to create. In CAD, *units* refers to the system used to define a unit distance. You decide if one unit in AutoSketch equals one nanometer, millimeter, inch, foot, furlong, mile, or light-year. In other words, one unit in AutoSketch can represent any linear distance. It is common in the United States to have one unit equal one inch (this chapter also follows this convention).

Choosing the Units-Display Format

AutoSketch can display distances in two different formats: decimal units and architectural units. The default format, *decimal* notation, is commonly used in electrical and mechanical drawings and in those that require very small or very large measurements. In electrical and mechanical inches, it is common to use decimal inches to measure distances. For example, the distance 1'-3 3/4" is represented as 15.750.

The amount of precision displayed by decimal units can be set from zero to six decimal places. Changing the displayed precision does not change the accuracy—AutoSketch always stores all points and calculates all measurements to six decimal places, regardless of the setting of the units-display precision. If the precision is set to two decimal places, and you enter a coordinate with three decimal places, AutoSketch displays a rounded-off figure; the original, more accurate number is stored in the database. The default precision for decimal notation is three decimal places.

The second unit-display format is *architectural*, which displays measurements in feet and inches. For example, 20.643' is displayed in the architectural-units format as 20'-7 23/32". The precision of architectural units can be rounded off to the nearest inch or carried down to 1/64". The default precision for architectural units is 1/4".

 Even though you may not need 1/64" precision, it is a good idea to set the architectural-units precision to the maximum. This decreases the likelihood of picking incorrect points due to round-off errors while drawing.

In the following exercise, you change the units display to architectural. Before you begin, note that the coordinates in the coordinate display box are in decimal form.

Changing Drawing Units

Continue from the previous exercise.

Choose **U**tility, *then select the Drawing Settings tool*	Accesses the Drawing Settings dialog box
Click on the Units button (located at the bottom of the right column)	Accesses the Units Display Settings dialog box
Click on the radio button next to Architectural (see fig. 5.2)	Sets the units display to architectural
Click on the radio button next to 1/4"	Sets the display precision to 1/4"
Click on OK	Closes the Units Display Settings dialog box
Click on OK	Closes the Drawing Settings dialog box, and makes changes to the settings

---

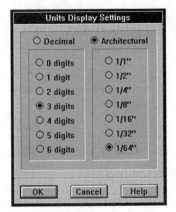

Figure 5.2:

The Units Display Settings dialog box.

The units are now displayed as feet, inches, and 1/4-inch increments. With AutoSketch set to architectural units, you can use the following formats for entering distances from the keyboard:

- 56.576453
- 4'-8-37/64
- 4'8-37/64"
- 4' 8 37/64

 While architectural units are activated, you cannot input a decimal distance with a foot-mark suffix (for example, 22.750'). AutoSketch returns an invalid input-error message.

In architectural units display mode, AutoSketch assumes that you are specifying inches if you do not indicate feet with the quote mark (this is why the inch marks have been omitted in some of the keyboard-input examples).

Understanding Snap and Grid

Snap and Grid function like graph paper in manual drafting. By using Snap and Grid, you can quickly and accurately pick points with the cursor.

Snap, when activated, forces the cursor to move in increments of a user-specified distance.

Grid, when activated, displays grid points as dots on the screen. The grid gives you a visual frame of reference for distance while drawing entities and indicates graphically the limits of a drawing.

The grid and snap spacings do not have to be set to the same distance. For example, Snap can be set to 1/4-inch, and Grid can be set to one inch. Usually, the grid spacing is set to a larger value than the snap spacing.

The aspect ratio (X distance to Y distance) of the Grid and Snap settings does not have to be square. For example, the aspect ratio can be set to four units by six units.

The snap and grid spacings are set in the Grid/Snap/Limits Settings dialog box (see fig. 5.3). You can access the Grid/Snap/Limits Settings dialog box by double-clicking on the Grid or Snap tool in the vertical Assist toolbox. You can turn Snap and Grid on or off by clicking on the Snap and Grid tools in the Assist toolbox.

Often, Snap can cause difficulties when you try to select an entity. If this happens, turn off the Snap tool.

In the following exercise, you set the snap and grid settings for the bathroom project.

Changing the Snap and Grid

Continue from the previous exercise.

Double-click on the Grid tool on the vertical Assist toolbox	Accesses the Grid/Snap/Limits dialog box (See fig. 5.3)
Click on OK in the warning dialog box	Ignores the irrelevant dialog box
*Double-click in the Snap X: text box, and type **6***	Sets Snap to 6"

Notice how all the text boxes changed to 6. Next, you turn off this feature and set Grid larger than Snap.

Click on the Grid=Snap check box to turn it off	
*Double-click in the Grid X: text box, and type **24***	Sets Grid to 2'
Click on OK	Closes the Grid/Snap/Limits Settings dialog box

Move the cursor around the drawing area. Notice how its operation has not changed.

Click on the Grid tool in the vertical Assist toolbox	Turns on the grid, and redraws the screen
Click on the Snap tool in the vertical Assist toolbox	Turns on Snap

Move the cursor around the drawing area again. Notice how the cursor now jumps exactly six inches at a time.

Figure 5.3:

Grid/Snap/Limits Settings dialog box.

The next step in making a production drawing is to lay down the organizing groundwork for drawing objects.

Organizing Drawings with Layers, Colors, and Linetypes

Some of the most useful tools of CAD are the ones that help you organize drawing elements. These tools give you the ability to draw entities on different layers, control layer visibility, assign different colors to individual entities, and assign different linetypes to different entities.

Layer, color, and linetype are characteristics or properties of every entity drawn in AutoSketch. These properties are stored in the drawing database, along with an entity's control points.

How To Use Layers

In CAD, *layers* are analogous to sheets of acetate, which are stacked on top of each other in manual drafting. If you are not familiar with the use of acetate sheets in manual drafting, you can visualize layers as if they were sheets of glass. A different type of

133

information is drawn on each pane. When all the panes are stacked on top of each other and viewed from the top, you see a composite view of the entire drawing.

AutoSketch gives you 10 layers that you can use to organize your drawing. Each layer can be made invisible by turning it off. By controlling the layer visibility, you can turn off layers that contain unnecessary information or get in the way of the drawing process.

Turning off unnecessary layers shortens the time it takes AutoSketch to redraw the screen.

Until now, you have been drawing on layer 1, which is the default layer. This is fine until you decide that you want to view just the walls or see only the plumbing fixtures of the bathroom addition. It is common, for example, in the architectural field to work with structural engineers who are only interested in the walls and wall openings. If you have organized the drawing information by layer, you can open the drawing, make the unnecessary layers invisible, and show the engineers a plot of the needed information.

What types of information should you separate into layers? First, you need to decide what information your drawing will contain and how to group it. Most CAD drawings fall into one of the following two categories:

- **Architectural drawings**. *Architectural drawings* are usually organized by structure component. Some common structure components are existing structure, planned structure, electrical, and plumbing. There are other elements that are related to the drawing itself, such as dimensions, annotations, title block and border, and text, which also are placed on separate layers. One layer is usually used as a *scratch*, or *construction*, layer.

- **Mechanical drawings.** *Mechanical drawings* are usually organized by object component and material. Fasteners, assemblies, auxiliary views, steel components, plastic components, and so on, are commonly put on separate layers. The same nonobject-component related layers of architectural drawings are also used in mechanical drawings (dimension, text, and so forth).

Later in this section is a table with an example of a layer, color and linetype structure.

Controlling Layers in AutoSketch

Layers are controlled through the Layer Settings Dialog Box. You can access this dialog box from the Drawing Settings dialog box by choosing the Layer option. You can also double-click on the Current Layer display button on the vertical status bar.

To change the current layer, click on the radio button to the left of the layer you want to be current. You can also change the current layer by clicking on the scroll arrows on the Current Layer display on the vertical status bar.

Changing the Current Layer

Continue from the previous exercise.

Click on the down arrow of the Current Layer display button   Sets the current layer to 10

Double-click on the Current Layer display button (the current layer number itself)   Accesses the Layer Settings dialog box (see fig. 5.4)

Notice that the current layer is now 10, as indicated by the radio button.

Click on OK

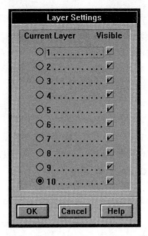

Figure 5.4:

The Layer Settings dialog box.

The dialog box shows the current layer and the visibility status of each layer. Only one layer can be the current layer; the other nine can be either visible or invisible. New entities are drawn on the current layer. To make a layer invisible, remove the checkmark from the box to the right of the corresponding layer by clicking on the checkmark.

 You can make the current layer invisible, but this practice is confusing and is not recommended. If the current layer is invisible, new entities remain on the screen until the next redraw is performed.

Specifying Entity Colors

Color is an entity property that is useful for visualizing the organization of entities in a CAD drawing. Color in a CAD drawing can be used for two purposes. The first is to assign the same color to all entities on a given layer, which makes it easy to identify all the entities on a specific layer at a glance. The second use of color CAD programs is to specify the pen thickness used to draw the entity when plotted; some multi-pen plotters change pens to plot the various entity colors.

AutoSketch supports up to 255 colors, and each color has a specific number. The numbers 1 through 8 are the default colors shown in the Color Palette, as follows:

1=red	5=blue
2=yellow	6=magenta
3=green	7=black
4=cyan	8=grey

The Color Palette on the Vertical Status bar displays eight colors. By double-clicking on any of the eight colors, you can assign a new color to the pallet by using Available Colors in the Color Settings dialog box.

For most purposes, there is no need to change the basic eight colors of the default palette.

So far, all the entities you have drawn have been in the default color—black. To change the current color, select a different color button from the pallet on the vertical status bar, and begin drawing. All new entities are drawn with the new current color.

In AutoSketch, color is assigned to individual entities. If you have chosen to assign a color to all entities on a layer, and you change layers, you also have to change the color to match the existing entities on the current layer.

Drawing a Grey Border

Continue from the previous exercise.

Click on the grey color button in the Color Palette on the vertical status bar	Sets the current color to grey
Choose **D***raw, then double-click on the Polyline tool*	Opens the Polyline Settings dialog box
In the Polyline Width text box, type **1.5***, and choose* OK	Sets the width to 1.5", and closes the dialog box
Polyline First point: **12,12** ↵	Defines the first point of the polyline
To point: **516,12** ↵	Selects the points of the polyline
To point: **516,396** ↵	
To point: **12,396** ↵	
To point: **12,12** ↵	Closes the polyline

In the previous exercise, the polyline width of 1.5" was determined by taking the intended width of the border (0.031") multiplying it by the scale factor (48), and rounding the result to the nearest one-half inch. When plotted, the border is 0.031 inches wide.

You now have a grey border drawn on layer 10. Although the layer and color properties for the border entities are not correct, they will be changed in a later exercise.

Specifying Entity Linetypes

Linetype is another property that can be assigned to entities. *Linetypes* are used in both manual drafting and CAD to convey information about a drawn object. For example, a dashed line is used to represent a hidden feature of an object.

AutoSketch offers 10 linetypes, and each linetype has a unique pattern that can be scaled in the Line Type Settings dialog box. As the scale changes, the relative size and spacing of the pattern also change.

To change the current linetype, use the up or down arrow buttons on the Current Linetype display. You can use the Line Type Settings dialog box to change the current linetype and set the linetype scale. The Line Type Settings dialog box can be accessed by double-clicking the line on in the Current Linetype display box on the vertical status bar or by choosing the Linetype option from the Drawing Settings dialog box.

Figure 5.5 shows the Line Type Settings dialog box, which displays the current linetype, all available linetypes, and appearances of the various linetypes at the current linetype scale.

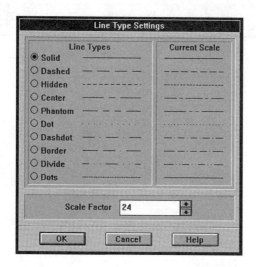

Figure 5.5:
The Line Type Settings dialog box.

In the sample drawing of the bathroom addition, the default linetype-scale factor of 1 is too small to show a line's pattern properly. The correct linetype scale is somewhat subjective, but a good starting point is a value that is one-half of your drawing's scale factor.

Wide polylines, text, dimensions, pattern fills, and leaders are not affected by the current linetype.

Like the color property, linetypes are assigned on an entity-by-entity basis, depending on the current linetype. If you change to a layer that you have assigned a specific linetype, you also have to change the current linetype before drawing new entities.

The following table outlines the layer, color, and linetype scheme for this chapter's example. You can use this scheme for your drawings, or you can modify it to conform to your standards.

Table 5.1 Entity-Property Organization			
Layer No.	*Layer Name*	*Color*	*Linetype*
1	Existing Structure	Grey	Continuous
2	New Structure	Black	Continuous
3	Electrical	Red	Continuous
4	Plumbing	Magenta	Continuous
5	Hidden Objects	Cyan	Dashed
6	Dimensions	Blue	
7	Text	Green	
8	Border	Green	Continuous
9	Scratch	Yellow	Continuous

Once you have developed your entity-property organization, write it down, and keep it handy for quick reference.

Changing Entity Properties

No matter how well you plan and organize your entities, mistakes happen, or you may change your mind about how to organize your drawing. For example, you may change the layer but forget to change the color and linetype, or you may discover that the color yellow doesn't show up well on your monitor. AutoSketch has a tool called Property(Change) that solves your entity-property problems.

With the Property(Change) tool, you can change an entity's color, layer, linetype, pattern properties, polyline width, and dimension properties. You can choose which entity properties get changed with the Property Settings dialog box, which you can access by double-clicking on the Property(Change) tool or through the Property option of the Drawing Settings dialog box. Figure 5.6 shows the Property Settings dialog box.

Figure 5.6:
Property Settings dialog box.

Changing the property of existing entities is a two-step process. First, set the current properties to the desired new values. For example, if you want to change the entities on the Existing Structure layer to layer 10, the color to red, and the linetype to phantom, make these property values current. Then choose the Property(Change) tool, and select all the entities you want to change.

To make the selection of entities with the Property(Change) tool easier, turn off all unnecessary layers. This reduces the amount of clutter on the screen.

Changing Entity Properties

Continue from the previous exercise.

Double-click on the Current Layer button	Accesses the Layer Settings dialog box
Click on the layer 8 radio button	Sets layer 8 current
Click on OK	Accepts changes
Click on the color green on the Color Palette	Makes green the current color
Choose **E***dit, then the Property(Change) tool*	
`Change Property Select object:` *Select all the entities with a crosses box*	Changes the border to the current property settings

---

Now that you have some strategies for organizing your drawings, and you have set up your drawing, the next step is to save your settings and entities.

Using Prototype Drawings

A *prototype* is a drawing that contains standardized settings and objects that are used as a basis for new drawings. For example, suppose you are producing an architectural floor plan for a five-story building. If the scale, title block, and outline of the structure are basically the same, you can use a prototype drawing with these objects and settings as the starting points for each floor. You are then assured that each drawing contains the same settings and parameters.

Faking Prototype Drawings in AutoSketch

AutoSketch does not support the use of prototype drawings as a feature, but prototype support can be easily faked. The basic technique for creating a prototype drawing is to start a new drawing, make your standard settings and objects, and then name and save the drawing. To use a prototype drawing as the basis for a new drawing, open the saved prototype drawing, then save the prototype with a new name before making any edits to the drawing.

Now that all settings are made, and all objects are drawn for an A-size architectural drawing, it is a good time to save the drawing as a prototype drawing. In the following exercise, the current drawing is saved as PROTOA-A, and a new drawing is started—named MYCHAP05, with PROTOA-A as the prototype drawing. MYCHAP05 is the name of the drawing file for the bathroom addition.

Saving and Using a Prototype Drawing

Continue from the previous exercise.

Set the current layer to 2, the current color to black, and the polyline width to 0.

Choose **F**ile, *then* **S**ave, *and name the drawing* PROTOA-A

Choose **F**ile, *then* **N**ew   Starts a new drawing

Now you start a drawing based on the prototype drawing.

Choose **F**ile, *then* **O**pen, *and open the* PROTOA-A *drawing*

Choose **F**ile, *then* Save **A**s, *and save the drawing as* MYCHAP05

You now have a drawing named MYCHAP05 that is based on the prototype PROTOA-A.

 It may seem like too much work to set up a drawing, but the effort you put into planning and setting up a drawing properly greatly speeds up the design and drafting process. Also, once you have a prototype drawing completed, future setup time is almost zero.

Understanding Coordinate-Entry Methods

In Chapter 4, you were introduced to the concept of the Cartesian-coordinate system, which you used to specify points while using the tools. In this system, a point is located with an X,Y coordinate pair, on an imaginary grid, with an origin at (0,0), and stretching infinitely in the X and Y directions. Most CAD programs use this method of point specification. It is easy to understand, and is a universal way to define a point in a 2D plane. Three-dimensional CAD programs add the Z component to the Cartesian-coordinate system to specify points anywhere in 3D space.

There are many ways to specify points in the Cartesian-coordinate system. AutoSketch supports three methods: absolute, relative, and relative polar.

Using Absolute Coordinates

All the points you have specified so far have been expressed as absolute coordinates. When you specify an *absolute coordinate*, you are specifying the distance from the Cartesian-coordinate system origin. You specify a distance in the X axis, followed by a comma, then a distance in the Y axis. In the following exercise, you use absolute coordinates to draw the existing structure of the house that gets the bathroom addition.

Using Absolute Coordinates

Continue from the previous exercise with the MYCHAP05 drawing.

Set the current layer to 1, and the current color to grey.

Choose the Line tool

`Line Enter point: `**`9'6,5'10`** ↵	Starts creating the walls
`To point: `**`15'10,5'10`** ↵	
`Line Enter point: `**`15'10,5'10`** ↵	
`To point: `**`15'10,29'4`** ↵	
`Line Enter point: `**`15'10,5'10`** ↵	Starts the porch outline
`To point: `**`26'10,5'10`** ↵	
`Line Enter point: `**`26'10,5'10`** ↵	
`To point: `**`26'10,26'4`** ↵	
`Line Enter point: `**`26'10,26'4`** ↵	
`To point: `**`15'10,26'4`** ↵	

*Choose **E**dit, then select the Copy tool*

`Copy Select Object: ` *Pick* ① *(see fig. 5.7)*	
`From point: ` *Pick anywhere in the drawing area*	Defines a base point
`To point: ` *Move the cursor* ~~up~~ down *one snap unit, and pick a point*	Creates a 6"-wall outline
`Copy Select Object: ` *Pick* ②	
`From point: ` *Pick anywhere in the drawing area*	
`To point: ` *Move the cursor left one snap unit and pick a point*	

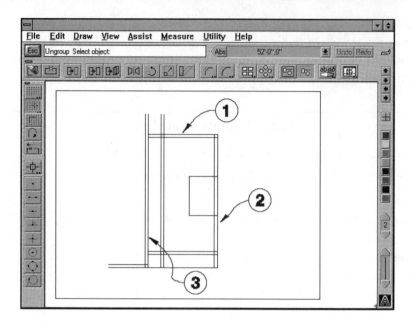

Figure 5.7:

Existing house structure, drawn with absolute coordinates.

As you see from the last exercise, specifying points using absolute coordinates is not practical. To calculate the distance of the line endpoints from the Cartesian-coordinate system origin (0,0) is tedious. In AutoSketch, as in most CAD programs, there are more practical ways to specify points.

Using Relative Coordinates

It is more common to know the distance from one end of an object to the other than to know the offset distance of the two endpoints from the drawing origin. In AutoSketch, as in most CAD programs, you can specify *relative coordinates,* which are points relative to the last point entered.

Relative coordinates must be entered in the following format:

r(*X offset*, *Y offset*)

The **r** in front of the parenthesis tells AutoSketch that the following coordinate is relative to the last specified point.

AutoSketch stores the last specified point in a system variable called /LPOINT. The position of a relative point is calculated by adding the X and Y offset to /LPOINT. If a negative number is specified for the offset, the line to be drawn is in a negative direction from the last point.

You can use the /LPOINT system variable whenever AutoSketch asks you to specify a point. This saves you from having to remember the last point.

If you use relative coordinates for specifying the first point during an editing session, AutoSketch uses 0,0 as the default last point.

In the following exercises, you add walls to the bathroom addition. Some of the existing structure lines are recycled to create part of the new structure. The /LPOINT system variable is used to copy entities in place and to draw lines end-to-end.

Using Relative Coordinates and the /LPOINT System Variable

Continue from the previous exercise. Set the current layer to 2, and the current color to black.

*Choose **D**raw, then the Line tool*

`Line Enter point:` **15'10,7'10** ↵

`To point:` **r(11',0)** ↵   Draws a line 11 units in the X direction and 0 units in the Y direction

*Choose **E**dit, then the Copy tool*

`Select Object:` *Pick the line you just drew*

`From point:` **/LPOINT** ↵   Specifies the last point

`To point:` **r(0,6)** ↵   Offsets the copied line up 6"

continues

*Choose **D**raw, then the Line tool*
`Line Enter point: 26'10,19'10` ↵
`To point: r(-4'6,0)` ↵   Specifies a negative offset for the
                                          endpoint

*Choose **D**raw, then the Line tool*
`Line Enter point: /LPOINT` ↵
`To point: r(0,0')` ↵ — 6'
*Choose **D**raw, then the Line tool*
`Line Enter point: /LPOINT` ↵
`To point: r(4'6,0)` ↵
*Choose **E**dit, then the Multi-copy tool*
`Select object:` *Pick* ①   (FIG. 5.8) ?
`From point: /LPOINT` ↵
`To point: /LPOINT` ↵   Copies the patio outline in place
`To point: r(0,-6)` ↵
Press Esc, *then choose the Multi-copy tool*
`Select object:` *Pick* ②
`From point: /LPOINT` ↵
`To point: /LPOINT` ↵   Copies the patio outline in place
`To point: r(-6,0)` ↵
Press Esc, *then choose the Multi-copy tool*
`Select object:` *Pick* ③
`From point: /LPOINT` ↵
`To point: r(2',0)` ↵
`To point: r(6,0)` ↵
Choose the Property(Change) tool,
and pick all the copied grey walls,
including lines at ① *and* ②
Save the drawing

Using Relative Polar Coordinates

Sometimes it is difficult or impossible to determine the X and Y
offsets for a relative point if you just know the angle and distance

of a point from the previous one. For example, if you have a 12'
wall at 45°, what is the X and Y offset of end? You can use your
knowledge of trigonometry to calculate the end, or you can use
relative polar-coordinate entry and let AutoSketch do the calculations. Relative polar coordinates are used to specify a point that is
a specific distance and angle from the previous point.

Angles for polar coordinates are measured counter-clockwise
from the X axis. If a negative polar angle is specified, the angle
is measured clockwise from the X axis.

Polar coordinates, like relative coordinates, must be entered in a
specific format:

> **p**(*distance from last point*, *angle from X axis*)

The **p** before the parenthesis tells AutoSketch that the following
coordinate is in the form of (distance, angle) from the previous
point.

In the following exercise, you add two doors and more walls by
using relative polar coordinates to specify points.

Using Polar Coordinates

Continue from the previous exercise.

Choose **E**dit, *then the Copy tool*

`Select Object:` *Pick line at* ①
(See fig. 5.8)

`From point: /LPOINT` ↵

`To point: p(6,270)` ↵   Copies line with polar specified
offset

`Select Object:` *Pick line at* ②

`From point: /LPOINT` ↵

`To point: p(6,0)` ↵

`Select Object:` *Pick line at* ③

`From point: /LPOINT` ↵

`To point: p(6,90)` ↵

Choose **D**raw, *then the Line tool*

continues

```
From point: 25'11,19'10 ↵
To point: p(2'8,150) ↵
```
Draws a 2'8" door with polar coordinates

```
From point: 19'4,7'10 ↵
To point: p(2'8,-30) ↵
```
Draws a door with a negative polar angle

```
From point: 15'4,14'4 ↵
To point: p(3',0) ↵
```
Choose **E**dit, *then the Multi-copy tool*
```
Select object: Pick the last line you drew
```
```
From point: /LPOINT ↵
To point: p(6,90) ↵
To point: p(4',90) ↵
To point: p(6,90) ↵
```
Save the drawing

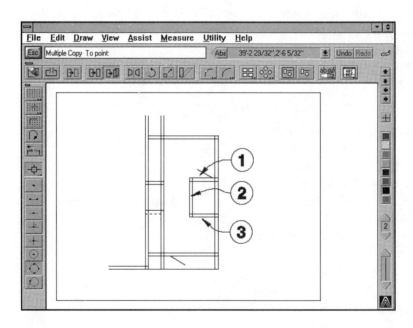

Figure 5.8:

Doors and walls, drawn with relative polar coordinates.

Controlling the Coordinate Display

The *coordinate display*, located on the horizontal status bar, displays coordinates of the cursor in three different ways (or it can be turned off). By default, the current position of the cursor is displayed in absolute coordinates. The position of the cursor can also be displayed in relative coordinates and relative polar coordinates.

You change the display by clicking on the Coordinate Type button on the left side of the coordinate display. This button displays the current display type. Abs means absolute coordinates, Rel means relative coordinates, and Pol means polar coordinates. The button displays Off when the coordinate readout is turned off.

If you click on the coordinate-window button (the down arrow on the right side of the coordinate display), you can display all the coordinate-display modes, as well as the last specified point. The window Control menu for the coordinate window enables you to select which coordinate display types show in the window.

Changing the Coordinate Display

Click on the Coordinate Type button on the horizontal status bar	Changes the display to polar coordinates

Move the cursor and watch the coordinate display update.

Continue clicking on the Coordinate Type button to cycle through the different display options or to turn the display off. Move the cursor after changing the display format.

Double-click in the display text box *Click on* OK	Enables you to set the units
Click on the coordinate-window button at the right side of the display box	Displays all the coordinate methods in a window
Click on the window control button, and turn off **A**bsolute *and* **L**ast Point	
Click on the coordinate window, and drag it to the upper right corner of the screen (see fig. 5.9)	

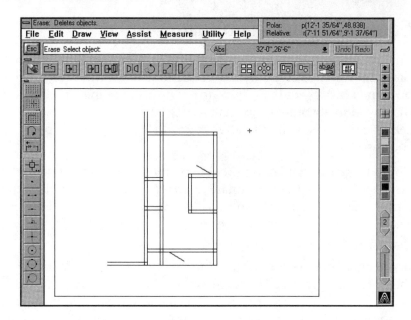

Figure 5.9:

The position of the coordinate window after moving it.

The coordinate-display window can be moved anywhere on the screen by clicking in the window and dragging it.

Using the View Tools

The previous exercises have kept you at the same view magnification. Sometimes this is not practical, especially if you need to work on a small detail of a drawing. The View tools enable you to zoom in and out, and pan the drawing around the drawing area.

Zooming In and Out

In CAD, changing the apparent size of the drawing in relation to the drawing area is called *zooming*. You zoom in to see more detail, but less of the drawing; you zoom out to see more of the drawing, but less detail. Zooming in and out does not change the actual size or scale of any entities.

In AutoSketch, the Zoom Box tool enables you to zoom into a specific area of the drawing. To use the Zoom Box tool, you specify the two opposite corners of a rubberband box, and AutoSketch magnifies the area so that it fills the entire drawing area. The Zoom Box tool can be invoked by pressing F10, or it can be invoked from the View toolbox.

With the Last View tool, you can go back to the previous view of the drawing after zooming in or out, or by panning.

 You can only go back one view operation. For example, if you zoom in three times, use the Last View tool to go back to the second zoom, and then use the Last View tool again, you return to the third zoom, not the first. If you use the Last View tool before using another view tool, you see an error message saying that no last view exists.

The Zoom X tool enables you to zoom a specific factor of the current view. For example, a factor of .75 reduces the current view by 25 percent, showing you more of the drawing. A zoom factor of 2.0 makes the drawing twice as large, showing more detail. This tool is used when you want to zoom in or out without changing the position of the drawing in the drawing area.

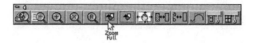

The Zoom Full tool zooms to the extents of the drawing. The *extents* is the area that encloses all the entities (even entities outside the limits) of a drawing. This tool is used to view the entire drawing, and is useful for finding entities that may have accidentally been drawn far away from the main drawing.

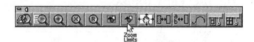

The Zoom Limits tool zooms to display the area of the current limits of the drawing. This tool is useful for establishing an overall view of your drawing if you have set your limits properly.

In the next exercise, you zoom in to the small room of the bathroom addition drawing to add a window and a toilet. Often, when you zoom in, it is necessary to set the snap increment to a smaller value to work on details. Figure 5.10 shows the drawing before the Zoom Box tool is used.

Figure 5.10:
Before zooming.

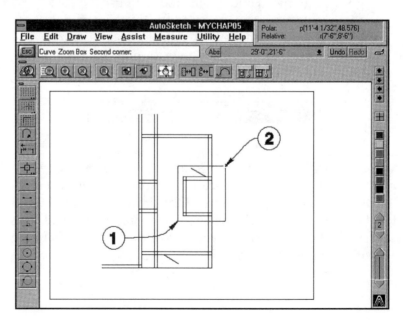

Using Zoom

Continue from the previous exercise.

*Choose **V**iew, then the Zoom Box tool*

`Zoom Box First corner:` *Pick* ① *(see fig. 5.10)*	Sets the first point of the zoom box
`Zoom Box Second corner:` *Pick* ②	Specifies the opposite corner for the zoom box, then AutoSketch zooms to the area
Double-click on the Snap tool, and set the snap spacing to 1"	Sets Snap to a small value for working on a detail

*Choose **D**raw, then the Line tool*

`Enter point:` *Draw a line from 26'4",17'10" to r(6",0)*

`Enter point:` *Draw a line from 26'4",15'10" to r(6",0)*

`Enter point:` *Draw a line from 26'7",10'10 to p(2',90)* ➔ 15'

Change the layer to 4, and the color to magenta for adding the plumbing fixtures.

Choose the Box tool, and draw a box from 23'6",14'6" to r(2'2",9")	Draws the toilet tank using relative coordinates

Choose the Ellipse tool

`Center of ellipse:` *Pick point 24'7", 16'*

`Axis endpoint:` *Pick point r(6",0)* 6"

`Other axis distance:` *Pick point r(0,8")*

Figure 5.11 shows the zoomed view and new window and toilet.

*Choose **V**iew, then the Last View tool*	Returns to the previous view of the drawing
Choose the Last View tool again	Returns to the zoomed-in view
Choose the Zoom X tool, and enter **.125**	Zooms to beyond the limits
Choose the Zoom Full tool	Zooms to the border, just inside the drawing limits

Save the drawing

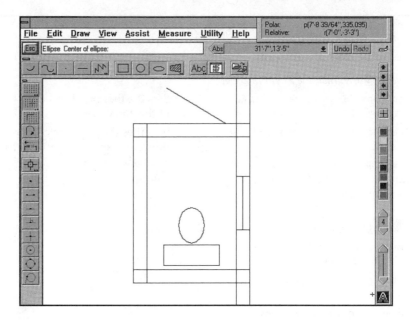

Figure 5.11:

Window and toilet added while zoomed-in.

Panning the Drawing

Sometimes you want to stay at the same view magnification but want to work in an adjacent area. In CAD, moving the view without changing the magnification is called *panning*. It is similar to panning a video camera to view a different part of a scene.

AutoSketch has two ways to pan the drawing: by using the Pan tool or the scroll buttons on the vertical status bar.

When you click on the Pan tool, you are prompted for a reference point, then a destination point. After the two points are specified, AutoSketch moves the reference point to the destination point. You can pick the points with the cursor or enter them from the keyboard. Usually you use the cursor to specify points for the Pan tool.

In the following exercise, you zoom in to draw two sinks, and then pan to add some shelves. Figure 5.12 shows the view before zooming and panning.

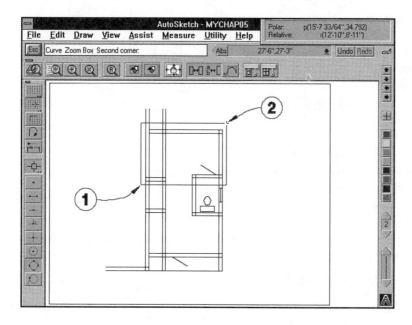

Figure 5.12:

The view before zooming and panning.

Using Pan

Continue from the previous exercise.

Choose **V**iew, *then the Zoom Box tool*

Zoom Box First corner: *Pick* ① (*See fig. 5.12*)	Sets first point of the zoom box
Zoom Box Second corner: *Pick* ②	Specifies the opposite corner for the zoom box, then AutoSketch zooms to the area

Set the current layer to 2, and the current color to black.

Choose **D**raw, *then the Line tool, and draw a line from 18'4",23'10" to r(8',0)*

Set the current layer to 4, and the current color to magenta.

continues

Choose the Ellipse tool, and draw two sinks; one at 20'4",24',10", and one at 24'4",24'10"

SIZE ?
19'6, 24'10   19'8, 24'9
23'6, 24'10   23'8, 24'9

Set the current layer to 2, and the current color to black.

Double-click on the Current Linetype display

Click on the Hidden Linetype radio button

SCALE ? 20

Choose OK

Choose the Line tool, and draw a line from 16'10",19'4" to r(0,6'6")

*Choose **V**iew, then the Pan tool*

`Pan reference:` *Pick a point near the bottom of the drawing area*

`Pan destination:` *Pick a point straight up near the top of the drawing area*

Repeat the use of the Pan tool until the screen shows the entire lower closet (see fig. 5.13).

*Choose **D**raw, then the Line tool, and draw a line from 16'10",8'4" to r(0,6'6")*

Set Current Linetype back to Solid.

*Choose **V**iew, then the Zoom Full tool*

Save the drawing

Using the Aerial View

Aerial
View

As your drawing gets larger and more complex, you need a way to keep from getting lost in the entities. The Aerial View is your road map to the drawing—it gives you an overall view of your drawing, and shows you the current view in relation to the entire drawing. It also enables you to dynamically change the current view without using the View tools.

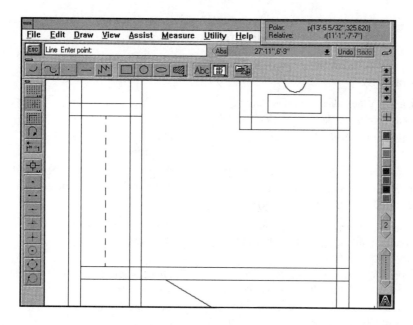

Figure 5.13:
View of the lower closet after panning.

When you click on the Aerial View button at the top of the vertical status bar (the little airplane), a small window appears in the upper right corner of the screen. The entire drawing appears in the window with the colors reversed. The current view is shown as a box with normal colors within the inverted color area. You can move or resize the view box to pan or zoom the current view.

You can change the size of the current view (zoom in or out) by clicking on and dragging the small box at the lower right corner of the view box. You can also zoom in or out by clicking and dragging a new view box anywhere in the Aerial View window.

If you place the cursor in the Aerial View window, and double-click with the left mouse button, you zoom in by the current setting of the Zoom X tool. If you double-click with the right mouse button, you zoom out by the current setting of the Zoom X tool.

To pan the current view, click and drag the green crosshairs in the view box, and release it when you are satisfied with the view.

Using the Aerial View

Continue from the previous exercise, or open any fairly complex drawing.

*Choose **V**iew, then the Zoom Box tool,
and zoom in on the room with the toilet*

Click on the Aerial View Button	Displays the Aerial View window

Notice that the entire drawing appears in the Aerial View window with the colors inverted, and the current view of the toilet room appears in normal colors (see fig. 5.14).

Click on the green crosshairs in the view box, and drag the view box to cover the sink area	Pans the view of the drawing
Click anywhere in the Aerial View window, and drag the new view box	Displays new zoomed view of drawing
Double-click twice anywhere in the Aerial View window	Zooms in twice by the Zoom X magnification setting
Double-click with the right mouse button anywhere in the Aerial View window	Zooms out by the Zoom X magnification setting
Double-click on the Aerial View window Control-menu button	Closes the Aerial view

Improving Accuracy with the Assist Tools

The Assist tools are the most-used tools of all CAD programs, including AutoSketch. You have already been introduced to two of the Assist tools to help you draw quickly and accurately: the

Grid tool and Snap tool. These tools, as well as the rest of the Assist tools, are invaluable and are used frequently. By default, AutoSketch puts the Assist toolbox at the left side of the screen for easy access.

The Assist tools can be in two states: on or off. The tool's icon is highlighted in the Assist toolbox when it is on. Some of the tools in the Assist tool box can be double-clicked on to access the tool's settings dialog box.

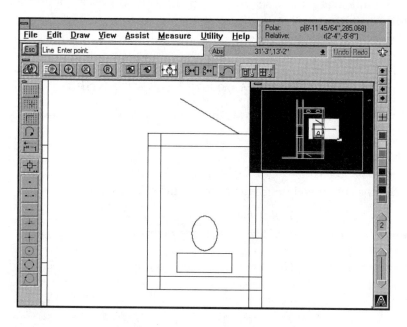

Figure 5.14:
The Aerial View window.

Using the Ortho Tool

The word *ortho* is short for *orthagonal*, which means right-angled. The Ortho tool operates similarly to a drafting machine by enabling you to easily draw lines or locate points, horizontally or vertically. The Ortho tool, when active, restricts picked points to right angles from the previously picked point.

The Ortho tool is primarily used with the Line and Polyline drawing tools; and with the Move, Copy, and Multi-copy editing tools.

 Although the Ortho tool can also be used with other tools, its usefulness is limited.

In the following exercise, you rough-in some doorway openings with the Ortho tool, in conjunction with the Line and Multi-copy tools.

Drawing and Copying Lines with Ortho

Continue from the previous exercise, and zoom to the view in figure 5.15.

*Choose **D**raw, then the Line tool*

From point: *Pick point 14'11",24'10"*

Move the cursor and notice the action of the rubber-band line.

Click on the Ortho tool to turn it on

Move the cursor again, and notice how the rubber-band line is only drawn horizontally or vertically.

To point: *Pick point r(1'3",0)*   Draws an orthagonal line

*Choose **E**dit, then the Multi-copy tool, and select the last line drawn*

From point: *Pick a point near the end of the line*

To point: *Pick point r(0,4'6")* r(0,-4'6)   Copies the line with the Ortho tool on

To point: *Pick point r(0,11'6")* r(0,-11'0")

To point: *Pick point r(0,15'6")* r(0,-15'6;)

Press Esc

Save the drawing

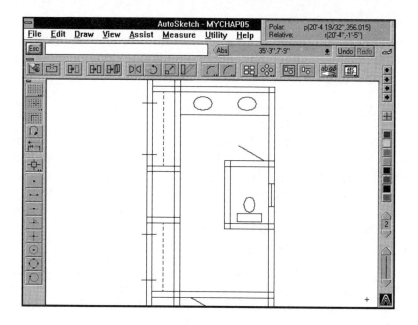

Figure 5.15:
Roughed-in doorway openings.

As you learn more of the tools that help you draw accurately, you are entering points from the keyboard less frequently. The next section explains the Attach tool and its settings. The Attach tool almost eliminates the need to enter points from the keyboard.

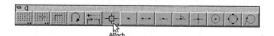

Understanding the Attach Tool

All entities have geometric-reference points. For example, arcs, lines, and polyline segments have endpoints and midpoints; circles and ellipses have centers and quadrant points.

As you have drawn the bathroom addition, you see that many of the entities do not fall conveniently on snap points. You can make the snap distance smaller, but doing so makes picking points more difficult. With the use of the Attach tool, you can accurately pick any geometric reference point on any entity without the use of snap.

When you use the Attach tool and its settings, you pick near the intended point, and AutoSketch locates the exact attachment point on that entity.

The Selection-Area Box

The Attach tool looks within a specific area around a picked point to locate an attachment point. This area is called the *selection-area box*. The size of the selection-area box and its visibility can be changed by altering these settings in the Selection Area Settings dialog box (accessed from the Drawing Settings dialog box). The selection-area box size is based on a percentage of the screen height. By default, the selection-area box is not visible.

An additional feature of AutoSketch that helps you align and pick points is the *crosshairs*, which can be turned on and off by clicking on the Crosshairs button on the vertical status bar, directly above the Color Palette.

In the following exercise, you make the selection area bigger and make the box visible so that picking attachment points is easier. You also turn on the crosshairs.

Setting the Selection-Area Box

Choose **U**tility, *then select the Drawing Settings tool*

Click on the Selection Area button	Displays Selection Area Settings dialog box (see fig. 5.16)
Set Selection Area to 2	Sets the selection-area box to 2% of drawing area
Click on the box to the left of Show Selection Area box	Makes the selection-area box visible
Click on OK — ► CLOSES SELECTION AREA CLICK ON OK AGAIN —	► Closes the Drawing Settings dialog box
Click on the crosshairs button	Turns on the crosshairs

Figure 5.16:

Selection Area Settings dialog box.

The familiar arrow cursor is now replaced with the selection-area box and the crosshairs.

The Attach Tool Settings

The Attach tool settings can be used by themselves, or they can be used in combination with each other. If too many of the settings are on, however, AutoSketch may pick a point other than the one you intended to pick.

 AutoSketch decides which point best fits the combination of settings, and the best point may not be the point you had intended to pick. Only use one or two settings at a time to avoid confusion.

Like the Assist tools, the Attach tool's settings can be either on or off. Double-clicking on an attach setting's icon automatically activates the Attach tool with the selected setting and turns off all other settings.

The Intersect setting enables the Attach tool to pick the point at which any two entities intersect each other. The Attach tool can only find an intersection of a curve frame and another entity, not the curve itself.

See Chapter 8 for more information on the Curve tool.

The Center attach setting enables the Attach tool to connect to the center point of a circle, an arc, or an ellipse. All other entities do not have center points. When you use this setting with the Attach tool, pick the actual circle, arc, or ellipse entity—not near the center point.

The Perpendicular attach setting enables the Attach tool to form a 90-degree angle line to an entity you select. Usually, only the second point of a line or polyline segment is used with the Perpendicular attach setting.

If you specify a circle or arc as the selected entity, the line is drawn from the first point to the perimeter of the circle or arc, as if the line would continue through to the center point of the circle or arc. The Perpendicular setting does not work predictably with ellipses.

All other attach settings should be off when using the Perpendicular setting.

To become familiar with the Attach tool and its settings, you will work on a drawing of a bracket. In the following four exercises, you use the Attach tool to construct an accurate drawing of a bracket without the use of Snap or Grid, or without entering points from the keyboard. Once you have finished the bracket drawing, you will use the Attach tool to finish the bathroom addition.

Using Center, Intersect, and Perpendicular

Start AutoSketch, and open the BRACKET5 drawing. IN   WSK DEMO\lc DIRECTORY

Turn off Snap and Grid

Double-click on the Center attach setting

Activates the Attach tool, and turns on the Center attach setting

Click on the Perpendicular attach setting

Turns on the Perpendicular attach setting

Next, you draw two construction lines that you will later erase.

*Choose **D**raw, then the Line tool*

`Enter point:` *Pick* ① *(see fig. 5.17)*

Attaches the line to the center of the circle

Notice how the Attach tool picked the center of the circle, even though you picked the perimeter of the circle.

`To point:` *Pick bottom horizontal line*

Draws a perpendicular line from the center of the circle to the bottom line

`Enter point:` *Pick* ②

`To point:` *Pick the line on the far left*

*Choose **E**dit, then the Copy tool*

`Select Object:` *Pick small circle*

Turn off the Perpendicular attach setting

Turn on the Intersect attach setting

`From point:` *Pick* ① *again*

`To point:` *Pick the intersection of the two construction lines*

Copies the small circle to the exact intersection of the two construction lines

Erase the two construction lines

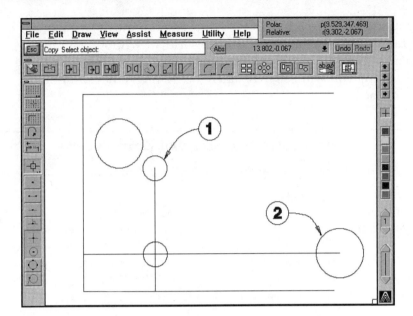

Figure 5.17:
BRACKET drawing, before erasing the construction lines.

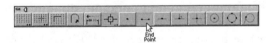

The End Point attach setting enables the Attach tool to attach to an endpoint of any entity that is not a circle or an ellipse. It also attaches the corner of a box, polyline, pattern fill, or curve frame.

When the End Point attach setting is on, the Attach tool grabs the end closest to the point picked on the entity. The End Point attach setting ignores circles and ellipses because these objects have no endpoints.

With the Midpoint attach setting on, the Attach tool picks a point that lies exactly halfway between the two endpoints of a line, arc, polyline segment, or curve frame. The Midpoint setting also ignores circles, ellipses, and text because none of these objects have a midpoint.

The Quadrant attach setting enables the Attach tool to find the 0°, 90°, 180°, and 270° points of a circle, an ellipse, or an arc. If you place a circle at 0,0, the quadrant points are located where the circle crosses each axis of the Cartesian-coordinate system. Arcs must have a point that passes through one of the quadrants for the Attach tool to work properly with the Quadrant setting enabled.

In the following exercise, you use the Attach tool to draw the right side of the bracket and add a dashed line to show the bracket bend.

Using Endpoint, Midpoint, and Quadrant

Continue from the previous exercise.

Double-click on the End Point attach setting	Activates the Attach tool with only the End Point setting on
Click on the Quadrant attach setting	Turns on the Quadrant attach
Choose **D**raw, *then the Line tool*	
`Enter point:` *Pick* ① *(see fig. 5.18)*	Attaches to the end of the line
`To point:` *Pick* ②	Attaches to the 90° point of the circle
`Enter point:` *Pick* ③	Attaches to the 270° point of the circle
`To point:` *Pick* ④	
Double-click on the Midpoint attach setting	Activates the Attach tool with Midpoint
Set the current linetype to dashed	
`Enter point:` *Pick anywhere on the top line*	Attaches to the midpoint of the line
`To point:` *Pick anywhere on the bottom line*	
Set the linetype back to solid	
Save the drawing	

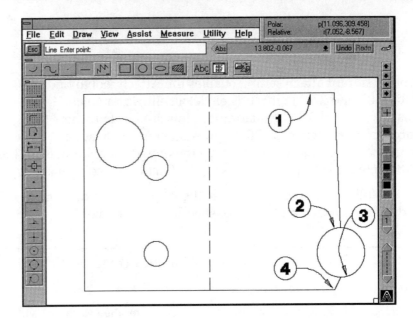

Figure 5.18:
The right side of
the bracket and
bend line.

The Tangent attach setting enables the Attach tool to draw a
tangent line from a first point to a point on an arc, a circle, or an
ellipse. The first point can also be a tangent point on another arc,
circle, or ellipse.

All other attach settings should be off
when using the Tangent setting.

In the next exercise, you use the Tangent attach setting to draw the
outline of the bracket cutout.

Using Tangent

Continue from the previous exercise.

Double-click on the Tangent attach setting	Activates the Attach tool, and turns on the Tangent setting

Choose **D**raw, *then the Line tool*

`Enter point:` *Pick* ① *(see fig. 5.19)*

Move the cursor around the outside of the circle. Notice how the rubber-band line is drawn tangent to the circle at all times.

`To point:` *Pick* ②   Draws a line tangent to two circles

`Enter point:` *Pick* ② *again*

`To point:` *Pick* ③

`Enter point:` *Pick* ④

`To point:` *Pick* ⑤

Save the drawing

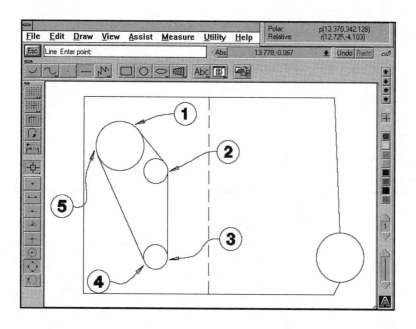

Figure 5.19:

The bracket with the cutout outlined.

Now the only thing left to do is to clean up the cutout and the notch. To do this, you use End Point and the Break tool in the following exercise.

Cleaning Up with End Point

Continue from the previous exercise.

Double-click on the End Point
attach setting

*Choose **E**dit, then the Break tool*

`Select object:` *Pick top circle of cutout*

`First break point:` *Pick* (1)
(see fig. 5.20)

`Second break point:` *Pick* (2)

`Select object:` *Pick top small circle*

`First break point:` *Pick* (3)

`Second break point:` *Pick* (4)

`Select object:` *Pick bottom circle*
of cutout

`First break point:` *Pick* (5)

`Second break point:` *Pick* (6)

`Select object:` *Pick the circle for the*
notch

`First break point:` *Pick* (7)

`Second break point:` *Pick* (8)

Save the drawing

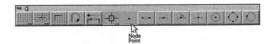

The Node attach setting is used to attach to a text entity's insertion point. The insertion point for a text string can be on the lower left corner, the bottom center, or the lower right of a text string.

Text is covered in detail in Chapter 6.

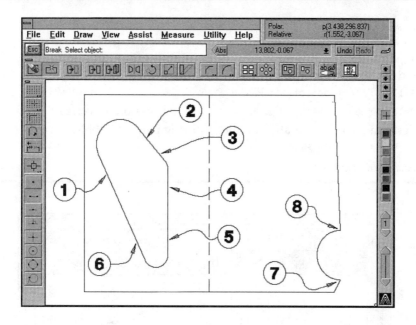

Figure 5.20:
The completed bracket.

In the following exercise, you use a trick of the Fillet tool to clean up line intersections. If the fillet radius is set to zero, the Fillet tool trims to the intersection of two lines. This happens because the result of a zero-fillet radius is a sharp corner.

 For the rest of this chapter, adjust the view by zooming and panning as needed to make performing the exercises easier. As you become more familiar with the tools, the exercise instructions become more general.

Cleaning Up Intersections Without Attach

Open the MYCHAP05 drawing you created in previous exercises, and zoom to the view in figure 5.21.

Turn off the Grid, Snap, and Ortho tools

continues

Choose **E**dit, *then double-click on
the Fillet tool*

Type **0** *in the* Fillet Radius:
text box, then choose OK

`Fillet Select object(s):` *Pick at* ①

`Select second object:` *Pick at* ② Squares off the corner

Perform the fillet operation on the following pairs of bubbles: ③ and ④; ⑤ and ⑥; ⑦ and ⑧; ⑨ and ⑩.

Save the drawing

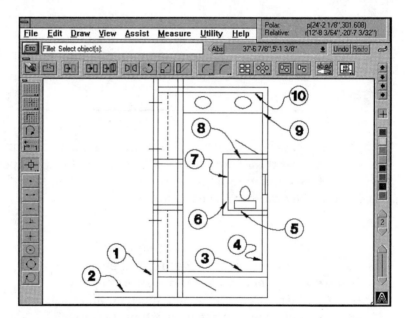

Figure 5.21:

Wall intersections, cleaned up with the Fillet tool.

Knowing which tools to use and when is a skill that you develop with experience. For example, in the previous exercise, you could have cleaned up the wall intersections with the Break and Attach tools, but it was more efficient to use the special feature of the Fillet tool.

In the following exercise, you use the Break and Attach tools to break out some wall sections. You also continue to use the corner-making feature of the Fillet tool. Figure 5.22 shows the drawing before breaking and cleaning up the walls.

In the following exercises, depending on your view magnification, you may need to make the size of the selection-area box smaller to prevent AutoSketch from getting confused about which lines you want to fillet.

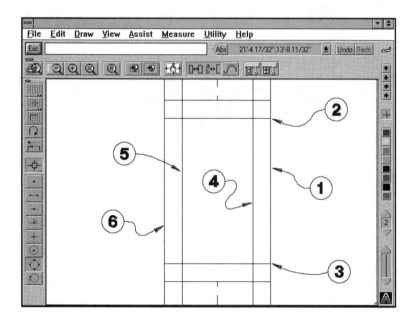

Figure 5.22
Wall sections before removal.

Removing Wall Sections

Continue from the previous exercise, and zoom to the view in figure 5.22.

Double-click on the Intersect attach setting

continues

*Choose **E**dit, then the Break tool*

`Select object:` *Pick the line at* ①

`First break point:` *Pick* ②

`Second break point:` *Pick* ③

Continue to break out the walls from the doorway to the bathroom addition. Break the lines at ④ ⑤, and ⑥.

Use the Fillet tool to trim the line intersections at ①, ②, ③, and ④ (see fig. 5.23).

Use the Break and Fillet tools, with the Intersect attach setting, to create the doorways for the closets. Figure 5.24 shows the closet doors removed.

Save the drawing

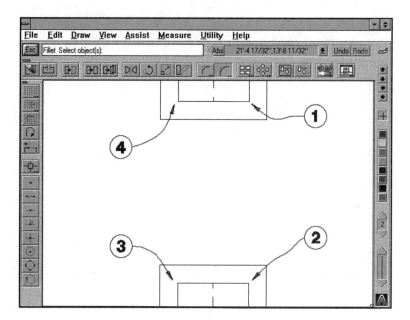

Figure 5.23:

Cleaned-up line intersections in the bathroom doorway.

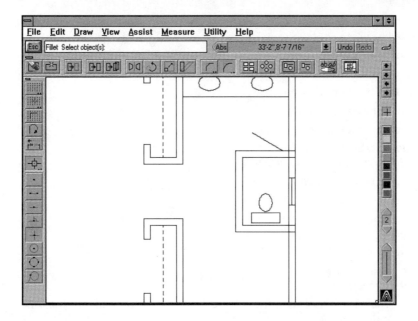

Figure 5.24:

Bathroom addition, with doorway sections removed.

Because AutoSketch's Arc tool is somewhat limited in its capabilities, it is often easier to use the Circle tool and break out the necessary arc segment. The Attach tool is indispensable for this work-around.

In the following exercises, you use the Circle and Break tool technique to draw the swing arcs on the doors. You also use the Attach tool to easily construct and break out the doorways.

Drawing Arcs with the Attach, Circle, and Break Tools

Continue from the previous exercise, and zoom to the view shown in figure 5.25.

Activate the Attach tool, and turn on the End Point and Intersect attach settings

*Choose **D**raw, then the Circle tool*

continues

`Center point:` *Pick* (1)
(see fig. 5.25)

`Point on circle:` *Pick* (2)

*Choose **E**dit, then the Break tool*

`Select object:` *Pick the circle*

`First break point:` *Pick* (3)

`Second break point:` *Pick* (2)

*Turn off the Intersection attach
setting, and turn on Perpendicular*

*Choose **D**raw, then the Line tool*

`Enter point:` *Pick* (1)

`To point:` *Pick anywhere on the line
directly under* (1)

`Enter point:` *Pick* (3)

`To point:` *Pick anywhere on the line
directly under* (3)

Use the Attach tool with the Intersect setting on to break out the toilet
room doorway.

Repeat the Circle and Break tool technique on the other door.

Save the drawing

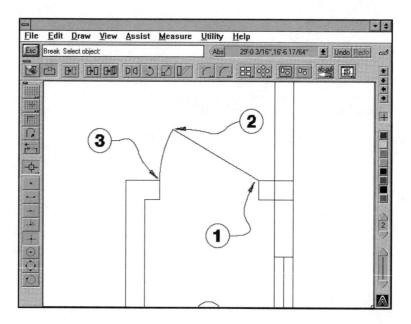

Figure 5.25:

Door swing arc,
drawn with the
Circle, Break, and
Attach tools.

178

The last exercise cleans up wall intersections by using the Break tool and the Fillet tool.

Cleaning Up Wall Intersections

Continue from the previous exercise, and zoom to the view shown in figure 5.26.

Double-click on the Intersect attach setting

*Choose **E**dit, then the Break tool, and break the line at ① between points ② and ③*

Choose the Fillet tool, and trim the intersections at ② and ③

Use the Break and Fillet tools to clean up all remaining wall intersections.

Save the drawing

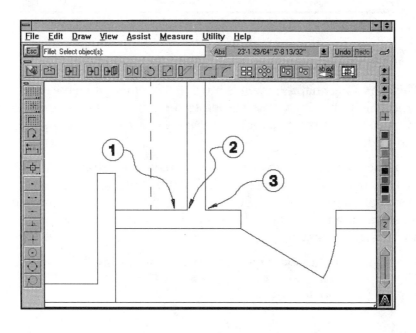

Figure 5.26:
Cleaned up T-wall intersection.

When all intersections have been cleaned up, your drawing should resemble figure 5.27.

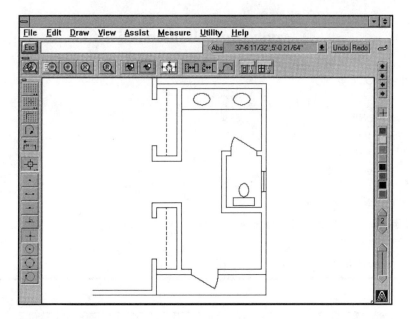

Figure 5.27:

The completed bathroom addition.

Summary

This was a big chapter; there is much to consider when creating production drawings. You learned to set up a production drawing by calculating a scale factor and setting the drawing limits, snap, and grid.

You also learned how to organize and make your drawing more clear by using the layer, color, and linetype-entity properties. Once you had everything set up and organized, you used a proto-type drawing to easily recall the settings and entities when starting a new drawing.

The View tools help you get close to areas requiring detail work. They also enable you to take a look at the "big picture" to keep from getting lost.

You learned that the Attach tool is one of the most important tools in CAD. It enables you to pick mathematically-precise geometric reference points on entities without effort. The effective use of the Attach tool is one of the most important skills you can develop to help you draw accurately and quickly.

Completing Your Drawing

A technical drawing often requires more than just graphic entities to convey the needed information. Text and dimensions can provide much of the necessary information required to build or manufacture the object. This chapter introduces you to the AutoSketch tools that help to annotate and detail your drawing. You will also use the measuring tools to provide you with distance, angle, and area measurements from your graphic entities.

The architectural drawing you created in Chapter 5 will be used for dimensioning. When the drawing is completed, the printing capabilities of AutoSketch are explained so that you will be able to produce hard copies of your drawings.

Applying Dimensions to Your Drawing

Chapter 2 discussed some standard drawing practices for technical drawings. One of the important aspects of creating an acceptable technical drawing is to dimension the drawing properly.

A *dimension* is a special label placed on a technical drawing to show the size or location of a component in the drawing. The process of placing these labels on a drawing is called *dimensioning*.

Many CAD users feel that it is easier to draw a professional-looking drawing in CAD because of the capability to move views and change dimension locations as the drawing nears completion. Dimensions also appear very crisp in a CAD drawing because text, arrows, and dimension lines are drawn by the computer.

Whether you do dimensioning with CAD or with manual drafting tools, it is still important to understand proper dimensioning formats and standards. Because these vary greatly between different disciplines, it is beyond the scope of this book to explain all of the standard dimensioning practices in use today.

For more information on how to apply dimensions to your work, ? YES?

Understanding Dimensioning Terminology

Most CAD software has the capability to *automatically dimension* graphic entities, which means that the software automatically generates leader lines, arrows (terminators), dimension lines, and dimension text. Figure 6.1 shows the parts of a standard dimension. These components are described in detail in the following sections.

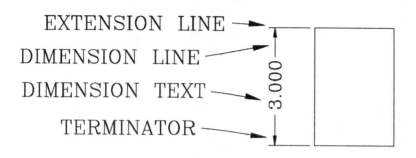

Figure 6.1:

Components of a typical dimension.

When you draw a dimension, AutoSketch produces the following components:

- **Dimension line.** The *dimension line* is drawn in the space between the two reference points. Dimension lines are often terminated with arrows, ticks, or dots. You must pick a point to show the location of the dimension line.

- **Extension line.** An *extension line* extends away from the object at the exact points referenced by the dimension. A small gap is placed between the object lines and the beginning of the extension line to help distinguish between the two. Notice that the extension lines also extend a small distance past the dimension line. You choose two points as the reference points for the extension lines.

- **Terminators.** *Terminators* can be placed at either end of the dimension line. Different disciplines often use different types of terminators. AutoSketch offers the option of an arrow, tick mark, dot, or no terminator.

- **Dimension text.** The dimension text is automatically generated by AutoSketch as it measures the distance between the two reference points. Many features of the dimension text may be altered to suit your drawing requirements.

Figure 6.2 illustrates the different types of dimensions AutoSketch can produce. Although the labels in the figure are the tool names AutoSketch uses, they are also generic (in the sense that these are common types of dimensions used on technical drawings).

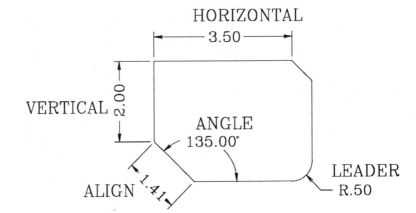

Setting Up for Dimensioning

AutoSketch has many settings that affect the appearance of your dimensions. Some of those settings, such as units, were covered in Chapter 5. The following list describes the key elements of the planning process.

- Create accurate scaled drawings. If your drawing contains scaling errors and misaligned entities, dimensioning will require a great deal of extra work.

- Plan ahead to determine the proper placement of dimensions and the logical order of dimensioning procedures.

- Use the object snap modes to accurately identify reference points.

- Create your dimensions on a separate layer and with a different color.

- Consider printing scale when determining dimension-feature sizes.

Expect to make mistakes when you first experiment with the dimensioning tools. Use the Undo or Erase tools to remove dimensions you want to redo.

Figure 6.3 shows the architectural drawing you created in Chapter 5, with the notes and dimensions that you will add in this chapter.

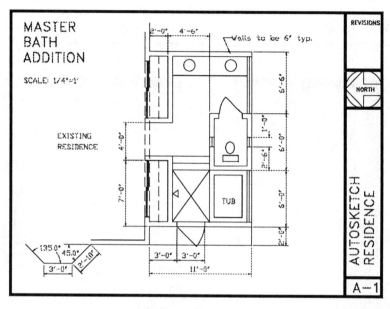

Figure 6.3:

The CHAP6 drawing, with text and dimensions.

The following exercise begins by opening the drawing you started in Chapter 5. You should begin by confirming all settings affecting dimensioning, and then you will be ready to begin dimensioning.

If you want to use the drawing provided for this chapter, it is named CHAP6, and it is provided on the disk included with this book.

Setting Up for Dimensioning

Start up AutoSketch for Windows.

Choose File, *then* Open — Activates the Open dialog box

Double-click on CHAP6.SKD — Opens the drawing (see fig. 6.4)

continues

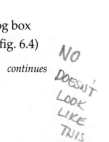

Click on the arrow button above the layer number in the vertical status bar

Changes current layer to 2

Choose the red color button

Changes current color button to red

Confirm that your settings match those in table 6.1.

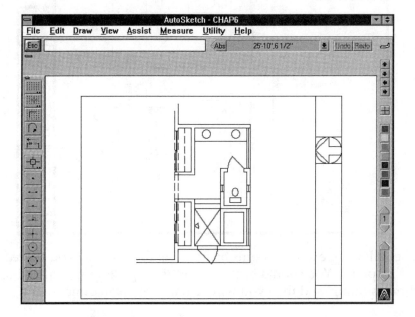

Figure 6.4:
The CHAP6.SKD drawing.

The last five drawings you have used in AutoSketch are listed at the bottom of the File menu. You can double-click on one of these file names to open the drawing. This method is much faster than using the Open dialog box.

Table 6.1 lists all the settings you should have current before beginning to dimension.

188

Table6.1 Current Settings For Dimensioning				
GRID	SNAP	UNITS	LAYER	COLOR
2', ON	6",OFF	ARCH, 1/4"	2	red

The settings that control the appearance of a dimension are shown in the Dimension Settings dialog box (see fig. 6.5).

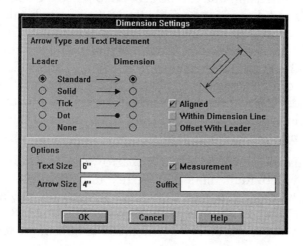

Figure 6.5:

Dimension Settings dialog box.

You can access this dialog box by clicking on the Drawing Settings tool found in the Utility toolbox, then choose the Dimension button.

 When a tool containing a double dot in the lower right corner of the icon is chosen from the toolbox, a double-click on the tool enables you to first modify the settings associated with that tool.

The Dimension Settings dialog box enables you to control the following visible features of a dimension:

- The terminator of a dimension line or leader can be chosen from one of five options shown on the left-hand side of the dialog box. Because these selections are chosen by clicking on radio buttons, selecting any of the options cancels out the previous option. A different terminator may be chosen for a leader than for a dimension. A picture of the terminator is shown next to the label.

- Dimension text can be placed above the dimension line, or the dimension line can be broken to place the text within it. Aligned dimensions enable the text string to be aligned with the dimension line instead of being horizontal. The Offset With Leader option is useful for placing the text in another location when the dimension line is very short. Each check box can be activated or turned off independently of the others. As you activate the check boxes, the illustration of the dimension shown in the upper right corner of the dialog box changes.

- You can specify your text and arrow size in the text boxes provided. Remember that the text must be properly sized on the hard copy. If your drawing is scaled down by a factor of 48, 6" text on your drawing becomes 6/48, or 1/8", on your hard copy. The arrow size defaults to 80% of the text size.

- When the Measurement check box is activated, the reference points are measured and dimension text is generated.

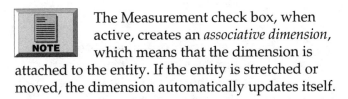 The Measurement check box, when active, creates an *associative dimension*, which means that the dimension is attached to the entity. If the entity is stretched or moved, the dimension automatically updates itself.

- You can add a suffix to the dimension text by entering the text string into the Suffix text box. This is useful for text strings such as "reference", "in", or "mm".

The current text font also affects the appearance of dimensions. This setting is discussed later in this chapter.

Applying Horizontal and Vertical Dimensions

You are now ready to begin dimensioning the drawing. The first dimensioning tool you will use is the Horizontal Dimension tool, which requires three points to be specified. The first two points are the reference points on which the dimension is based. (A *reference point* is often a corner point or center point of an entity, which is used to show the size or location figures of that entity.)

It is important to use Attach tools to precisely locate the points because AutoSketch measures the exact distance. The third point specifies the location of the dimension line. The first two reference points do not need to be aligned horizontally—AutoSketch measures the horizontal distance only between the two points.

The Vertical Dimension tool, also found in the Measure toolbox, works much the same as the Horizontal Dimension tool. Three points are used. The first two are the two points between which the vertical measurement is taken, and the third point shows where to place the dimension line.

Try using these tools in the following exercise.

Using the Horizontal Dimension Tool

Choose **V**iew, *then the* Zoom Box *tool, and zoom up to a view similar to figure 6.6*

Choose **M**easure, *then double-click on the* Horizontal Dimension *tool*

Opens the Dimension Settings dialog box

Modify the dialog box as necessary so that it matches the settings shown in figure 6.5.

6" TEXT TOO BIG
USE 4"

continues

Choose OK	Closes dialog box
Double-click on the Intersect *tool*	Activates the Intersect tool
Horizontal Dimension From point: *Pick near* ① *(see fig. 6.6)*	Specifies the first reference point
To point: *Pick near* ② point	Specifies the second reference
Dimension line location: *Pick near* ③ location	Specifies the dimension-line
Horizontal Dimension From point: *Pick near* ②	
To point: *Pick near* ④	
Dimension line location: *Pick near* ③	

Click on the down-arrow button in the vertical status bar five or six timesuntil you see a view similar to figure 6.7. Continue using the Horizontal Dimension tool to create the three horizontal dimensions near the bottom of the drawing.

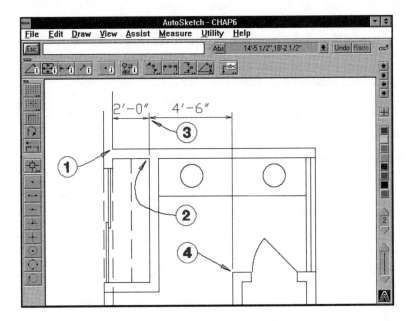

Figure 6.6:

Applying horizontal dimensions.

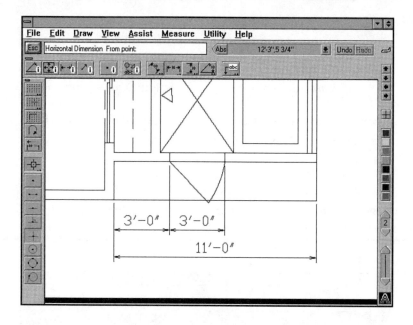

Figure 6.7:
Additional horizontal dimensions.

Automatic dimensioning works well when the graphic entities have been accurately placed. The first two points must be precisely located, and the third point specifies where to place the dimension.

The Grid and Snap tools help place the dimension lines so that adjacent dimensions line up properly with each other.

In the following exercise, continue placing dimensions on the drawing by using the Vertical Dimension tool.

Creating Vertical Dimensions

Choose **V**iew, *then the* Zoom Full *tool*	Shows full view
Choose the Zoom X *tool, then type* **1.35** ↵	Shows the view seen in figure 6.8

continues

Choose **M**easure, *then the* Vertical
Dimension *tool*

`Vertical Dimension From point:` *Pick the corner near* ① *(see fig. 6.8)*
Specifies the first reference point

`To point:` *Pick near* ②
Specifies the second reference point

`Dimension line location:` *Pick near* ③
Locates the dimension line

`Vertical Dimension From point:` *Pick near* ②

`To point:` *Pick near* ④

`Dimension line location:` *Pick near* ③

Continue using the Vertical Dimension tool to create the vertical dimensions on the right side of the drawing.

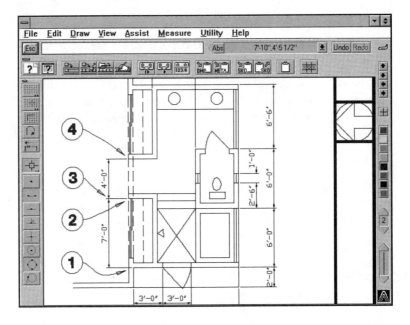

Figure 6.8:

Using the Vertical Dimension tool.

The Intersect tool worked well for the dimensions you placed on this drawing. Sometimes other Attach tools, such as End Point or Center, are preferred. Notice that the one-foot dimension for the bathroom window was too short for the text to be placed between the arrows. AutoSketch places it outside the arrows on the side that was chosen as the second reference point.

You can use Undo or Erase to try some dimensions a second time for better results.

Creating Aligned Dimensions

The Align Dimension tool measures the absolute distance between two points. Unless the two points are in vertical or horizontal alignment, the dimension is placed on the angle formed by a line connecting the two points. A designer or detailer must decide when aligned dimensions are preferred over horizontal and vertical alignment.

In the following exercise, you add a bay window to the existing wall to demonstrate the use of the Align Dimension tool.

Using the Align Dimension Tool

From the **V**iew toolbox, use the Zoom Full tool, then the Zoom Box tool to obtain the view shown in figure 6.9. Change to layer 1 and color black.

*Choose **D**raw, then the* Line *tool*

Line Enter point: *Using the* End Point   Begins the line
tool, pick near ④ *(see fig. 6.9)*

To point: `r(-2',-2')` ⏎

Line Enter point: `/LPOINT` ⏎

To point: `r(-3',0)` ⏎

Line Enter point: `/LPOINT` ⏎

continues

To point: **r(-2',2')** ↵

Change back to layer 2 with a color of red.

Choose **M**easure, *then the* Align Dimension
tool

Align Dimension From point: *Using the*
Intersect *tool, pick near* ①

To point: *Pick near* ②

Dimension line location: *Pick near* ③

Align Dimension From point: *Pick near* ②

To point: *Pick near* ④

Dimension line location: *Pick near* ⑤

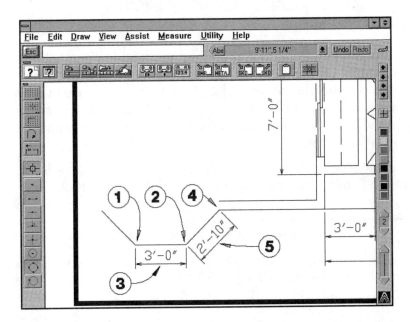

Figure 6.9:

Using the Align
Dimension tool
for dimensioning.

The first time you used the Align Dimension tool, it worked just
like the Horizontal Dimension tool. The second dimension you
placed was more typical of the way the Align Dimension tool is
used.

Dimensioning Angles

In the last chapter, you learned how to use polar coordinates to draw lines at precise angles. Often, an angular dimension is needed in a technical drawing to show the values of these angles.

Angle
Dimension

The Angle Dimension tool also requires three picks. The Attach tools are not needed because the first two selections prompt you to pick the two lines from which the angle is being measured. You can pick the line in the most convenient location. The third pick enables you to drag the location of the dimension arc, which can be placed at a position that best fits the rest of the drawing. If the dimension text cannot fit into the specified dimension arc, you are prompted for a fourth pick to place the text.

Continue to add the angular dimensions in the following exercise. First, the number of decimal places shown on the angular dimension should be specified by using the units settings.

Creating Angular Dimensions

Choose **U***tility, then the* Drawing Settings *tool*	Opens the Drawing Settings dialog box
Click on the Units *button, then choose* 1 digit *of accuracy displayed, and choose* OK, *and* OK *again*	Changes the angular dimensions to one place of accuracy
Choose **M***easure, then the* Angle Dimension *tool*	

`Angle Dimension Select first line:` *Select the line near* ① *(see fig. 6.10)*

`Select second line:` *Select the line near* ②

`Dimension line arc location:` *Pick near* ③

continues

MAX
DEMO
FILE
SIZE

Angle Dimension Select first line:
Select the line near ④

Select second line: *Select the line
near* ⑤

Dimension line arc location:
Pick near ⑥

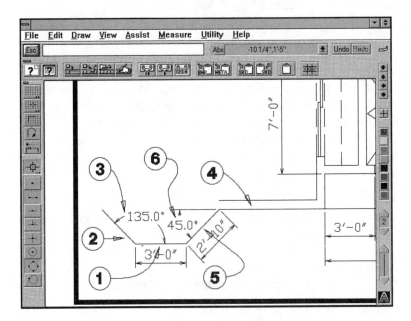

Figure 6.10:
Creating angle
dimensions.

Because you do not have much extra room to place the dimensions, you may have to try a few times before you are satisfied with the text and dimension arc location. You may have noticed that AutoSketch also provides an extension line for dimensioning so that the angles are always less than 180 degrees. In figure 6.10, the angle between the line at bubbles 4 and 5 is really 225 degrees, but AutoSketch added the extension line for the 45-degree angle dimension instead.

Labeling Features with the Leader Tool

A leader is very helpful when placing labels or showing sizes of certain features that do not lend themselves to regular dimensioning tools.

A *leader* begins with a terminator, normally an arrow. The leader line, drawn with a series of specified points, connects the terminator with the leader text. Display of leaders, including the text height, is controlled by some of the same settings that control other types of dimensions. The text font used is controlled by the text settings, which are covered in the next section. When you are prompted to enter the text string, you are placed into the Text Editor, shown in figure 6.11, which gives you great power and flexibility for creating leader notes.

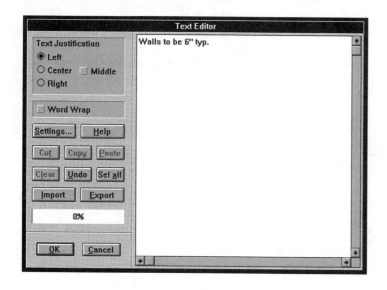

Figure 6.11:

The Text Editor, used with the Leader tool.

The following exercise places a leader on the drawing to indicate a typical wall thickness. After the points for the leader location are chosen, you enter the text string that appears with the leader.

Using the Leader Tool

Zoom to the view shown in figure 6.12.

Choose **M**easure, *then the* Leader *tool*

Leader Start Point: *Pick a point*
near ①

To point: *Pick near* ②

Text location: *Pick near* ③   Opens Text Editor

Confirm that your text-justification settings match figure 6.11. Then type
Walls to be 6" typ., and click on the **O**K button. This is a good time to
save the drawing.

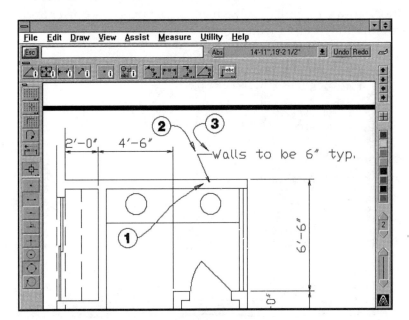

Figure 6.12:

Creating the
leader.

You have now completed dimensioning your first drawing. The
following section introduces you to the text capabilities of
AutoSketch.

Adding Text to a Drawing

Text is often necessary on technical drawings in the form of labels, notes, descriptions, or other necessary data. AutoSketch contains many useful features for placing text in drawings. Figure 6.13 shows some of the features that you control for text placement and appearance; figure 6.14 shows the Text Settings dialog box, which controls those features.

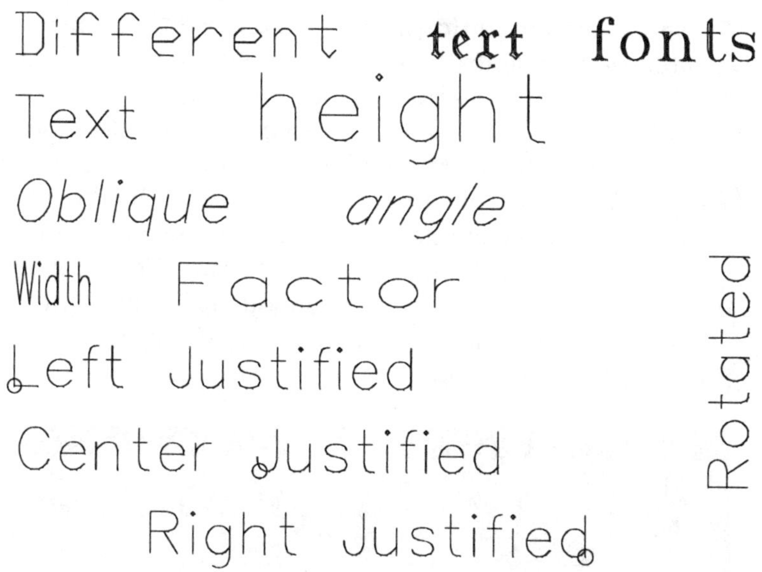

Different text fonts
Text height
Oblique angle
Width Factor
Left Justified
Center Justified
Right Justified

Rotated

Figure 6.13:
Text display and placement

The terms used in many CAD software packages for text creation are as follows:

- **Fonts.** *Fonts* are separate files of alphanumeric characters used to display text. Some font types are more appropriate than others for use in technical drawings. The trade-off for using complex text fonts in a drawing is slower redraw time and greater amounts of memory used. Some of the AutoSketch text fonts are shown in figure 6.14.

- **Text height.** *Text height* must be specified, and is usually proportional to the rest of the graphic entities. Your printing scale determines the text height you use. Many technical drawings require text height to be between 1/8" and 1/4" on the final hard copy.

- **Angles and width factor.** The *oblique angle*, *rotation angle*, and *width factor* can be adjusted to control the appearance of text. Subtle use of these features can help improve the appearance of notes or title block information.

- **Text-justification options.** *Text-justification* options are helpful for placing text. *Left justification* is the default—the text string is placed starting at the point you pick. *Right justification* or *center justification* moves the text into proper alignment after the text string has been completely entered. The *middle-justification* option modifies any of the three types of justification. When middle is activated, the pick point indicates the vertical center of the text string. This enables text to be centered, top to bottom, about a chosen point. Figure 6.15 shows the left-, center-, and right-justification points and how the Middle option modifies those points.

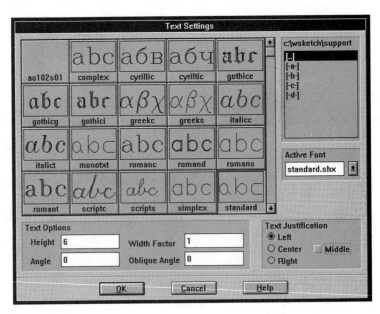

Figure 6.14:

The Text Settings dialog box.

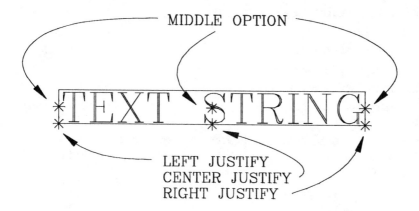

Figure 6.15:

Text-justification points.

Through the use of icons for text fonts, radio buttons for justification, and text boxes for other text settings, the Text Settings dialog box gives you complete control over your text placement and appearance.

The Quick Text tool from the Draw toolbox prompts you to pick the text location, and then enter your text string. You can double-click on the tool to bring up the Text Settings dialog box and make any changes in the current text settings before entering text.

You begin adding text to your drawing in the following exercise.

Inserting Text with the Quick Text Tool

Use the Zoom Full tool to view the entire drawing. Click on the Snap and Grid tools to activate them. Change to layer three, and choose a different color to help separate all your drawing entities.

Choose **D**raw, *then double-click on the* Quick Text *tool*	Opens the Text Settings dialog box

Change your settings to match those shown in figure 6.14, then choose **O**K.

Quick Text Enter point: *Pick near* ① *see fig. 6.16)*	Locates the start point of text (
Enter text: **TUB** ↵	
Enter point: *Pick near* ②	

continues

```
Enter text: EXISTING ↵
```

```
Enter point: Pick near ③
```

```
Enter text: RESIDENCE ↵
```

```
Enter point: Pick near ④
```

```
Enter text: SCALE: 1/4"=1[p] ↵
```

Double-click on the Quick Text *tool box*   Opens the Text Settings dialog

Change the font by choosing the romand icon, change the text height to 5", choose the Center justification and the Middle option, and then choose **O**K.

```
Quick Text Enter point: Pick near the
center of the north arrow at ⑤
```

```
Enter Text: NORTH ↵
```

```
Enter Point: Pick a point centered in
the column near ≈ ⑥
```

```
Enter text: REVISIONS ↵
```

Double-click on the Quick Text tool, and change the text height to 12", then choose **O**K. Enter the "A-1" text string centered in the box in the title block near ≤.

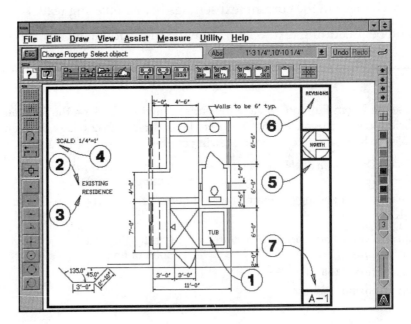

Figure 6.16:

Placing text in the drawing.

The Quick Text tool is a simple tool for placing text according to the current settings. When text strings or notes become long and complex, the Text Editor is available for creating text.

The Text Editor tool brings up the Text Editor dialog box (see fig. 6.11), which enables you to create long text strings as if you were using a regular word processor. When you choose the **O**K button, the text is placed into your drawing. The same justification features found in the Text Settings dialog box are used in this dialog box. If you choose the **S**ettings button, you access the Text Settings dialog box.

Many of the other features of the Text Editor are covered in Chapter 10, in which you learn to import and export text from other software applications.

The Text Editor tool is also found in the Edit toolbox. You can use it to edit text strings that have already been placed in the drawing.

The last two text strings are placed in the drawing by using the Text Editor tool.

Using the AutoSketch Text Editor

Choose **D**raw, *then double-click on the* Text Editor *tool*

Opens the Text Settings dialog box

Match your settings with those shown in figure 6.17, then click on OK.

`Text Editor Enter point:` *Pick near* ①

Locates the text *(see fig. 6.18)* start point, then activates the dialog box

Enter text, and choose **O**K.

continues

`Text Editor Enter point:` *Pick near* ②

Click on the **S**ettings button in the Text Editor dialog box, enter 90 in the Angle text box, then choose **O**K. Enter the text string AUTOSKETCH, press Enter, enter RESIDENCE, and choose **O**K. Save the drawing before continuing in this chapter.

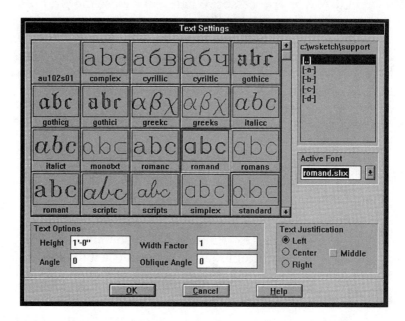

Figure 6.17:
Current text settings.

The Quick Text and Text Editor tools, along with all the settings that affect text, give you great flexibility for placing text strings in your drawing. If your text size or placement still needs minor adjustments, consider using editing tools such as Move or Scale to modify your text appearance.

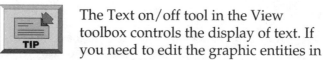

The Text on/off tool in the View toolbox controls the display of text. If you need to edit the graphic entities in a drawing with a large amount of text, your graphics redraw much faster with the text display turned off.

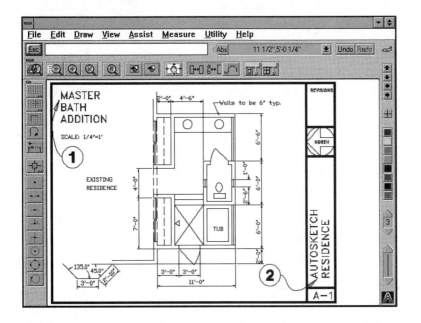

Figure 6.18:

Creating text strings with the Text Editor tool.

Using the Additional Measure Tools

Chapter 2 pointed out that the greatest difference between a manual drawing and a CAD drawing is the database that constitutes a CAD drawing. If a design has been properly completed using CAD, the database should be useful for many activities requiring size or area information. The Measure toolbox contains a group of tools that provide this information.

The information tools presented in this section work much like the dimensioning tools discussed earlier in this chapter except that the information is displayed in an information box.

 Each of the icons representing tool information contains an "i", which stands for *information*. This is an easy way to distinguish these tools from the dimensioning tools.

As in dimensioning, it is very important to use proper Attach tools to obtain accurate information. In some cases, it is not possible to use the Attach tools for a given distance or location. Depending on the zoom scale and the accuracy of the information you require, it may be possible to visually pick the points requested by the information tools.

 The data shown in the information box is displayed according to the current units settings.

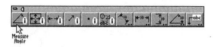

The Measure Angle tool prompts for three points. The first point is the base point of the angle; the second and third points are the two points that form the angle. The angle displayed always has fewer than 180 degrees.

The Measure Area tool is very useful for displaying the area and perimeter of a designated space in your drawing. You are prompted to pick points around the perimeter, ending back at the first point chosen. If the area you are measuring (a pond, for example) has an irregular shape, choose enough points around it for a close approximation. This tool provides valuable information for purchasing materials such as roofing or flooring. Facility managers often use this tool to determine the square footage of offices, shop floor space, and parking areas.

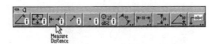

Measure Distance

The distance between any two chosen points is shown with the Measure Distance tool. This tool is very useful for checking clearances or distances not dimensioned on a drawing.

Measure Bearing

The Measure Bearing tool works much like the Measure Angle tool except that the bearing is taken from the 0-degree point of the Cartesian coordinate system, or the 3:00 position. Only two points are required to obtain a bearing. This information is useful for determining which polar coordinate angles must be used.

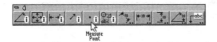

Measure Point

The Measure Point tool is used to obtain the exact coordinates of a selected location. The X and Y coordinates are given from the absolute zero position on the Cartesian coordinate system.

Show Properties

Using the Show Properties tool is a good way to look at the database of the drawing. Every entity in the drawing contains coordinate information, such as start points, endpoints, radii, and so on. Other information, such as color, layer, and linetype are also stored for each entity. To use the Show Properties tool, pick an entity, and the information box displays the properties of the entity. Depending on the type of entity chosen, the information box displays the properties relevant to that entity type. Figure 6.19 shows the information box of a dimension.

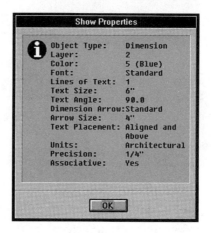

In the following exercise, you experiment with the Measure tools,
which display information.

Using the Angle, Bearing, and Distance Measuring Tools

Zoom in to the area shown in figure 6.20. Snap and Grid should be
turned off. Activate the End Point and Intersect Attach tools.

Choose **M**easure, *then the* Measure Angle
tool

`Angle Base point:` *Pick* ①
(see fig. 6.20)

`First direction:` *Pick* ②

`Second direction:` *Pick* ②, *then*   Angle is 45 degrees
choose OK

Choose the Measure Bearing *tool*

`Bearing Base point:` *Pick* ①

`Enter point:` *Pick* ②, *then choose* OK   Bearing is 135 degrees

Choose the Measure Distance *tool*

`Distance From point:` *Pick* ①

`To point:` *Pick* ②, *then choose* OK   Distance is
2'6"

Choose the Measure Point *tool*

Point coordinates: *Pick* ①   Displays the X and Y
(see fig 6.21), then choose OK   coordinates

Choose the Measure Area *tool*

Area First perimeter point: *Pick* ①

Next point:

Continue picking corner points ② through ⑧, then pick ① a second time. The area is 60.5 square feet, and the perimeter is 39 feet.

Choose the Show Properties *tool*

Select object:

Try choosing several different types of entities to see the information displayed on each of them. Figure 6.19 shows the information box when the 4' dimension is chosen.

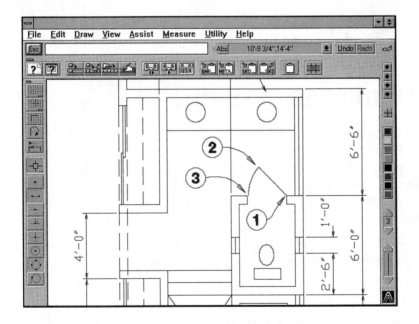

Figure 6.20:
Using the measure tools.

Now that the drawing has been completed, the final step is to print the hard copy of the drawing. The final section in this chapter explains how to print from AutoSketch.

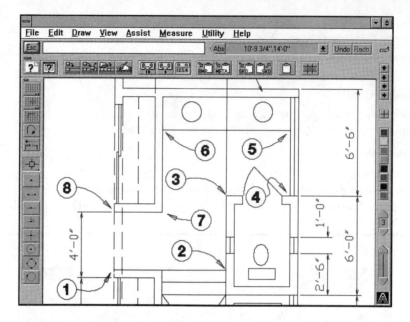

Figure 6.21:

Sample pick points for measuring an area.

Plotting and Printing

The terms *plotting* and *printing* really have the same meaning in AutoSketch for Windows. Because all hard-copy output devices are controlled by the Windows Print Manager, AutoSketch sends the information to the Print Manager. Your hard-copy device(s), whether it is a printer or a plotter, must be configured for Windows.

A plotter generally has more features, such as pens of different color and thickness, pen speed, and paper size.

Your dialog boxes and printing options may look slightly different than the samples shown in this book because of different hardware and configuration settings.

This process is discussed in Chapter 2, and is explained in detail in your Windows Reference Guide.

Using the Print Command

The Print command, found in the File menu, creates a hard copy of your drawing by instructing the Print Manager to print one copy of your drawing, fitting all of the graphic entities on to the current paper size. Before you continue learning how to change and adjust all your print settings, try using the Print command to make sure your printer is working properly.

Using the Print Command

Choose File, *then* Print   Printing message appears

A hard copy of your existing drawing should be output on your printer or plotter.

 If your printer or plotter does not function properly, try using it with one of your other Windows applications, such as Write or Paint. If that also fails, your output device is not properly configured with Windows. If your printer or plotter perform well with other Windows applications, continue reading in this chapter to see if the AutoSketch settings are correct.

Managing Your Print Settings

The other command in the File menu that affects your hard copy output is the Print Settings command. Figure 6.22 shows the Print Settings dialog box.

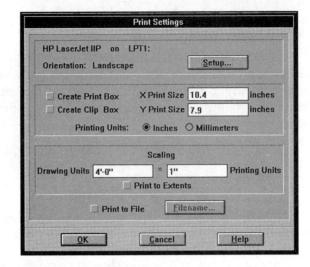

Figure 6.22:

The Print Settings dialog box.

Examining the Printer Defaults

At the top of the Print Settings dialog box, the current printer from Print Manager is displayed. To change to another printer, you have to open the Print Manager window and select another printer.

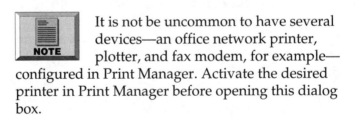

It is not be uncommon to have several devices—an office network printer, plotter, and fax modem, for example—configured in Print Manager. Activate the desired printer in Print Manager before opening this dialog box.

The **S**etup button opens another dialog box, as shown in figure 6.23, which enables you to view and change the settings associated with the current printer. Again, your settings features may vary, depending on your hardware.

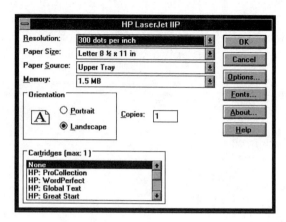

Figure 6.23:
The Printer Setup dialog box.

Specifying Paper Size and Print Boxes

The paper size must be established to determine how the graphic entities will fit on the paper. Technical drawings are usually created in a *landscape* orientation instead of a *portrait* orientation. This means that the paper is the longest in the horizontal direction instead of the vertical direction.

Although an A-size drawing sheet is usually 11" wide by 8 1/2" tall, the X and Y sizes shown in figure 6.22 reflect a 1/4" minimum border area that the printer or plotter cannot reach. Depending on the drawing size and output device, some borders are larger than this. The paper size can be specified in inch or millimeter units, depending on which radio button is selected.

A *print box* is generated from these settings if a check mark is placed in front of the Create Print Box. This box, as seen in figure 6.24, shows you exactly how the graphic entities will fit on the paper. This feature is a great improvement over some other software packages, in which trial-and-error methods of printing can waste a good deal of time.

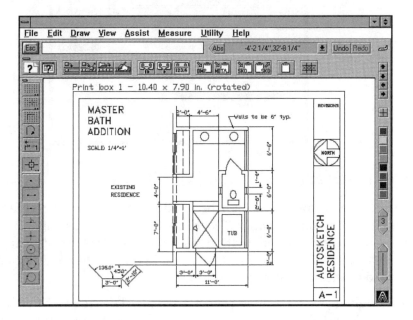

Figure 6.24:

A print box, shown on the existing drawing.

A print box can be treated like any other entity. It can be moved, scaled, or erased. You may want to place it on a layer on which it can be turned off when you are not using it.

A *clip box* is used to select only a portion of a drawing for printing. It can be used inside a print box or with no print box.

Scaling Your Graphic Entities to Your Paper Size

The issue of scaling should be addressed when you begin your drawing because it affects settings such as text height and linetype scaling. These settings should be calculated so that they appear correct on the final hard copy.

The Print to Extents check box, if activated, instructs AutoSketch to determine the scale factor needed to fit all the graphic entitles on the paper. It is often necessary to print to a specific scale factor, such as 10:1 or 1/4"=1' (1:48). You can enter these numbers directly into the text boxes to specify the scale factor.

Printing to a File

Instead of sending your output to a hard-copy device, you have the option of storing the formatted output in a file for later use. If you create a drawing at home but want to plot it at work, plotting to a file works very well. Some word processors, such as WordPerfect, can import graphic entities from a plot file. If you place a check mark in the Print to File box, you can use the Filename button to name the file. If you do not name it here, you are asked for a file name when you use the **P**rint command.

Finish this chapter by printing once more, this time using all the print settings.

Using the Print Settings To Print Your Drawing

Erase any existing print boxes on your drawing. If necessary, open the Windows Print Manager to select the printer you want to use.

Choose **F**ile, *then* Print Se**t**tings box	Opens the Print Settings dialog
Click on the **S**etup *button, and confirm appropriate settings, then choose* OK	Opens the Printer Setup dialog box

Change any other settings in the Print Settings dialog box so they conform to figure 6.22 or to your own preferences, then choose **O**K.

Choose **P**rint	Prints the drawing

217

Your graphic entities should be properly scaled on your paper and centered, as shown in figure 6.24.

Summary

This chapter covered several important steps for finishing your CAD drawings and printing them. The dimensioning tools are easy to use, and they take a lot of the manual effort out of dimensioning. They also make your drawing look professional. If you have had no previous experience with dimensioning, however, take some time to learn the dimensioning practices that are acceptable for your type of work.

If you are very familiar with dimensioning, the way AutoSketch automatically produces dimensions may vary from your manual methods. Remember that automatic dimensioning is only really useful if the graphic entities are properly scaled and positioned.

Adding text to your drawing can be as simple as picking a locating point and entering the text. AutoSketch provides some very powerful features for text appearance and placement.

The measure tools, which show information about the graphic entities, give you an appreciation for the database that is the heart of the CAD drawing. The measure tools are especially helpful when you access drawings that are unfamiliar to you.

Finally, the hard copy output is needed to share the CAD information in a printed form. You must understand the link between AutoSketch and the Windows Print Manager, and you must have some knowledge of the computer hardware you are using to create acceptable hard copies.

This completes Part Two of this book, which is designed to get you started on the AutoSketch for Windows CAD software. When you have mastered these CAD drafting fundamentals, turn to Part Three, in which you learn many of the common advanced CAD drafting techniques.

Advanced
CAD Drafting
Techniques

Creating and Inserting Parts
Using Pattern Fills, Polylines, Arrays, and Splines
Creating Special Types of Drawings
Using AutoSketch with Other Applications
Practicing with AutoSketch
Using Macros To Enhance AutoSketch Performance

Creating and Inserting Parts

The first six chapters of this book covered most of AutoSketch's drawing tools, editing tools, and methods for increasing your drawing efficiency. This chapter shows you how to place external, predrawn objects, assemblies, and symbols into a drawing whenever needed.

The capability to insert external objects into a drawing is one of the most powerful features of CAD. It automates repetitive drawing tasks that are so time-consuming and tedious in manual drafting. In AutoSketch, external objects that are inserted into a drawing are called *parts*.

 Parts replace plastic templates, which are used in manual drafting to repetitively draw standard objects.

A part is made up of entities that have been saved to disk as an AutoSketch drawing file. A part can contain any number or type of entities, and any AutoSketch drawing can be inserted as a part. A part can also be opened and edited like any other AutoSketch drawing.

In this chapter, you learn how to group entities together so they act as one entity. Grouped entities are easily moved, copied, scaled, or otherwise edited. When grouped entities are used as a part, you can manage and manipulate many parts quickly.

Understanding Parts

Parts are divided into the following two categories:

- **Components**. *Components* are real-world objects, such as desks, tables, chairs, sinks, toilets, and so on. They are drawn at their real-world size.

- **Symbols.** *Symbols* represent other objects, such as electrical receptacles, pipe valves, surface quality, and so forth. They are sized according to plot size and scale factor.

There are two ways to make a part in AutoSketch: use the Part Clip tool or make a drawing that contains only the part's entities.

Understanding Parts and Entity Properties

The properties of each entity (layer, linetype, and color) are maintained in each part when it is created. When a part is inserted into a drawing, the entities have the same properties they had when the part was created. For example, if you create a part of a red desk on layer 8, its entities are red and inserted on layer 8 every time you insert the desk part.

Entity properties must be taken into consideration when a part is created. Create your parts with your entity-property organization scheme in mind. If you do not plan ahead when creating your parts, it is easy to become disorganized and have entities scattered on inappropriate layers.

The following conditions apply to the entities of an inserted part:

- **Layer.** The layer assignments of the individual entities at the time of the part's creation are maintained. If you make a layer invisible, and an entity within a part was created on that layer, the entity disappears.

- **Linetype.** If a part is created with linetypes other than solid, the current linetype scale affects individual entities within the part when it is inserted.

- **Color.** The current color does not affect the entities of an inserted part; the color of the entities at the time the part was created is maintained.

You can edit the properties of a part's entities after they have been inserted into a drawing, or you can edit the part's entity properties before inserting the part into a drawing. Editing an existing part is covered later in this chapter.

Making Parts with the Part Clip Tool

The Part Clip tool enables you to save entities to a separate AutoSketch drawing file. The Part Clip tool is located in the File pull-down menu.

There are two ways to come up with entities for parts to use with the Part Clip tool. The first way is to draw the part from scratch, and then clip it. The second (easiest) way is to open a drawing with the object or symbol already drawn, and then clip the entities for the part.

If you do not have the time or the desire to create your own parts, you can buy libraries of predrawn parts from third-party vendors. The full-feature version of AutoSketch also comes with an extensive selection of parts you can use.

Once you have the entities created for the part, the next step is to clip them to a drawing file. When you activate the Part Clip tool, AutoSketch displays the Part Clip File dialog box, in which you can name the part file.

After naming the file, AutoSketch prompts you to specify the part-base location. Next, you are prompted to select the entities you want to include in the part. The entities you select are highlighted. When you have selected all the entities for the part, choose any drawing or editing tool to save the part to disk.

Naming the Part

Naming the part is an important part of the part-creating process. Follow a consistent naming pattern to keep similar parts organized. For example, you may want to name doors according to style and size: a 32" standard door can have the file name DRSTD32.SKD.

Always construct your file-name pattern to show information from general to specific. AutoSketch sorts the file names of parts alphabetically and numerically. In the example DRSTD32, the first two characters identify the part type (door). The next three characters identify the style (standard). The last two numbers identify the size (32").

In AutoSketch, the Part Clip File dialog box is used to name the part before you actually clip it. It operates exactly like the Save File As dialog box. The subdirectory used to store parts is separate from the drawing subdirectory, so it is easier to keep parts organized and separated from project drawings.

You can have several different parts subdirectories to organize different kinds of parts. For example, you may want to create one subdirectory for drawing symbols, one for house parts, one for furniture, one for electronic parts, and one for trees and plants. Figure 7.1 shows the Part Clip File dialog box.

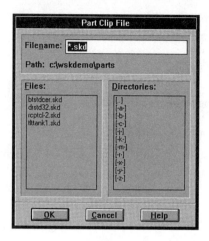

Figure 7.1:
Part Clip File
dialog box.

Specifying a Part-Base Location

The *part-base location* is a point, relative to a part's entities, that is used to place the part when it is inserted into a drawing. All of a part's entities are inserted at the same distance from the insert point as they were from the part-base location when the part was created.

The part-base location should be a point that is convenient for placing the part when it is inserted. For example, you may want the part-base location for a desk to be one of the desk's corners; a tree symbol may have its center as the part-base location. The base point can be on one of the part's entities or away from the entities.

In the following exercise, you create a part from entities in an existing drawing.

Clipping a Part

Open the CHAP7 drawing, or open your MYCHAP05 drawing from Chapter 5, then save it as MYCHAP07.

Use the View tools to display the view in figure 7.2

Choose **File**, *then* Part **Clip**

continues

225

Note that the current parts directory is PARTS.

Type **TLTTANK1** *in the* Filename:
text box, then choose OK

Double-click on the Midpoint
attach setting

`Part Clip Part-base location:` *Pick* ①
(see fig. 7.2)

`Select object:` *Pick* ②

`Crosses/Window corner:` *Pick* ③   Highlights the
                                          toilet entities

Choose **D**raw, *then select any Draw tool*   Ends the process,
                                                       and saves the part

Double-click on the Endpoint
attach setting

Choose **F**ile, *then* Part **C**lip

Type **DRSTD32** *in the* Filename:
text box, then choose OK

`Part Clip Part-base location:` *Pick* ④

`Select object:` *Window the door entities*
from ⑤ *to* ⑥

Select any Draw or Edit tool   Ends the process,
                                        and saves the part

Erase the door and toilet entities

Now you have clipped some parts. The next step is to insert the parts into a drawing.

Inserting Parts with the Part Tool

Once you have created your parts, you can insert them over and over again into any drawing. The Part tool, located in the Draw toolbox, is used to insert parts into an AutoSketch drawing.

The Part tool, when activated, brings up the Select Part File dialog box. The Select Part File dialog box is similar to the Open Drawing File dialog box. Small icons of each part are displayed in the dialog box. Double-clicking on one of the icons selects that part for insertion. The directory list box enables you to change the current parts subdirectory. The current parts subdirectory is displayed at the top of the directory list. The Select Part File dialog box is shown in figure 7.3.

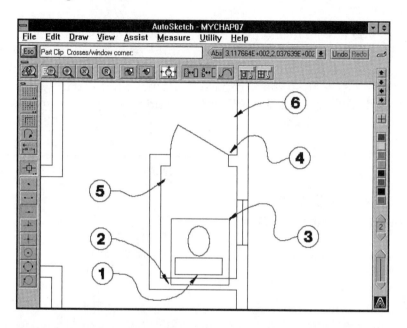

Figure 7.2:

Clipping the toilet and door parts.

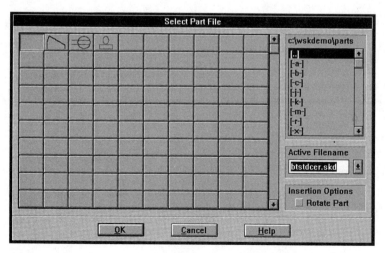

Figure 7.3:

Select Part File dialog box.

The Active Filename text box displays the file name of the last inserted part. If you click on OK, AutoSketch automatically inserts the last part. The Active Filename text box has a drop-down list box that enables you to select a part by file name rather than visually.

Once you have indicated what part you want to insert into your drawing, AutoSketch prompts you for the part-insertion point. The part's entities are the same distance from the insertion point that they were from the part-base location when the part was created. You can pick a point with the cursor, or you can enter a point from the keyboard.

Inserting Parts

Continue from the previous exercise.

Choose **D**raw, *then the Part tool*	Displays the Select Part File dialog box
Click on the TLTTANK1 *icon, then choose OK*	Makes the TLTTANK1 the current part
Turn on Snap	
Part To Point: *Pick point 24'7",14'6"*	Inserts the toilet at the picked point
Turn off Snap	
Choose the Part tool	
Double-click on the DRSTD32 *icon*	
To point: *Pick* ① *(see fig. 7.4)*	
Save the drawing	

Drawing standard components with parts is much quicker than drawing them from scratch. Next, you learn how to rotate a part as you insert it into your drawing.

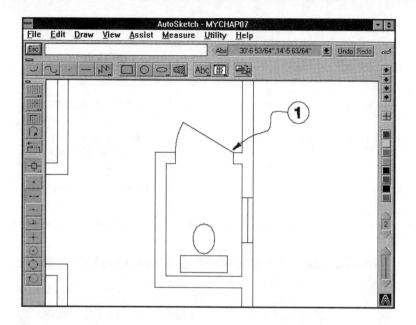

Figure 7.4:
The inserted toilet and door parts.

Rotating Parts at Insertion Time

Sometimes, when you insert a part, it is not oriented properly—when parts are inserted, they are oriented the same as when they were created. The Rotate Part insertion option of the Select Part File dialog box enables you to rotate the part to any angle.

When you enable the Rotate Part option, you are prompted for a reference point, then a second point or angle to indicate the rotation angle. If you pick a second point, the angle is calculated from the first point to the second point. You are asked to specify the rotation angle before specifying the insertion point.

In the following exercise, you insert the door part again, except this time you rotate it 180° to fit the outside doorway.

Rotating Parts

Continue from the previous exercise, and zoom or pan to the view of the outside door shown in figure 7.5.

continues

229

*Choose **D**raw, then the Part tool*

Make sure DRSTD32 is the active file name.

Turn on the Rotate Part insertion option

Choose OK

`Reference point:` *Pick* ① *(see fig. 7.5)*	Specifies the first point for the rotation angle
`Second point or angle:` *Pick* ②	Specifies the second point for the rotation angle, and rotates part to angle
`To point:` *Pick* ① *again*	Picks the insertion point

Save the drawing

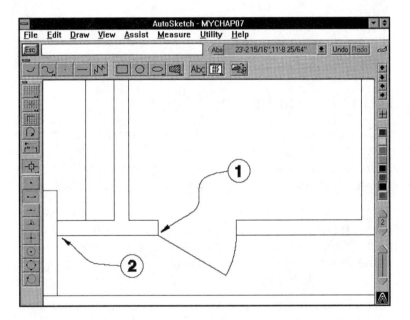

Figure 7.5:
The rotated door part.

Scaling Parts

AutoSketch does not have a feature to scale parts at insertion time—you must scale a part after it has been inserted. The Scale tool in the Edit toolbox enables you to make entities larger or smaller.

Parts that are components rarely need to be scaled because they are drawn actual size (1:1 scale); parts that are symbols may need to be scaled according to drawing scale factor.

The Scale tool asks you to select the entities to be scaled, and prompts you for a base point. The base point is important because AutoSketch uses it as a point of reference. If you pick a base point in the center of an object, the object increases or decreases around its center. If the base point is located to the right of the object, the object grows or shrinks to the left.

In the following exercise, you insert a symbol part for a two-outlet electrical receptacle and scale it to the bathroom addition's drawing-scale factor.

Scaling a Part

Continue from the previous drawing, and zoom to the view in figure 7.6.

Turn on Snap

*Choose **D**raw, then select the Part tool*

*Insert the RCPTCL-2 part with a
0° rotation angle in an open space
in the drawing area*

The symbol is scaled for a 1:1 drawing scale, and looks like a red dot in the drawing area. Next, you scale the part by the drawing scale factor of 48.

*Choose **E**dit, then select the Scale tool*

`Scale Select object:` *Select the red dot
with the window-selection method*

`Base point:` *Pick near the red dot of the
outlet symbol*

`Second point or scale factor:` **48** ↵

*Copy and rotate the outlet symbol to
the positions in figure 7.6*

Save the drawing

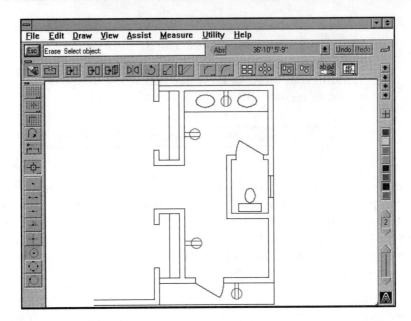

Figure 7.6:

The scaled, rotated, and copied outlet.

It is not easy to edit a part's entities after a part has been inserted. The entities of a part are separate and often must be selected individually. If there are many other entities nearby, entity selection becomes even more difficult.

Because AutoSketch does not have a way to scale parts at insertion time, it is easier to create a set of prescaled symbol parts for a specific drawing-scale factor than it is to scale parts after inserting them. Store each set of symbols in a separate directory for easy organization.

Grouping Entities

The Group tool enables you to combine entities into an object that behaves like a single entity. Every entity of a group is selected when one entity of the group is selected. Grouped entities are easily copied, scaled, moved, arrayed, and otherwise edited. The Attach tool operates exactly the same on grouped entities as on non-grouped entities.

Scale

Any set of commonly associated and repeated entities should be grouped for efficient editing. Parts are excellent candidates for grouping. Grouped entities, when inserted as a part, are inserted as a single object and can be easily edited. The Group tool does not clip entities to an external drawing file; they reside only in the current drawing—unless they are clipped with the Part Clip tool.

In AutoSketch, there are several limitations to grouped entities. Groups are limited to 1,000 entities, and they can only be nested up to eight levels deep. The Break, Chamfer, and Fillet tools do not work on grouped entities.

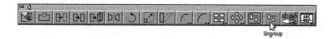

Ungroup

If want to edit grouped entities individually, the Ungroup tool returns grouped entities to their ungrouped state.

In the following exercise, you group entities for electrical symbols, clip the groups as parts, and then insert them into your bathroom drawing.

Making and Editing Groups

Continue from the previous drawing.

Erase all outlet symbols except the one at ① (see fig. 7.7)

*Choose **E**dit, then the Group tool*

`Group Select object:` *Window select the outlet symbol*   Highlights the entities

*Choose **F**ile, then Part **C**lip*   Groups outlet entities, and starts clipping the part

continues

Double-click on the RCPTCL-2 file name

Choose Yes *to overwrite existing file*

`Part-base location:` *Use the Attach tool with the Center option and pick* ① *(see fig. 7.7)*

`Select object:` *Pick grouped symbol at* ①

Highlights all the outlet entities

All the entities highlight because they were grouped.

Choose **D**raw, *then select the Part tool*

Clips the symbol, and opens the Select Part File dialog box

Insert the outlet symbols with the Rotate Part option enabled, as shown in figure 7.7

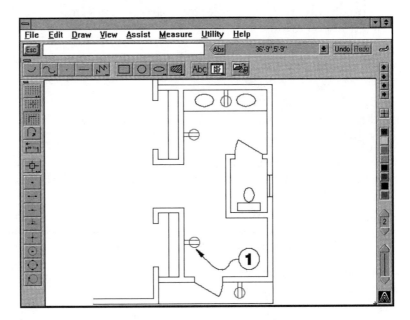

Figure 7.7:

The grouped outlet symbols.

If you want to copy an outlet symbol to add more receptacles, you only need to pick one of the symbol's entities to select the entire group.

Modifying Existing Parts

Any part can be opened and edited like any other drawing. You can change entity color, linetype, or layer; group the entities; or change the part-base location. Changes to a part only show up when the part is inserted into a drawing—existing parts are not updated; they must be erased and then reinserted.

All the parts you used in this exercise have *preset values*, which are layers, linetypes, colors, and scale settings that are determined as the parts are created. Sometimes parts need to be modified to incorporate them into your drawing.

Changing a Part's Entity Properties

Continue from the previous exercise.

Turn off Snap if it is on

*Choose **D**raw, then the Part tool, and insert the BTSTDCER part in a clear area of the drawing*

Notice that the color and layer of the bathtub does not match the bathroom addition's entity-property organization.

Erase the bathtub

Save the drawing

*Choose **F**ile, then **O**pen*

Use the subdirectory list box to change to the \WSKDEMO\PARTS subdirectory

Open the BTSTDCER part

Set the current layer to 4 and the current color to magenta

Use the Property(Change) tool to change the bathtub's entities to the current property settings

Save the drawing

Open your MYCHAP07 drawing

continues

Use the Part tool to insert the
BTSTDCER part again

Notice that the bathtub's entities are now inserted on the correct layer and are the correct color.

Erase the bathtub
Save the drawing

Although the bathtub's entities now have the correct entity properties, the part-base point is not in a convenient location. AutoSketch has a feature that enables you to change the insertion-base point of a drawing.

Changing the Part-Base Location

If you are unsatisfied with the position of a part's base location, you can change it. To change the location of the part base for a drawing, use the Part Base option of the Drawing Settings dialog box.

The Part Base option displays the Part Base Settings dialog box, shown in figure 7.8, which enables you to change the part-base point of a drawing. The default part-base location for a new drawing is 0,0.

Figure 7.8:
Part Base Settings dialog box.

In the following exercise, you modify the bathtub part by changing the part-base location.

Changing the Part-Base Location

Continue from the previous exercise.

Open the bathtub part

*Choose **M**easure, then select the Measure Point tool*

Double-click on the Endpoint attach setting

`Point coordinates:` *Pick* ① *(see fig. 7.9)*

`Coordinates: 12'3", 23'5"`   Displays the information box

Click on OK

*Choose **U**tility, then select the Drawing Settings tool*   Opens the Drawing Settings dialog box

Click on Part Base   Opens the Part Base Settings dialog box

Type **12'3"** *in the* Part Base X: *text box*

Double-click on the Part Base Y: *text box, then type* **23'5"**

Click on OK   Closes the Drawing Settings dialog box

*Press F12; or choose **F**ile, then **S**ave*   Saves the part with the new part-base location

Open the MYCHAP07 drawing

Insert the bathtub at ② *(see fig. 7.10)*

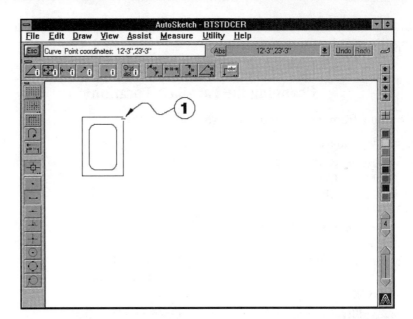

Figure 7.9:

The new part-base location.

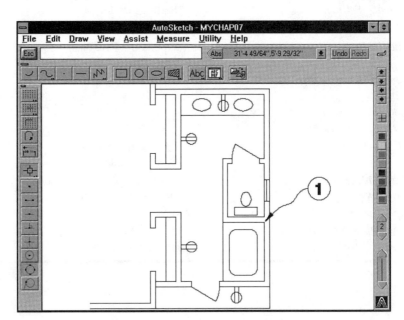

Figure 7.10:

The updated bathtub, inserted into the bathroom addition.

Inserting and Combining Drawings

All parts or drawings that are saved can be inserted into any drawing. The Part tool in the Draw toolbox enables you to combine drawings into an assembly drawing. It is common practice to create drawings independent of one another, and then combine them into one final drawing before plotting.

For example, if there are six parts to make up an assembly drawing, six different people can each work on a part as a separate drawing, and then combine the parts to form the final drawing.

The benefits of this method are numerous, particularly if each individual drawing is made up of a number of parts or details. As long as the six people are using the same drafting standards and scale, the drawings can be combined easily with a little planning.

Summary

In this chapter, you learned how to use CAD to complete drawings faster by using the Part and Group tools. These tools enable you to use the assembly-line technique of prebuilt components to complete a drawing in less time than drawing everything manually from scratch.

This chapter also discussed the Part Clip and Part tools, which enable you to insert predrawn entities into a drawing. The Group tool enables you to edit grouped entities as if they were a single entity.

In Chapter 8, you explore more AutoSketch tools that enable you to draw smooth spline curves and enhance drawing clarity with automated hatch patterns.

Using Pattern Fills, Polylines, Arrays, and Splines

This chapter continues to explore some of the more advanced CAD drafting techniques. Several of the AutoSketch tools covered (Polyline, Curve, Array, and Pattern) are commonly found in other CAD packages. The challenge is not just in learning how to use the tools—it is in developing CAD drafting techniques that enable you to create a technically accurate and visually pleasing drawing using a given set of drawing tools.

The best way to learn the tools, as well as the techniques, is to practice them on a variety of drawings. The drawing of the AM/FM cassette recorder shown in figure 8.1 uses several features of AutoSketch you have probably not used up to this point.

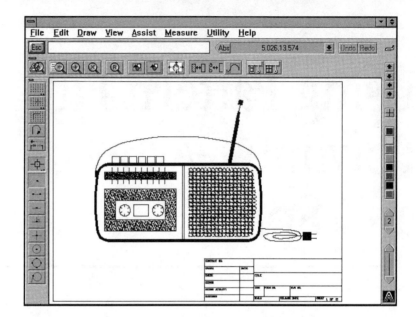

Figure 8.1:

The completed AM/FM cassette recorder drawing.

Beginning the Drawing

A productive way to begin a new drawing is to retrieve a drawing that already has a border, title block, and any other standard components you need in your drawing. You can do this by beginning a new drawing and inserting a part that contains all this information. (Inserting parts was demonstrated in Chapter 7.)

Another way to open an existing drawing is to use a border and title block, and then rename the drawing. Opening an existing drawing is the way you begin the drawing for this chapter because the settings are already specified, and you are ready to begin drawing.

Retrieving a Border and Title Block

A drawing called CHAP8.SKD is provided on the LC DISK included with this book. The first thing you should do when you

open the drawing is to save it as another name, so that the drawing is available to use again as the starting point for another new
drawing.

The border is sized for an A-size drawing sheet. Because the object
to be drawn needs a C-size drawing sheet to contain the complete
part at full scale, you scale up the existing border and title block.
The first drawing exercise in this chapter shows you how to
perform these steps.

Beginning the Drawing

Begin AutoSketch and open the drawing CHAP8.SKD. Move your cursor
around the border, and watch the coordinate display. Note that the
border appears to be about 7.5 units tall by 10 units wide, with the lower
left corner at 0,0.

Choose **File**, *then* Save **A**s, *enter* **MYCHAP8** *in the text box*	Renames the drawing
Choose **E**dit, *then the* Scale *tool*	
`Scale Select object:` *Use a window to select the entire drawing*	
`Base point:` **0,0** ↵	Scales from the 0,0 point
`Second point or scale factor:` **2** ↵	Doubles the border size
Click on the Grid *tool to display the grid*	
Double-click on the Grid *tool*	Displays Grid/Snap/Limits dialog box

Change Grid to .5 and Snap to .125, and change the drawing limits to 20"
by 15". Notice that choosing OK resizes the drawing screen to the new
limits. Save your drawing.

Your drawing now appears, as shown in figure 8.2.

 If you do not change your drawing
limits, the grid is only displayed in the
lower left half of your border. (The
grid is displayed only in the area defined by your
current drawing limits.)

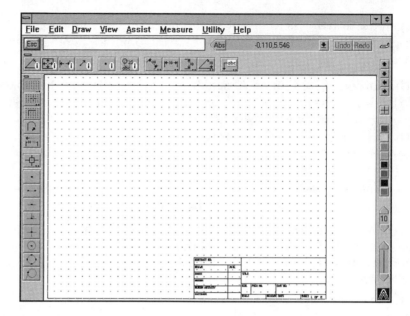

Figure 8.2:

The resized border and title block.

Establishing Proper Drawing Standards

Before you proceed any further with this drawing, some sound CAD drafting practices should be reviewed. If you have access to a C-size plotter, you can print this drawing at full scale, which means that features such as text size and dimension arrows may be sized accordingly. The standard units for this drawing are decimal, with three places of accuracy.

You should establish a layer and color scheme. Table 8.1 shows an example of such a scheme. The layer numbers are assigned to each of the different types of graphic entities, and a separate color may also be used for each layer. This arrangement helps keep the drawing well organized, and enables you to display only the layers with which you are currently working.

Table 8.1 Layer and Color Settings		
Layer	Entity Type	Color
2	Object Lines	7-black
3	Dimensions	4-cyan
4	Notes	5-blue
5	Hatch	2-yellow
8	Construction Lines	6-magenta
10	Border, Title Block	7-black

If you are using a color printer or plotter, you can use other color combinations for better clarity. For multiple pen plotters, you may want to assign colors based on the width of the pen used for that color.

Try to remember to use the correct layers and colors when creating graphic entities. If you forget, you can use the Property Change tool to quickly reassign the correct properties to your existing entities.

The macro language can be used to switch layers, linetypes, and colors in one operation. For more information about macros, refer to Chapter 12.

Beginning a Drawing by Using Construction Lines

In the exercises in this chapter, you draw the AM/FM cassette recorder by using several of the more advanced drawing tools.

Before going too far, it is often a good idea to "rough out" an object to size it properly and locate it on the drawing sheet.

The following exercise shows you how to lay out your drawing on layer 8, which is reserved for construction entities. You place an 11" by 5" rectangle on your drawing and perform several modifications to create the necessary points for the polyline.

Creating the Construction Entities

Set the current layer to 8 and the color to magenta.

Choose **D**raw, *then the Box tool*

`Box First corner: 3,4 ↵`

`Second corner: r(11,5) ↵`   Draws a rectangle

Choose **E**dit, *then double-click on*   Displays Fillet
the Fillet tool   Settings dialog box

Set the fillet radius to .75", and fillet each corner of the rectangle, as shown in figure 8.3. Use the Break tool with the Midpoint attach tool to break the rectangle at ① and ②.

Choose the Stretch tool

`Stretch First corner:` *Pick* ③   Begins crossing window

`Crosses/window corner:` *Pick* ④

`Stretch base:` *Using the End Point tool,*
pick near ①

`Stretch to: r(-.125,0) ↵`

Stretch the other side .125 to the outside.

As you become more experienced with computer-aided drafting, you learn how the proper use of construction entities, along with the appropriate Attach tools, help you to create an accurate drawing without entering all the coordinates. The next tool you learn to use in this drawing is the Polyline tool.

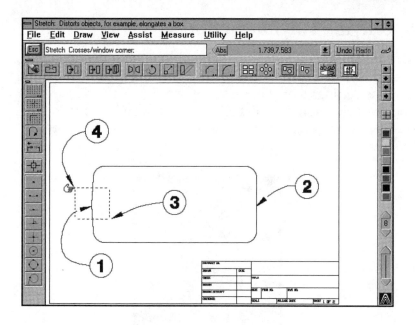

Figure 8.3:
Stretching out the side of the rectangle.

Using Polylines Creatively

You have already used the Polyline tool several times in previous drawing exercises. Perhaps the most obvious use of a polyline is for drawing connected lines. Instead of specifying a start point and an endpoint for each line segment, AutoSketch prompts only for endpoints after the first segment is drawn.

Another good reason to use a polyline is to group several basic entities, such as lines and arcs, into one complex entity. This process is similar in effect to using the Group tool, as explained in Chapter 7.

Specifying Polyline Settings

Many of the normal settings, such as layer, color, and linetype, affect polylines in the same way that they affect lines and arcs. The Polyline Settings dialog box, shown in figure 8.4, is displayed by double-clicking on the Polyline tool. You can also access this dialog box by using the Drawing Settings tool in the Utility toolbox.

Figure 8.4:

The Polyline Settings dialog box.

Polyline Width

The default width of a polyline is 0, which means that the width of the polyline appears on your drawing screen as the width of one pixel. Your graphics resolution determines the pixel width. The line width on the hard copy depends on the standard line width on your printer or plotter. A polyline is unique in that it can be assigned a specific line width, which is helpful for borders or highlighted areas. It is also used for special entities, such as walls in an architectural drawing, which are always drawn showing their full width.

The next exercise shows you how to highlight the border on your drawing by placing a wide polyline around it.

Drawing a Wide Polyline

Choose **D**raw, *then double-click on the* Polyline tool	Opens Polyline Settings dialog box

Set the Polyline Width to .06", confirm that the Solid Fill radio button is active, then choose OK. Change the current layer to 10 and the color to black.

Polyline First point: *With the End Point tool active, pick* ① *(see fig. 8.5)*

To point: *Pick* ②, ③,   Draws polyline
④, *and then* ① *again*

Polyline First point: *Pick* ⑤, ⑥, *then pick* ⑦ *twice to end the polyline*

Zoom up on the title block, as seen in figure 8.6, to see the width of the polylines.

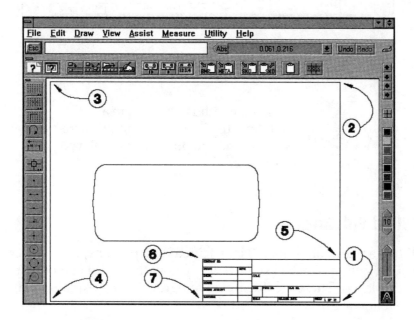

Figure 8.5:
Drawing the wide polylines.

The first polyline drawn in the previous exercise was a *closed polyline.* By choosing the start point as the last point, the polyline is closed, and the tool is terminated. To draw an *open polyline,* pick the last point twice to terminate the command.

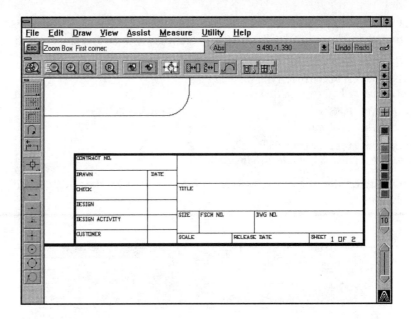

Figure 8.6:
Viewing the
wide polylines.

When a width is assigned to a polyline, the linetype setting is disregarded and the polyline is displayed as a continuous linetype.

Filled Polylines

When a width other than 0 is specified for a polyline, three different fill settings can be used to specify how the width of a polyline is displayed. These are illustrated in figure 8.7 and explained in the following list.

- **Solid Fill.** The *solid fill setting* fills in the width of the polyline with the current color.

- **Blank Fill.** The *blank fill setting* shows only the edges of the polyline.

- **Pattern Fill.** When the *pattern fill setting* is active, the polyline width is filled with a pattern. The pattern is based on the current pattern settings, which can be accessed by clicking on the Change Patterns button in the Polyline Settings dialog box. Pattern fills are discussed later in this chapter.

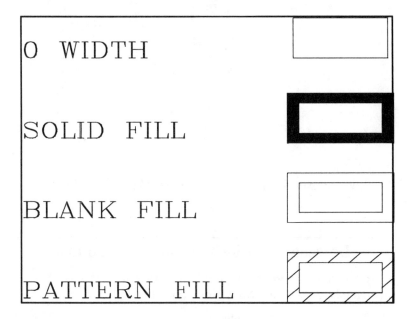

Figure 8.7:
Polyline-width settings.

Drawing Arc Segments in a Polyline

Because the term *polyline* implies many line segments, it is easy to forget that polylines can also be made up of arcs. The Polyline tool first prompts for a *"first* point," then it keeps prompting for a *"to* point." This tool joins line segments by placing the start point at the endpoint of the previous segment and using the new point for an endpoint.

The Arc Mode tool enables arcs to be created in a polyline. The campground exercise in Chapter 1 used the Polyline tool to draw a curved road. It appeared rather choppy because of the line segments. When the Arc Mode tool is activated, both polylines and pattern-fill boundaries are drawn using arc segments. The start point of the arc is the endpoint of the previous segment. The next prompt reads Point on arc:; the last prompt reads Arc segment endpoint:. The Arc Mode tool enables you to create arcs using three points.

The following exercise illustrates the use of the Arc Mode option with the Polyline tool.

Drawing a Polyline with the Arc Mode Tool

Zoom to the view shown in figure 8.8. Change to layer 2 (color black). Activate the End Point and Midpoint Attach tools.

Choose **D**raw, *then double-click on the Polyline tool*

Set the Polyline Width to .125", confirm that Solid Fill is chosen, then choose OK.

Polyline First point: *Pick* ①
(see fig. 8.8)

To point: *Pick* ②

To point: *Click on the Arc Mode tool to activate it*

Point on arc: *Pick* ③

Arc segment endpoint: *Pick* ④

Point on arc: *Pick* ⑤

Arc segment endpoint: *Pick* ⑥

Point on arc: *Pick* ⑦

Arc segment endpoint: *Pick* ⑧

Point on arc: *Click on the Arc Mode tool to deactivate it*

252

continues

`To point:` *Pick* ⑨

`To point:` *Click on the Arc Mode tool*
to activate it

`Point on arc:`

Continue picking points by using the End Point and Midpoint tools to locate accurate points on the construction geometry until the polyline is closed.

Double-click on the Polyline tool

Change the settings to Blank Fill, choose OK, and turn off the Arc Mode tool.

`Polyline First point:` **8.875,9** ↵

`To point:` **8.875,4** ↵

Click on the Polyline tool to terminate the polyline, then save the drawing.

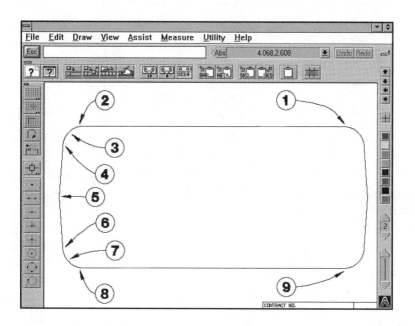

Figure 8.8:

Using the construction geometry to draw a polyline.

Your drawing should now be similar to figure 8.9, with one solid filled polyline and one blank filled polyline.

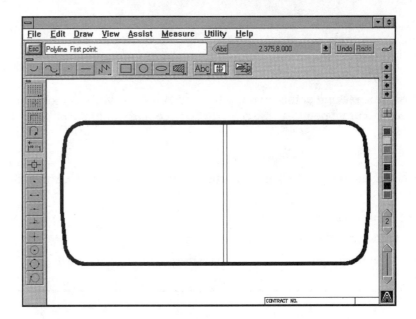

Figure 8.9:

A solid filled polyline and a blank filled polyline.

NOTE A box entity that has been modified with the Break tool becomes a polyline. The Property tool in the Edit toolbox can modify the construction geometry, which was two polylines, into a wide polyline similar to the one you just created.

Most of the editing commands work on polylines, just as they do on separate lines and arcs. The Break tool enables polylines to be broken up into individual entities.

Applying Pattern Fills

The Pattern Fill tool defines a boundary, and fills that area with a selected pattern of grouped entities. This tool enables you to use some of the many different hatch patterns provided in AutoSketch to highlight certain parts of your drawing. Some disciplines have special patterns to represent various types of materials. Figure 8.10 shows some of the many patterns provided by AutoSketch.

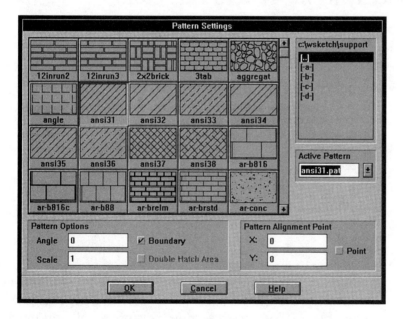

Figure 8.10:
The Pattern Settings dialog box.

Choosing a Pattern

All AutoSketch patterns are contained in individual files with a PAT extension. Users can also create their own pattern files. The Pattern Settings dialog box can be displayed by double-clicking on the Pattern Fill tool or through the Drawing Settings tool in the Utility toolbox.

You can set the active pattern by clicking on a pattern icon, by using the drop-down list from the text box, or by entering the name of the pattern file.

 If you cannot locate pattern files, check in the upper right corner of the Pattern Settings dialog box to be sure your current drive and directory are correct.

Specifying the Pattern Fill Settings

After you have selected the proper pattern, you can choose the following options that affect the appearance and placement of the pattern:

- **Angle.** The angle of the pattern can be rotated from its defined orientation. For example, in an isometric view, a brick pattern can be rotated at an angle of 30 degrees.

 A pattern, such as ANSI31, is defined at a 45-degree angle. Specifying an additional 45-degree rotation creates a vertical hatch pattern.

- **Scale.** Specifying the scale factor for a pattern is much like determining the linetype scale. A pattern for a civil engineering drawing that shows several city lots has a large scale factor applied. Showing a section view of a small part may require a scale factor of less than 1.

 A pattern scale factor equal to half the drawing scale is a good starting point.

- **Boundary.** Every pattern needs a boundary to define the area of the pattern. The boundary is drawn much like a polyline. If the boundary is to be displayed around the pattern, the boundary box should be checked.

- **Double Hatch Area.** This option is available only when the pattern file CRSSHTCH.PAT is active. This places pattern lines in opposing directions, creating a cross-hatch.

- **Pattern Alignment Point.** The origin point of the drawing is the point from which the pattern begins to generate. If the pattern is not properly aligned to the area it must fill, the pattern can be shifted to a new alignment point. This new alignment point can be specified with an X and Y location, or a point can be picked on the drawing if the Point check box is activated.

Whenever a pattern is applied, AutoSketch enables you to view the finished pattern, then either accept it or go back to the Pattern Settings dialog box for further setting adjustments. This feature is very convenient because it is frustrating to undo the pattern and draw the boundary again if the settings are not correct.

The following drawing exercise places a pattern fill on the right side of the AM/FM cassette recorder to show the grill covering the speaker. The coordinates for all the boundary points are given.

 It may be easier to pick the points using the absolute coordinate display with Snap turned on.

Placing a Pattern Fill on the Drawing

Change to layer 5 (yellow). Click on the Snap and Grid tools to activate them.

Choose **D***raw, then double-click on the Pattern Fill tool*	Opens the Pattern Settings dialog box
Click on the CIRC *pattern icon*	Specifies the Active Pattern

All other settings should match figure 8.10.

Choose **O**K

```
Pattern Fill First point: 9.25,8.75 ↵   Begins boundary
To point: 13.25,8.75 ↵
To point: Click on the Arc Mode tool        Activates Arc Mode
Point on arc: 13.5, 8.625 ↵
Arc segment endpoint: 13.625,8.375 ↵
Point on arc: 13.75,6.5 ↵
Arc segment endpoint: 13.625,4.625 ↵
Point on arc: 13.5,4.375 ↵
Arc segment endpoint: 13.25,4.25 ↵
Point on arc: Click on the Arc Mode tool     Turns off Arc Mode
To point: 9.25,4.25 ↵
To point: 9.25,8.75 ↵
```

Examine the results, then choose **M**odify. Change the scale to .25, and remove the check mark from the Boundary box.

Choose **O**K, *then* **A**ccept

Your completed pattern fill should resemble figure 8.11.

Depending on the shape of the area to be filled, the creation of the boundary can range from a few simple picks to a fairly complicated chain of line and arc segments. Notice how similar the boundary-creation techniques are to those for a polyline. The scale of the pattern is sometimes hard to predict until you actually see the results.

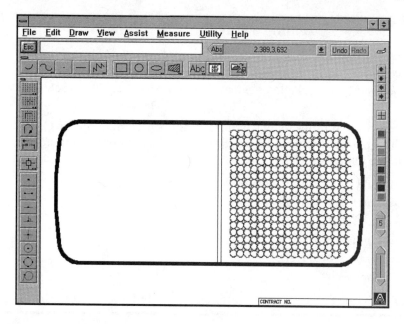

Figure 8.11:
The completed pattern fill.

Using Pattern Fills To Fill a Polyline

One of the options for filling a wide polyline is to use a pattern fill. Now that you have learned how to draw polylines and apply pattern fills, this is easy to do.

The Polyline Settings dialog box contains a button labeled Change Patterns. When the Pattern Fill radio button is activated, the Change Patterns button brings up the Pattern Settings dialog box, in which you can make any needed changes to the pattern.

In the next exercise, you use this technique to draw the door containing the cassette tape.

Filling a Polyline with a Pattern

*Choose **D**raw, then double-click on the Polyline tool*
Opens the Polyline Settings dialog box

Click on the Change Patterns *button*
Opens the Pattern Settings dialog box

Change the settings to match those in figure 8.12, then choose **O**K. Change the polyline width to .75, activate the Pattern Fill option, and choose OK.

```
Polyline First Point: 3.5,5 ↵
To point: 8,5 ↵
To point: 8,7 ↵
To point: 3.875,7 ↵
To point: 3.875,5.375 ↵
To point:
```

Click on the Polyline tool to terminate the polyline. Save your drawing.

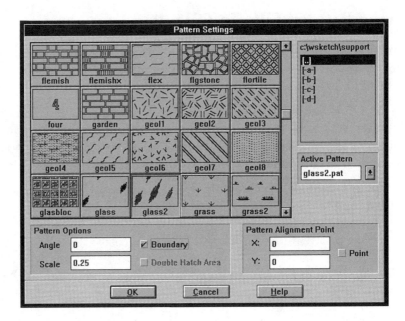

Figure 8.12:

Pattern Settings for the polyline fill.

Your drawing should resemble figure 8.13 when you finish the exercise.

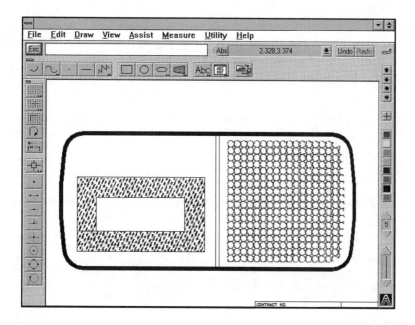

Figure 8.13:

The completed pattern-filled polyline.

Controlling the Graphics Display

Now that your drawing is starting to take shape, you may notice that a considerable amount of time is required to redraw the screen. One of the drawbacks of using powerful tools such as pattern fills is that many graphic entities are created. The drawing size increases and so does the redraw time.

Because you created entities on separate layers, some of the layers can be turned off. Layer 10, containing the title block, does not need be turned on at this point in the drawing. Because you will not be creating any more entities on layer 5, it can also be turned off temporarily. Turning off layers 10 and 5 reduces redraw time.

Two other tools found in the View toolbox can greatly affect redraw time. The Text on/off tool suppresses display of the text. This is helpful if there is a lot of text on the drawing. The Fill on/off tool suppresses the complete display of all patterns and fills. At this point in the AM/FM cassette recorder drawing, turning the Fill tool off greatly reduces redraw time.

Controlling the Graphics Redraw Speed

Double-click on the layer number button   Displays the Layer Settings dialog box

Turn the visibility of layer 5 off, choose OK, then choose the redraw button to see if the redraw time has improved. Make layer 5 visible again.

*Choose **V**iew, then the Fill on/off tool*   Turns Fill off, as shown in figure 8.14

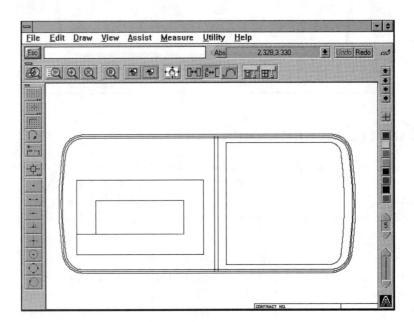

Figure 8.14:

The polylines and hatch pattern with Fill turned off.

Generating Ring and Box Arrays

The pattern-fill techniques place recurring patterns in an enclosed area. Many objects drawn in mechanical design have repeating patterns that are more precisely defined. The Array tools enable you to draw the base pattern, and give you special options to repeat those patterns on your drawing. Another advantage that an array has over a pattern fill is that items in an array can later be edited on an individual basis, whereas a pattern fill is one large entity that cannot be modified.

Similar to pattern fills, the Array tools have a settings dialog box, which can be accessed by double-clicking on the tool, or by using the Drawing Settings tool from the Utility toolbox. The finished array is temporarily displayed along with a dialog box that enables you to accept the array, modify it, or cancel the command.

Constructing a Ring Array

Many objects—such as gears, bolt-hole circles, and other circular patterns—can be drawn by using a ring array. First, the object to be repeated must be drawn and placed in proper position. Then the Ring Array tool can be used for multiple copies. Figure 8.15 shows the Ring Array Settings dialog box.

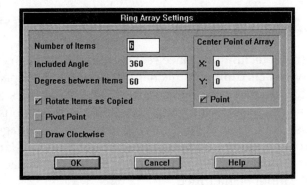

Figure 8.16 illustrates the results of the various settings.

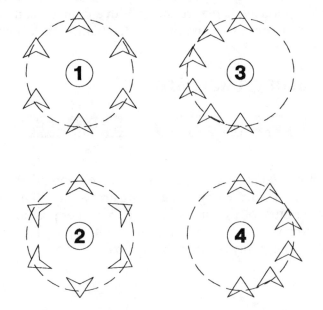

Figure 8.16:
Several types of
ring arrays.

The following list explains what the various text boxes, radio buttons, and check boxes control.

- **Number of Items.** The number of items in the array, including the original item, must be specified. The array in figure 8.16 contains six items.

- **Included Angle.** The default for this setting is 360 degrees. This number is automatically divided by the number of items to determine the angle between the items. The arrays at ① and ② have an included angle of 360 degrees; the arrays at ③ and ④ have an included angle of 180 degrees.

- **Degrees between Items.** This angle is automatically calculated, as explained in the previous paragraph, or it can be specified explicitly. If a number is entered into this text box, it is multiplied by the number of items to update the included angle value. The array at ① has an angle of 60 degrees; the array at ③ is 30 degrees between items.

- **Rotate Items as Copied.** This is a check box which, when active, rotates the items about the center point of the array as they are copied. The array at ① has this feature turned off; the array at ② has this feature activated.

- **Pivot Point.** If an additional pivot point is selected, the item is still arrayed about a center point, but is rotated about a pivot point chosen on the object. Specifying a pivot point automatically turns off the Rotate Items as Copied Check box because the object to be arrayed is now rotated about a specified point instead of the center point.

- **Draw Clockwise.** The default direction for an array is counterclockwise, as seen in the array at ③. (The original object is at the 12 o'clock position.) If the Draw Clockwise box is checked, the array is done in a clockwise direction, as shown in the array at ④.

- **Center Point of Array.** You can specify the center of the array by typing the X and Y coordinates in the text boxes. If the Point box is checked, you are prompted to pick a center point on your drawing.

In the following exercise, you continue your drawing by creating the cassette tape drive sprockets. Creating them requires the use of the Ring Array tool. All of the points required can be chosen with Snap set to .125 or entered as absolute coordinates.

Creating a Ring Array

Zoom to the view shown in figure 8.17. Change the layer to 2 (black). Activate Snap and Grid.

Choose **D**raw, *then the Box tool*

Box First corner: **5.5, 5.625** ↵

Second corner: **6.5, 6.375** ↵

Choose the Circle tool

Circle Center point: **4.875, 6.0** ↵

Point on circle: **5.25, 6.0** ↵

Double-click on the Polyline tool

Set the width to .08, and activate Solid Fill.

Polyline First point: **4.875, 6.375** ↵

To point: **4.875, 6.25** ↵

Specify that point a second time to end the polyline.

Choose **E**dit, *then double-click on the Ring Array tool*	Opens the Ring Array Settings dialog box

Change your settings to match those in figure 8.15.

Ring Array Select object: *Pick the polyline*

Center point of array: **4.875, 6.0** ↵

The array is shown, along with a dialog box, to accept or modify the array settings.

Choose **A**ccept

Choose the Copy tool

Copy Select object: *Window the entire array*

From point: **4.875, 6.0** ↵

To point: **7.125, 6.0** ↵

Remember that the Fill tool is turned off, so the polyline segments appear unfilled. You may decide whether to have fill turned on or off for the rest of the drawing exercises.

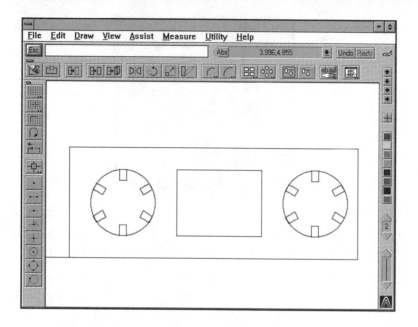

Figure 8.17:
The results of using the Ring Array tool.

Sometimes dialog boxes pop up and cover portions of your drawing. You can move these dialog boxes into a more convenient location by dragging the dialog box title bar.

Constructing a Box Array

The Box Array tool works like the Ring Array tool. Instead of placing multiple copies of an object in a circular pattern, the Box Array tool places objects into a rectangular grid. There are many creative ways to use the Box Array tool because of the settings options available. Figure 8.18 shows the Box Array Settings dialog box.

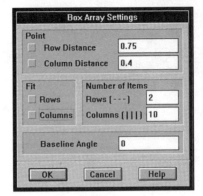

Figure 8.18:

The Box Array Settings dialog box.

The text boxes and check boxes in the dialog box control the size and features of the box array. Figure 8.19 shows a typical box array.

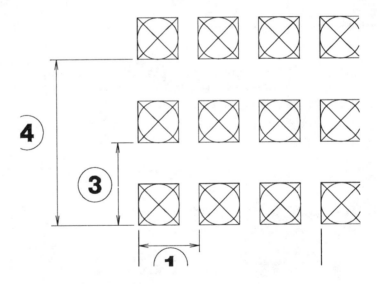

Figure 8.19:

A typical box array.

- **Row and Column Distance**. Figure 8.19 shows a box array with three rows and four columns. ① is the column distance, and ② shows the row distance. The distance values may be entered in the text box. If the check boxes are activated, the distance must be specified by picking two points on the drawing.

- **Number of Items.** You can use the text boxes to specify the number of rows and columns in a box array.

- **Fit.** The Fit check boxes, when activated, change the way AutoSketch interprets the Row Distance and Column Distance values. ③ and ④ show the fit value as the entire distance used by the rows and columns. When you try to fill a given area with an array, this may be an easier method of showing the row and column distances.

- **Baseline Angle.** The entire array can be rotated as it is created. The baseline angle, which defaults to 0, is specified in standard Cartesian coordinate-system degrees, with a positive number rotating counterclockwise.

Two box arrays are used in the next exercise. The first one places the markings for the radio dial. The second array creates the set of push buttons on the top of the radio used for cassette tape control.

Creating the Box Arrays

Zoom to the view shown in figure 8.21. Turn fill on and be sure that Snap and Grid are on. Make sure the Attach tool is off.

*Choose **D**raw, then double-click on the*   Opens Polyline
Polyline tool   Settings dialog box

Set the width to .5, activate Pattern Fill, and choose the TEXTURE pattern using the Change Patterns button.

```
Polyline First point: 3.5,8.25 ↵
To point: 8.375,8.25 ↵
```

Specify that point twice to terminate the polyline.

Double-click on the Polyline tool

Set the width to .05, and activate Solid Fill.

`Polyline First point:` **4,8** ↵

`To point:` **4,7.75** ↵

Choose **E***dit, then double-click on the*   Opens Box Array
Box Array tool   dialog box

Change the settings to match figure 8.18.

`Box Array Select object:` *Pick the last*
polyline drawn

Choose **A***ccept*   Accepts array as shown

Choose **D***raw, then the Box tool*

`Box First corner:` **4,9** ↵

`Second corner:` **4.5,9.5** ↵

Choose **E***dit, then the Box Array tool*

`Box Array Select object:` *Pick the box*
just drawn

Choose **M***odify from the dialog box*

Change the settings to match figure 8.20.

`Column spacing only First point:` **4,9** ↵

`To point:` **7,9** ↵

Accept the array, and save the drawing.

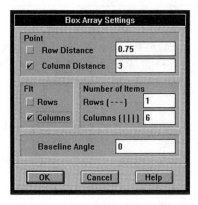

Figure 8.20:

The Box Array
Settings for the
push buttons.

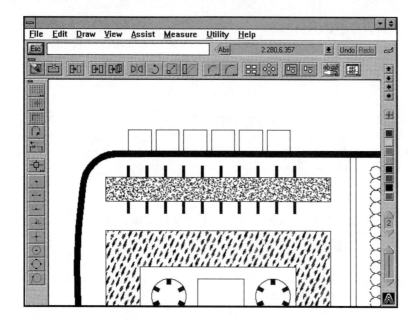

Figure 8.21:
The completed box arrays.

The AM/FM cassette recorder is nearing completion. A flexible handle must be added across the top, and a cord and antenna should also be included.

Understanding Spline Curves

A *spline curve* is used to create a free-form curve by using points to guide the shape of the curve. The manual drafting tools used to create curves are French curves and flexible splines. These tools connect features of a part with smooth flowing curves. For some technical drawing applications, a series of X,Y coordinates is collected from some calculations or measurements, and then the points are used as a framework for a smooth curve that represents the composite of the points.

Drawing Points

A *point* is a CAD entity represented by an X and Y coordinate. Three-dimensional CAD systems also assign a Z coordinate. The Point tool, found in the Draw toolbox, is not often used because it is hard to distinguish a single dot on the drawing.

 The Node attach tool enables you to locate existing points in your drawing.

In the following exercise, you place points on the drawing to use in constructing a curve.

Placing Points in the Drawing

Zoom to the view shown in figure 8.22. Draw a .38 solid filled polyline from 3,8.375 to 2.875,8.375; and from 14,8.375 to 14.125, 8.375 to create the handle swivels.

Choose **D**raw, *then the Point tool*

`Point Enter point:`

Enter the following point coordinates: **2.875,8.5; 3,9.5; 4,10; 8.5,10.5; 13,10; 14,9.5; 14.125,8.5**

Figure 8.22 has small circles drawn at each point to make the points more visible. Turn Grid off so that you can see the points you have drawn.

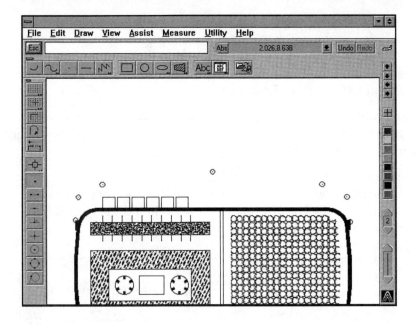

Figure 8.22:
Creating points with the Point tool.

Drawing the Curve

Curve

The points on the drawing can now be used to construct the curve. Double-clicking on the Curve tool brings up the Curve Settings dialog box, as seen in figure 8.23.

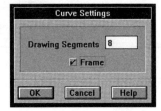

Figure 8.23:
Curve Settings dialog box.

273

The Drawing Segments text box can be changed to control the resolution of the curve. A curve is really made up of many short line segments. For this reason, the higher the number of segments, the smoother the curve. More segments also increase the drawing size and redraw time, however.

The Frame checkbox, when activated, displays line segments connecting the points used in the curves. This display helps to edit curves or view the control points of the curve.

Figure 8.24 shows a curve with the Frame checkbox activated so that the frame is also displayed. Notice that the curve does not pass through the control points—it uses the points to pull the curve into a smooth and gradual blend.

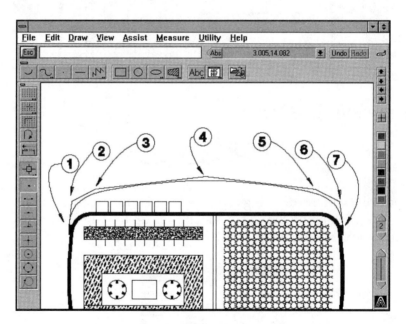

Figure 8.24:

The completed curve and the curve frame.

Continue working through the next drawing exercise to draw the curve.

274

Drawing a Curve

Double click on the Curve tool   Opens the Curve Settings dialog
                                               box

Change settings to match those in figure 8.23. Activate the Node attach
tool.

`Curve First point:` *Pick near the point*
at ① *(see fig. 8.24)*

`To point:` *Pick* ②, ③, ④, ⑤
⑥, *pick twice at* ⑦

The curve for the handle has now been created. Step back at this
point and study the design. The distance between the handle and
the top of the radio may be too small to comfortably place your
hand. You can easily modify a curve to a different shape.

Editing a Curve

Because a curve is defined by its control points, you can modify a
curve by changing these points. Many of the editing commands
can be used to do this. In the following exercise, you use the
Stretch tool to move three points up by .5". The curve then updates itself to these points.

Editing a Curve

*Choose **E**dit, then the Stretch tool*

`Stretch First corner:` *Pick* ①
(see fig. 8.25)

`Crosses/window corner:` *Pick* ②

`Stretch base:` *Pick near* ①

`Stretch to:` `r(0,.5)` ↵

*Choose **D**raw, then double-click on the Curve*   Opens the Curve
tool   Settings dialog box

Click on the Frame *checkbox*   Turns off Frame display, as seen
                                               in figure 8.26

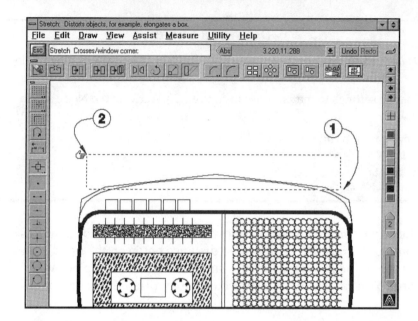

Figure 8.25:
Stretching the curve.

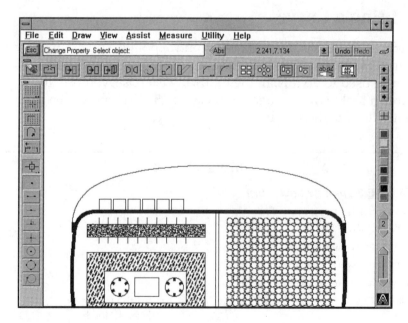

Figure 8.26:
The handle after stretching.

The original points are no longer needed. They can be erased or placed on the construction layer (6), which should be turned off.

Finishing the Drawing

The Curve tool also enables you to sketch the power cord on the radio. You may need to try it over a few times until you see how many points need to be chosen to create a suitable curve. Several wide polylines, drawn end-to-end with different widths, are used to draw the antenna. Figure 8.27 shows the radio with the power cord and antenna.

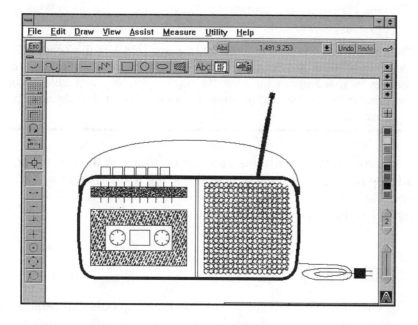

Figure 8.27:
The completed AM/FM cassette recorder.

Completing the Radio

Zoom to the view shown in figure 8.27. Use the Curve tool to sketch the power cord and a wide filled polyline for the plug. Turn off the Attach tool.

Double-click on the Polyline tool

Set the width to .2, and activate Solid Fill.

```
Polyline First point: 12,9 ↵
To point: p(3,80) ↵
```

Double-click on the Polyline tool, and change the width to .15.

```
Polyline First point: /LPOINT ↵
To point: p(.5,80) ↵
```

Double-click on the Polyline tool, and change the width to .1.

```
Polyline First point: /LPOINT ↵
To point: p(.5,80) ↵
```

Double-click on the Polyline tool, and change the width to .25.

```
Polyline First point: /LPOINT ↵
To point: p(.25,80) ↵
```

Click on the Polyline tool to terminate the polyline. Use the Zoom Full tool to view the entire drawing. Use Print Settings to review the printing settings for this drawing based on the printer you have available. If you can print to a C-size sheet, this drawing should print full scale. Save your drawing.

You may continue with this drawing by filling in the title block, adding notes and dimensions, and placing text to label the AM and FM tuning bar. Additional switches and dials can also be placed at the top of the radio.

Summary

This chapter discussed several of the drawing tools that can add a lot of flair and detail to your drawing with a minimum amount of effort. In addition to learning the function of the tools, it is important to be creative in applying these tools to complete various types of drawings.

The Polyline tool is useful for drawing connected lines. Only the endpoint of a segment is required because the start point is automatically taken from the end of the last segment. The width options of the polyline make the tool extremely powerful for filling in areas and showing wide features of a part. The Arc Mode is used to draw arc segments in a polyline.

Pattern fills can apply a variety of patterns in an area. The area is defined much like a polyline. Because a pattern fill is a single entity, it cannot be modified or changed once it has been completed. The scale of a pattern can be previewed because a dialog box enables you to accept, modify, or cancel a pattern fill before it is permanently placed into your drawing.

Box arrays and ring arrays are used to place copies of objects in a rectangular or circular orientation. These objects remain separate, and can be edited individually after the array is complete. Like the pattern fill, the array may be temporarily viewed before it is accepted.

The type of drawing you are working on greatly influences the way these tools are applied. Creating a drawing that looks great is much different than creating a drawing that includes all the detail needed for a complete manufacturing database.

Most of the drawing and editing tools have now been explained and demonstrated. Chapter 9 demonstrates how to create some special types of technical drawings using these tools.

Creating Special Types of Drawings

This chapter shows you techniques that you can use to create different types of drawings in AutoSketch. In this book, you have been introduced to most of the advantages that CAD has to offer. The capability to create presentation drawings adds to the list of advantages that electronic-drawing production can offer.

The drawings that are described in this chapter are probably not new to you if you have a manual drafting background. The techniques have been around for a long time. As you become more familiar with AutoSketch and increase your productivity level, these techniques can be used to add interest and depth to the final drawings. You begin by creating an isometric-block drawing.

Drawing in Isometric

In *isometric drawings*, objects can be measured on all axes for true distances. To learn about *isometric* techniques, you create a simple block drawing. CAD enables you to accurately draw in isometrics without the repetition that is associated with these drawings on the drafting board.

Isometrics are a quick way to give a drawing depth because the same scale is used on all of the entities in a drawing. Figure 9.1 shows the orthographic views of the block that is drawn in the first exercise.

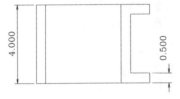

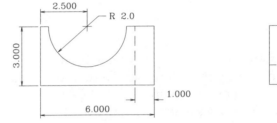

Figure 9.1:

Orthographic views of the block.

Isometrics are drawn with the three visible axes at 120 degrees apart (see fig. 9.2). The angles you work with are based on the 30/60/90-degree triangle that is a common tool in manual drafting.

An isometric drawing helps you visualize the object of the orthographic drawing.

Most of the lines in an isometric drawing can be created with the Line, Copy, and Break tools. In this chapter's exercises, you use many of the tools that have been covered in the previous chapters.

Figure 9.3 shows the completed isometric drawing that is drawn in the following exercise.

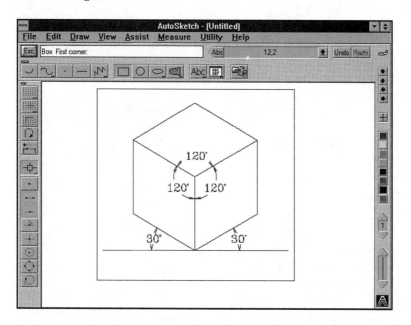

Figure 9.2:

The basic isometric layout.

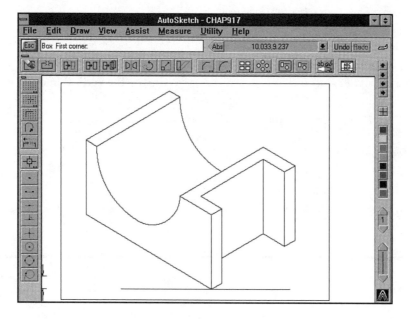

Figure 9.3:

The completed isometric drawing.

Drawing in Isometric

Choose **F**ile, *then* **O**pen

Double-click on the CHAP91 *drawing icon in the Open Drawing dialog box*

Choose **F**ile, *then* Save **A**s

Type **MY-9** *in the* Filename: *text box, then choose* OK

Double-click on the Current Layer button	Opens the Current Layer dialog box
Click on the visible box on layer 2, then choose OK	Displays layer 2

Choose **V**iew, *then select the Zoom Box tool*

Zoom Box First corner: **9,7** ↵

Second corner: **22,16** ↵	Magnifies the drawing

Choose **D**raw, *then select the Line tool*

Line From point: **15.5,8** ↵

To point: **p(6,150)** ↵

Double-click on the End Point attach tool to make it active

Choose **E**dit, *then select the Copy tool*

Copy Select object: *Pick at* ①
(see fig. 9.4)

From point: *Pick at* ②

To point: *Pick at* ③	Creates the vertical lines

Choose the Multi-copy tool

Multi-copy Select objects: *Pick at* ①

From point: *Pick at* ①

To point: **p(.5,30)** ↵

To point: **p(3,30)** ↵

To point: **p(.5,30)** ↵	Creates the sides of the vertical slot

To point: *Press Esc*

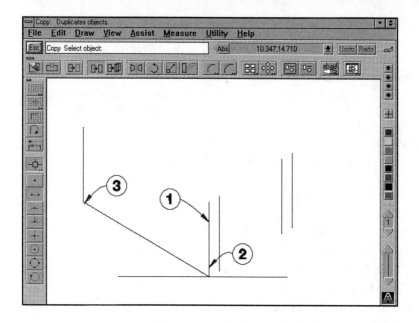

Figure 9.4:
Beginning the isometric drawing.

After the initial entity is drawn, the Multi-copy tool can repeat the entity as often as required. The End Point attach tool makes the job of picking points quite easy. In the following exercise, you complete the vertical slot, as shown in figure 9.5.

Creating the Vertical Slot

Choose **D**raw, *then select the Line tool*

`Line From point:` *Pick at* ①

`To point:` *Pick at* ②

Choose **E**dit, *then select the Multi-copy tool*

`Multi-copy Select object:` *Pick the last line drawn*

`From point:` *Pick at* ①

`To point:` *Pick at* ③

`To point:` *Pick at* ④

continues

```
To point: Pick at ⑤
To point: Press Esc
```
Choose **D**raw, *then select the Line tool*
```
Line From point: Pick at ②
To point: p(1,150) ↵
```

Draws a line for the depth of the vertical slot

Choose **E**dit, *then select the Multi-copy tool*
```
Multi-copy Select object: Pick at ⑥
From point: Pick at ⑥ again
To point: Pick at ④
To point: Pick at ⑤
To point: Press Esc
```
Choose **D**raw, *then select the Line tool*
Create the line at ⑦ (see fig. 9.5)

Draws the width of the slot

Choose **E**dit, *then select the Copy tool*
```
Copy Select object: Pick at ⑦ again
From point: Pick at ⑦
To point: Pick at ⑧
```

Creates the bottom of the slot

```
Copy Select object: Pick at ④
From point: Pick at ④
To point: Pick at ⑧
```
Click on the Intersect attach tool

Choose the Break tool and remove the section of the line at ⑨ (see fig. 9.5)
Press F12

Cleans up the drawing

Next, you create the half-circle slot that extends through the width of the part. Circles and arcs in isometric are drawn with a particular set of radius centers and endpoints that can be seen by making layer 3 visible (see fig. 9.6).

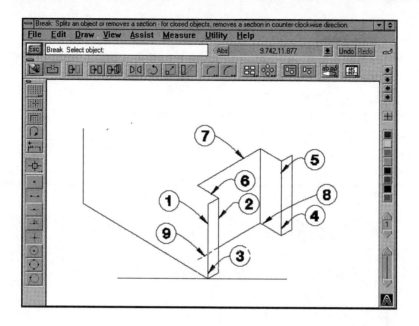

Figure 9.5:
The vertical slot.

Drawing Isometric Arcs

Choose **D**raw, *then select the Line tool*

`Line From point:` *Pick at* ①
(see fig. 9.6)

`To point:` **p(1.5,150)** ↵

`Line From point:` *Pick at* ②

`To point:` **p(.5,330)** ↵   Defines the top edge of the part

Double-click on the Current Layer button

Click on the visible box in layers 3 and 5, then choose OK   Displays the iso-circle setup and notes

Choose **D**raw, *then select the Circle tool*

`Circle Center point:` *Pick at* ③

`Point on the circle:` *Pick at* ④

`Circle Center point:` *Pick at* ⑤

`Point on the circle:` *Pick at* ⑥

Double-click on the Current Layer button

continues

Click on the visible box in layer 5,   Hides the text
then choose OK

Choose **E**dit, *then select the Break tool*

`Break Select object:` *Pick at* ⑦

`First point:` *Pick at* ⑥

`Second point:` *Pick at* ④   Removes part of the circle

`Break Select object:` *Pick at* ⑧

`First point:` *Pick at* ⑨

`Second point:` *Pick at* ⑥

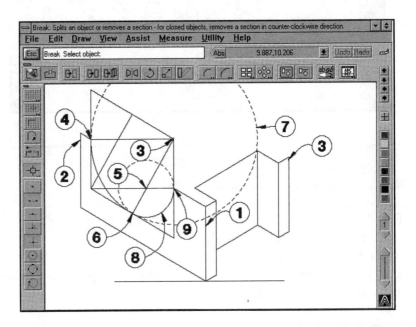

Figure 9.6:
Creating the isometric half circle.

Although this drawing looks complicated, this process will be beneficial after you experiment with isometric circles. In the following exercise, you finish the part by copying the objects to the back side and connecting the lines (see fig. 9.7).

Completing the Isometric Drawing

Double-click on the Current Layer button

Click on the visible box in layer 3, then choose OK   Hides the iso-circle setup

Choose the Copy tool, and create a crosses-selection box, as shown in figure 9.7

`From point:` *Pick at* (1) *(see fig. 9.7)*

`To point:` *Pick at* (2)   Grabs the half circle

Choose **D**raw, *then select the Line tool*

`Line From point:` *Pick at* (3)

`To point:` *Pick at* (4)

Choose **E**dit, *then select the Multi-copy tool*

`Multi-copy Select objects:` *Pick at* (5)

`From point:` *Pick at* (3)

`To point:` *Pick at* (6)   Copies the edge

`To point:` *Pick at* (7)

`To point:` *Press Esc*

Erase arc at (8)   Removes the hidden arc

Choose **V**iew, *then select the Zoom Limits tool*   Zooms to limits

Press F12   Saves the drawing

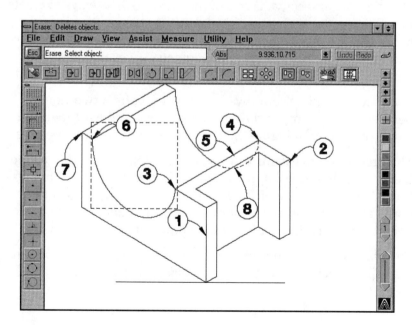

Figure 9.7:

Completing the isometric drawing.

Use these techniques to add interest to your drawings. As you continue with this chapter, you learn ways to set yourself apart from other users.

 Electronically produced drawings are only products of the person at the keyboard. Your skill level and creativity are restricted only by how well you can draw and how much time you spend with the drawing program. The computer itself does only what it is told to do.

In the next section, you create a two-point perspective drawing.

Creating a Perspective View

The perspective drawing is a unique tool that enables architects, engineers, and other artisans to create three-dimensional visions to describe an idea.

Drawing in perspective is one of the most realistic ways to create a presentation drawing. *Perspective drawing* enables the viewer of the drawing to see an object with the proper amount of distortion and foreshortening. This play of geometry gives the viewer an illusion of depth that is similar to the way you see objects every day.

The following exercise shows you how to set up a two-point perspective drawing, and figure 9.8 shows you the orthographic views of the object. Figure 9.9 shows the completed perspective.

The first step is to establish several points that are used to create the construction lines of the drawing. The *station point* is the position of the observer, which has a line of sight that looks at the object at a height of six feet above the ground line. The six-foot height is adjustable, as are all of the points that you set up.

The plan view of the object is rotated 45 degrees, and the picture plane just touches the corner of the plan. The *picture plane* is the point at which true height can be measured. All the heights in the drawing are created from this plane. As you set up the drawing, elements in plan and elevation are overlapped.

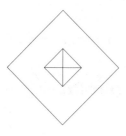

Figure 9.8:

Plan and elevation for perspective drawing.

Figure 9.9:

The perspective drawing.

The drawing can be very confusing at its beginning stages. If you put the construction lines on different layers, the drawing is easier to work on.

Begin the exercise by opening the CHAP93 drawing.

Setting Up the Perspective Drawing

*Choose **F**ile, then **O**pen*

Double-click on the CHAP93 drawing icon in the Open Drawing dialog box

*Choose **F**ile, then Save **A**s*

*Type **MY-93** in the Filename: text box, then choose OK*

Double-click on the Current Layer button

Click on the visible box on layers 9 and 10, then choose OK — Displays the main measuring lines and planes

Double-click on the Current Layer button

Click on the visible box on layer 8, then choose OK — Describes the method used to find the vanishing points

Double-click on the Current Layer button

Click on the visible box on layers 8 and 10, then choose OK — Removes the setup information

Click on the upward arrow in the current layer display — Makes layer 2 the current layer

Choose the magenta button in the color palette — Makes magenta the current color

*Choose **D**raw, then select the Line tool*

Double-click on the End Point attach tool

Click on the Perpendicular and Intersect attach tools

Line From point: *Draw line at* ① (*see fig. 9.10*)	Creates a height line
Continue drawing lines at ② *through* ⑨	Begins the drawing
Press F12	Saves the drawing

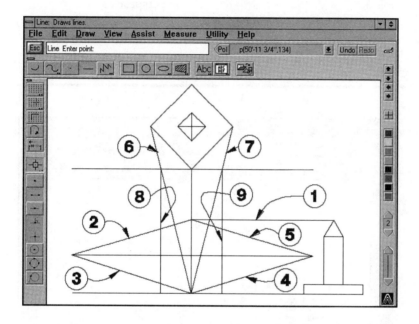

Figure 9.10:
Beginning the perspective drawing.

In the last exercise, you projected the points on the platform at ⑥ and ⑦ toward the picture plane. The intersection of the platform extents and the picture plane was dropped to the ground line. The place at which the points met the ground line extended back toward the vanishing point.

In the following exercise, you create the base of the object and the highest plane with the same concept. You establish the height of the platform from the elevation.

After you complete this step (see fig. 9.11), you perform some cleanup with the Edit tools to make your drawing look like figure 9.12.

Creating the First Platform

Choose the Line tool

`Line From point:` *Create the height line at* ① *(see fig. 9.11)*

Continue creating the lines at ② *through* ⑦   Draws the platform in perspective

Choose **E**dit, *then select the Break and Erase tools to depict the drawing shown in figure 9.12*

Press F12   Saves the drawing

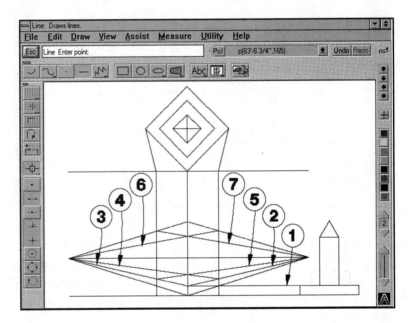

Figure 9.11:

The base platform setup.

Constructing the perspective is another skill that requires practice and patience. Once you fully understand the concept, creating a perspective becomes intuitive.

Continue with the following exercise, using the projection method shown in the previous steps. Figures 9.13 through 9.17 show the steps that are taken in this exercise.

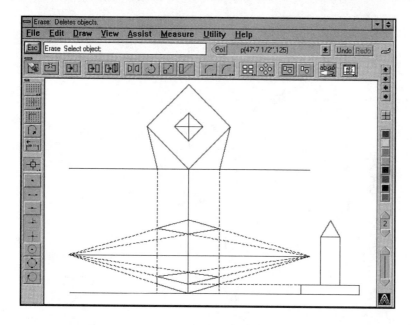

Figure 9.12:
The base platform.

Completing the Perspective

Choose **D**raw, *then select the Line tool*

`Line From point:` *See figure 9.13 to draw the lines from the tower out to the edge of the platform at* ①

Continue with the Line tool by creating lines from the station point to the lines that you projected out from the tower (see fig. 9.13) at ②

Create lines from the intersection of the picture plane and the projection lines (see fig. 9.14) at ③

Create a height line for the tower at ④ *in figure 9.14*

continues

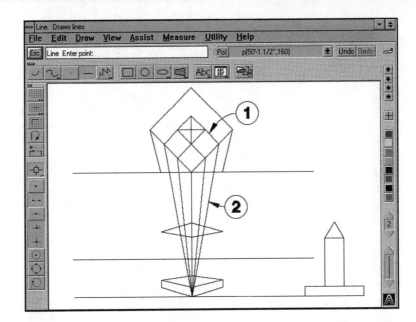

Figure 9.13:
Projecting the tower base.

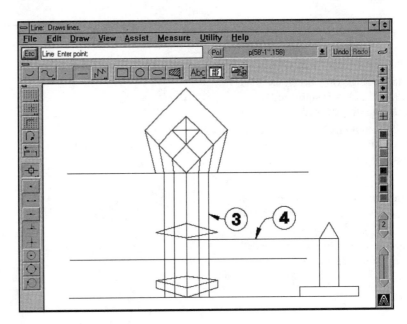

Figure 9.14:
Establishing the sides and height.

*Choose **V**iew, then select the Zoom Box tool*

`Zoom Box First corner:` *Create a box to move into the view shown in figure 9.15*

Magnifies the view

*Choose **D**raw, then select the Line tool*

`Line From point:` *Draw the line that is shown at ① in figure 9.15; start by picking at ②*

Transfers the height to the tower-projection lines

Continue with the Line tool, and outline the base of the tower where it meets the platform at ④ and ⑤

`Line From point:` *Create the line at ⑥*

Delineates the tower height

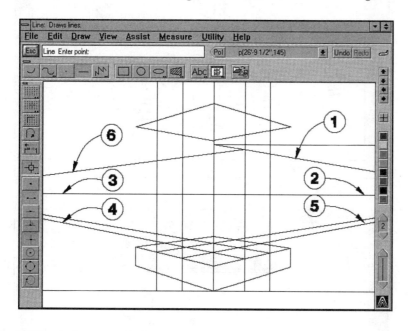

Figure 9.15:

Creating the intersection of the tower and the platform.

Use the Line tool to create the intersection in the highest plane for the point of the tower at ① in figure 9.16

Continue with the Line tool, and create the line at ② and the vertical lines at ④ and ⑤ in figure 9.16

Create the lines at ⑥ in figure 9.16

continues

*Choose **E**dit, then select the Erase and Break tools to clean up the drawing, as shown in figure 9.17*

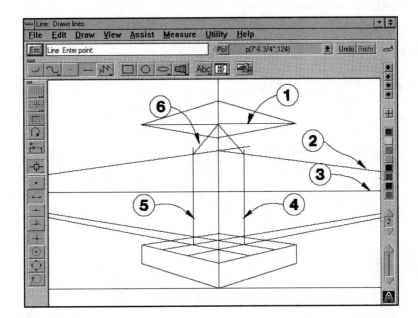

Figure 9.16:
Creating the sides and roof.

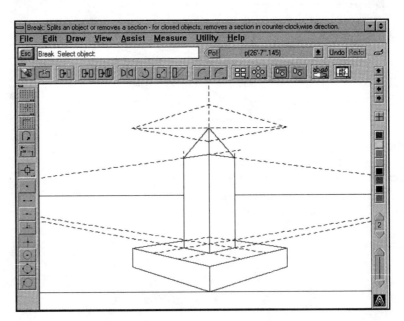

Figure 9.17:
Cleaning up the perspective.

Summary

This chapter showed you techniques that you can use to create drawings that are interesting and informative. Isometric drawings, in which objects can be measured on all axes for true distances, are an easy way to represent an object to a viewer.

Perspective drawings take time and skill to master. To learn more about perspective-drafting techniques, refer to books that deal specifically with the subject. Do not be afraid to experiment with the techniques you learned in the exercises.

Using AutoSketch with Other Applications

Several tools discussed in this chapter are not available in the training edition of AutoSketch. These tools include DXF, Copy Metafile, Copy Objects, and Show Clipboard. Object Linking and Embedding is also disabled. If you want to upgrade to the full version of AutoSketch, you should try the tutorials.

One of the nicest features of Windows application software is its consistent user interface—after you have mastered a Windows application, learning to use other Windows products becomes much easier.

Another useful feature of Windows application software is its capability to share information and data with other applications.

This chapter explains many of the common techniques of sharing data with other applications. The applications used (Write and Paintbrush, for example) are those included with your Windows software. Many of these same techniques also work for other Windows application software you may already own.

This chapter also discusses DXF data translation, which is a very popular way to exchange CAD graphics data between many packages that are not Windows-compatible. Several sample files have been included, and you are not required to have special knowledge of any of the other software applications discussed in this chapter. Figure 10.1 shows a technical document produced by using a variety of data-translation techniques.

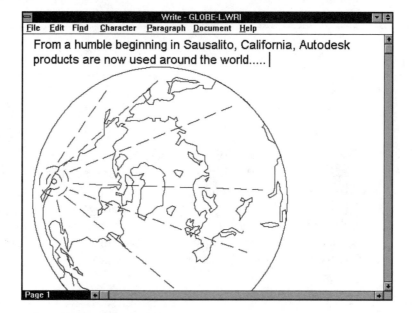

Figure 10.1:

A technical document, produced by using several types of data exchange.

 Because of the broad scope of applications and techniques covered in this chapter, additional information on these topics may be helpful. Refer to your Windows Reference Guide, other application software reference manuals, or books from New Riders Publishing, such as *Maximizing Windows 3.1.*

Understanding Special File Formats

Information in a computer is stored in a *file*, which has a *name* and a *format*. The DOS operating system permits a file name of up to eight characters, with an optional three-character extension.

The extension on a file name often helps distinguish between various file formats. Some software packages, such as AutoSketch, automatically assign a file-name extension, based on the type of file. Whether or not the software package assigns the file extensions, it is good practice to properly identify file formats by assigning proper extensions.

Computer files can be generally classified as the following file types:

- **Binary file.** A *binary file*, which contains information in machine-readable form, is extremely efficient for storing information because it is in a compiled—or compressed— format.

To see whether a file is binary, use the DOS TYPE command. If it is a binary file, it displays unreadable characters on the screen.

- **Text file.** Sometimes referred to as a *DOS text file* or *ASCII text file*, a *text file* contains standard alphanumeric text characters. This file format can be read or created by many types of software applications.

File Formats Used in AutoSketch

Different file formats are usually identifiable by the file's extension. AutoSketch uses some file extensions that are unique to AutoSketch; other file formats that AutoSketch supports are also used by other Autodesk products. AutoSketch is also capable of using file formats that are accepted as industry standards for data translations. A brief summary of these files is as follows:

- **SKD.** AutoSketch files are saved, in binary format, in a file with an SKD extension. Very little can be done with this file except for retrieving it as an AutoSketch drawing.

- **PAT.** A *pattern file* describes a pattern used by the Pattern Fill tool.

- **SHX.** A *shape file* contains all the characters used in a text font. Both the SHX files and the PAT files are compatible with AutoCAD.

- **DXF.** Autodesk initially developed the *Drawing Interchange File* to describe an AutoCAD drawing file in a standard text file. This format is now supported on many graphics software packages as a standard for graphics data exchange.

- **SLD.** A *slide file* is a graphics image that can be created or viewed by AutoSketch. This file type is used by many of the other Autodesk products and supported by some other desktop publishing software.

Other Popular Graphics-File Formats

Other file formats have emerged as standards for data translation, and are supported to some degree in many software packages. A variety of formats can be used, depending on the type of data being translated and the end use of that data.

- **DWG.** Technically, a DWG file is a graphics file that can only be read by AutoCAD. Because of the widespread popularity of AutoCAD, however, some other graphics software can read this file format directly. AutoSketch 1.0 for Windows cannot directly read a DWG file.

- **BMP.** A *bit-map file* contains an image defined by a series of dots. The dots can be monochrome or colored, and the resolution varies according to the application. AutoSketch can create a bit-map file but not read one. Sometimes called a *raster image*, a BMP file is similar to a PCX, TIF, or GIF file.

- **WMF.** A *Windows metafile* format is a picture-file format that retains entities, such as lines or circles, instead of turning them into a raster image.

Copying and Pasting with Other Windows Applications

In Chapter 7, you learned how to save entities from AutoSketch by using the Part Clip tool. This process saves the entities in the standard AutoSketch format (SKD). The SKD file can then be used repeatedly by inserting the entities into a drawing.

AutoSketch for Windows has several other tools, which are also found in many other Windows applications. These tools, located in the Utility toolbox, all work in a very similar manner, but they save the entities in different formats, depending on the application in which you work.

Copying and Viewing the Contents of the Clipboard

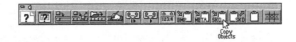

Copy
Objects

 The Copy Objects tool is not available in the training edition of AutoSketch.

The Copy Objects tool prompts you to choose the entities you want to copy (usually with a window). It does not alter your current drawing; it places a copy of those entities into the Windows *Clipboard*, which is a temporary storage area built into Windows.

The most recent group of copied entities is stored in the Clipboard and can be pasted, or transferred, back into any other Windows application that can support those entities.

The Show Clipboard tool is not available in the training edition of AutoSketch.

The Show Clipboard tool is useful for viewing the contents of the clipboard. Figure 10.2 shows the Clipboard, displayed as a result of using this tool.

Figure 10.2:
The Clipboard Viewer, displayed by the Show Clipboard tool.

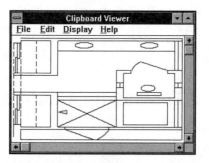

The Clipboard is a regular window that you can resize or move around on the drawing screen. The **S**ave command in the **F**ile menu enables you to save the contents of the Clipboard as a CLP file. Because the Clipboard contents are overwritten whenever new objects are copied, this sets aside the contents of the Clipboard in a file to be retrieved at a later time.

The following exercise uses the Copy Bitmap tool to place the entities that make up the master bath in the CHAP6.SKD file into the Clipboard. The Show Clipboard tool is then used to view the Clipboard.

Using the Copy Bitmap and Show Clipboard Tools

Begin AutoSketch, and open the file CHAP6.SKD, as shown in figure 10.3.

Choose **U***tility, then the Copy Bitmap tool*

`Copy Bitmap First corner:` *Begin a window near* ① *(see fig. 10.3)*

`Second corner:` *Pick near* ②

Choose the Show Clipboard tool   The Clipboard is displayed (see fig. 10.2)

Double-click on the Control-menu button of the Clipboard Viewer to close it

If your Clipboard tool is not available, use the windows Clipboard Viewer.

Now that the objects have been copied to the Clipboard, and you have viewed the objects in the Clipboard Viewer, you are ready to place the objects into another Windows application.

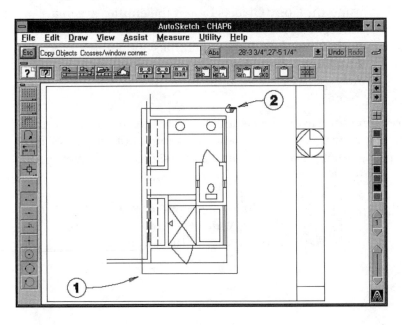

Figure 10.3:

Copying the objects.

Pasting the Contents of the Clipboard

The Paste Objects tool is very similar to the Part tool—they both insert entities into the drawing at specified locations. The Part tool retrieves a drawing file; the Paste Objects tool inserts the entities from the Clipboard.

AutoSketch prompts you for an insertion point, and then places the entities into the drawing. Other editing tools (such as Move, Rotate, or Scale) can be used to further refine the entities.

 AutoSketch pastes entities into a drawing only if the entities are in AutoSketch format. This means that the entities must be copied into the Clipboard by using the Copy Objects tool. If the entities are in a different format, AutoSketch displays a warning, stating that the Clipboard entities are not in AutoSketch format, and AutoSketch will not attempt to insert the entities.

Try using the Paste Objects tool to paste the entities currently in the Clipboard. First, paste the entities into another AutoSketch drawing; then paste those same entities into Paintbrush.

 The following exercise works only if the Copy Objects tool was used to copy entities to the Clipboard.

Pasting Entities from the Clipboard

*Choose **F**ile, then **N**ew*	Begins a new drawing
*Choose **U**tility, then the Paste Objects tool*	
`Paste To point:` *Pick near the lower left corner of the drawing*	Locates the insert point
*Choose **V**iew, then the Zoom Full tool*	Shows the entire bathroom

Exit AutoSketch. Double-click on the Paintbrush icon, shown in figure 10.4. This icon is located in the Accessories Program Group in the Windows Program Manager.

*Choose **E**dit, then **P**aste*	Pastes the entities into Paintbrush, as seen in figure 10.5

You may experiment with the Paintbrush program, then exit when you are finished.

You can use the Copy Objects tool to place selected entities from AutoSketch into the Windows Clipboard, then into many other applications. You can have several windows open on your screen at one time to quickly copy and paste from one window to another. The only limitation is the amount of memory available to concurrently run several applications, and the amount of screen space you allow each application.

Figure 10.4:

The Paintbrush icon in the Accessories Program Group.

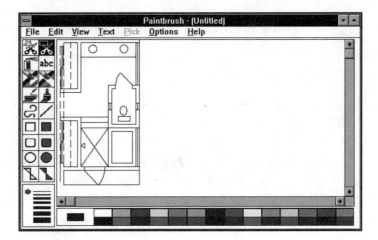

Figure 10.5:

Pasting entities from the Clipboard into the Paintbrush program.

 Many software packages have a tool named *Cut*, as well as a tool named *Copy*. The only difference is that the Cut tool removes objects from their original location when put into the clipboard; the Copy tool does not alter the original entities.

The Copy Bitmap and Copy Metafile Tools

Two other tools located in the Utility toolbox are similar to the Copy Objects tool.

The Copy Metafile tool saves the entities into the Clipboard in a different format from that of the Copy Objects tool.

The Windows metafile format is a widely used picture format for many Windows graphic applications. This format cannot be pasted back into AutoSketch because AutoSketch does not support this format.

Copy
Bitmap

The Copy Bitmap tool saves the entities to the Clipboard in a bit-map format, which uses a *raster image* to represent the graphics. Instead of graphic objects such as lines or arcs, the picture becomes a series of dots. This graphics format is widely supported, but it is difficult to edit because of the raster image.

Learning DXF Data Translations

DXF capabilities are not active in the training version of AutoSketch.

Most CAD software packages use a proprietary binary-file format to contain the graphics data generated by that software. With few exceptions, these packages cannot read or write to each other's format. Autodesk developed the Drawing Interchange Format (DXF) to exchange drawings between different drawing programs. This format has become very popular with many graphics software packages, and is commonly used for data exchange.

Examining the DXF File Format

A DXF file is an ASCII text file that uses words (*entity types*) and numbers (*entity coordinates*) to completely describe a graphics file in text format. Because this translation capability is built into AutoSketch, you do not have to interpret the contents of a DXF file.

A DXF file is quite easy to read after you become familiar with the way entities are listed and coordinates are displayed.

Figure 10.6 shows the beginning of the DXF file you will create in the next exercise.

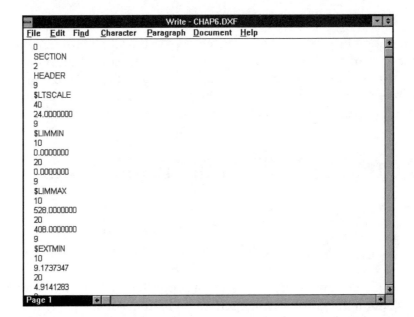

Figure 10.6:
A typical DXF file.

Exchanging graphics data between different software packages always contains an element of risk. Entity types, text fonts, and hatch patterns are not always compatible or available. Although AutoSketch attempts to translate graphic entities into its own entity types, it is not always possible.

Some data loss or corruption may occur between incompatible CAD software. You can minimize data loss by planning in advance for the limitations of the software to which you are translating.

Because DXF files can become extremely large, a binary DXF file format has also been developed for some applications. AutoSketch does not support a binary DXF format. Make sure that the DXF files you receive from other people are in ASCII format.

Creating a DXF File

A DXF file is easy to create in AutoSketch. Choose Export DXF from the File menu, and use the dialog box to name the file. You can use the same name as the drawing file because it has a different extension (DXF).

After the DXF file has been created, it can be read into another software package or viewed in a text editor, such as the Write program included with Windows or the MS-DOS Editor.

In the following exercise, you create a DXF file of the CHAP6 drawing and examine it in Write.

Exporting a DXF File

Open the CHAP6 drawing.

Choose File, then Export DXF	Opens the Export DXF File dialog box
Type **CHAP6** *in the text box and choose* **S**ave	Names and saves the file

Exit AutoSketch, then double-click on the Write icon from the Accessories program group, as seen in figure 10.7.

Choose File, then Open	Displays the Open dialog box, shown in figure 10.8

Change the current directory to C:\LAW and the File type to list text box to *.* . Double-click on CHAP6.DXF, and choose No Conversion. The DXF file should appear, as displayed in figure 10.6. After examining the text file, exit Write.

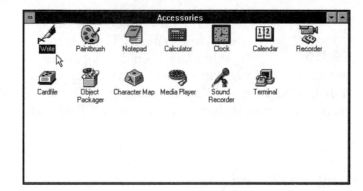

Figure 10.7:

The Write icon in the Accessories program group.

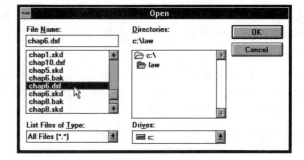

Figure 10.8:

The Open dialog box in Write.

By paging through the DXF text file, you may recognize variables or entity names from the drawing. You can modify this file by changing the layer, color, or linetype of an entity. By changing the coordinates, the entity shape and size can also be modified. This process is used by many third-party programmers to examine and manipulate drawing files.

Reading a DXF File

DXF files can be read into AutoSketch by choosing Import DXF from the File menu. If you are working in an existing drawing, the entities are added to your drawing at the same X,Y coordinates that were originally defined. If you are beginning a new drawing, the new drawing is defined by the contents of the DXF file. Figure 10.9 shows a dialog box that displays when a DXF file is imported, which presents you with several options (discussed in the following sections).

Figure 10.9:

The Import DXF Control Settings dialog box.

- **Explode Large Blocks.** Because AutoSketch groups are limited to 1,000 objects, extremely large AutoCAD blocks may be lost unless they are exploded.

- **Import Visible Attributes.** This option also imports text that has been defined as attributes.

A DXF file from AutoCAD, called GLOBE.DXF, is included on the disk for this book. In the following exercise, you import this DXF file into AutoSketch.

Importing a DXF File

Begin a new drawing in AutoSketch.

Choose **F**ile, *then* **I**mport DXF	Opens the Import DXF dialog box
Double-click on globe.dxf *(see fig. 10.10)*	Opens the Import DXF Control Settings dialog box
Choose OK	Imports the file
Choose **V**iew, *then the* Zoom Full *tool*	Shows the globe, as shown in figure 10.11
Choose **F**ile, *then* **S**ave, *and enter* **GLOBE**	Saves the file as GLOBE.SKD

When you import DXF files, you can use the Properties tool to see the AutoSketch entity type, as well as other properties such as layer and linetype. The Import DXF tool never prompts for a locating point because the entities are always placed according to the X and Y positions with which they were created.

Figure 10.10:

The Import DXF File dialog box.

If you plan to make extensive use of the DXF translations, prepare a few test drawings to exchange with the software packages you plan to use. This helps to work the bugs out of the translation process before you begin translating large production drawings.

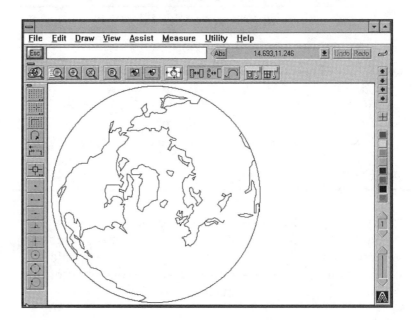

Figure 10.11:

The globe DXF entities, as they appear in AutoSketch.

Importing and Exporting Text

In Chapter 6, you learned about the Text Editor, which enables you to create and edit text strings. Compared to many other CAD packages, AutoSketch is quite powerful in its text capabilities. A word processor, however, is still more efficient for creating long text strings. This is especially important when standard notes or descriptions are used on multiple drawings.

You can save text strings by using the Part Clip tool. Creating a DXF file converts the text into an ASCII file format. The preferred method of moving text in and out of drawings is by using the Import and Export features that are built into the AutoSketch Text Editor.

Saving AutoSketch Text to a File

Text strings created in AutoSketch are part of the proprietary binary drawing file. To convert the text strings from your drawing into an ASCII text file, you can use the Export option from the Text Editor. This creates a text file with a TXT extension, which is compatible with most other word processing programs.

 Some word processors default to their own file format. They have a special command to specify an ASCII file, sometimes referred to as *DOS format* or *text format*.

The following exercise demonstrates the capabilities of AutoSketch to export text from a drawing to a file. You create the text string in AutoSketch, then place that text into a separate file named TEXT.TXT.

Exporting a Text File

Begin a new drawing in AutoSketch.

*Choose **D**raw, then double-click on the*   Displays the Text
Text Editor tool   Settings dialog box

Confirm that the settings are the same as in figure 10.12, then choose **O**K.

`Text Editor Enter point: 1,7` ↵   Locates text and displays the
     Text Editor

Type the text string shown in figure 10.13, then choose **O**K. The text appears in the drawing, as shown in figure 10.14.

*Choose **E**dit, then the Text Editor tool*

`Text Editor Select object:` *Click on*   Displays the Text Editor
the text

*Choose **E**xport, then type*   Names the text file
`\LAW\TEXT.TXT` ↵ *in the text box*

*Choose **O**K*   Leaves the Text Editor

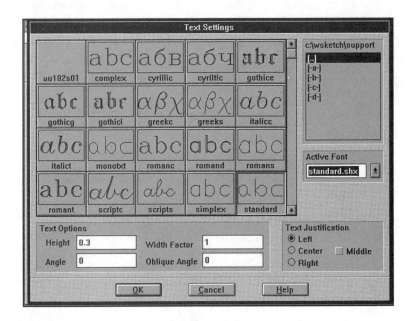

Figure 10.12:

The Text Settings dialog box.

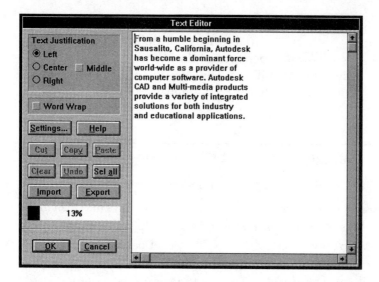

Figure 10.13:
The AutoSketch Text Editor.

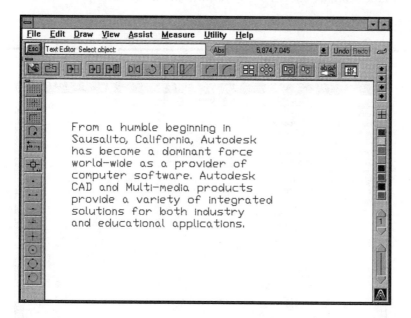

Figure 10.14:
The text string in AutoSketch.

Now that the text file has been created, you can bring it up in any other software package that can read an ASCII text file. Continue to use this text file by bringing it up in the Windows Write program and adding a sentence.

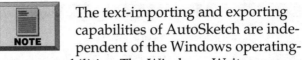

The text-importing and exporting capabilities of AutoSketch are independent of the Windows operating-system capabilities. The Windows Write program is used here only for convenience.

Modifying the Text File by Using Windows Write

Exit the drawing, and open the Windows Write program.

Choose **File**, *then* **O**pen	Displays the Open dialog box
Enter **\LAW\TEXT.TXT** *in the text box*	Opens the file
Choose **N**o conversion	Does not convert file into Write format

Add the sentence shown in figure 10.15 to the text string.

Choose **File**, *then* **S**ave, *and* E**x**it	Saves the file, and ends the program

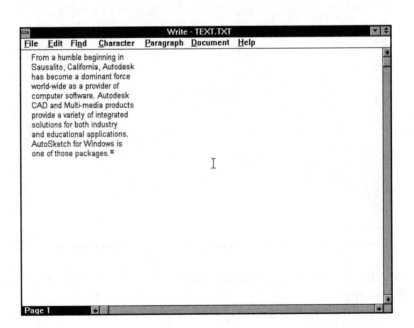

Figure 10.15:

The modified text in Write.

The text string can be created entirely in Write or in any other package that writes the ASCII file format. If the file is converted into the Windows Write format, it is not completely compatible to import back into AutoSketch.

Reading a Text File into an AutoSketch Drawing

The Import button in the AutoSketch Text Editor enables you to import text files. The Import Text File dialog box displays, which enables you to select or type a file name (the maximum size file is 2,048 characters). After a text file has been imported, many modifications—such as font, text height, and placement—can be specified.

In the following exercise, you use the TEXT.TXT file again. This time, you import it into the GLOBE AutoSketch drawing, and modify it for better fit and appearance.

Importing a Text File

Open the GLOBE drawing in AutoSketch.

Choose **D**raw, *then the Text Editor tool*

Text Editor Enter point: **26,20** ↵   Locates the text, and opens the Text Editor

Choose Import, *then enter*   Displays the text,
\LAW\TEXT.TXT ↵   as shown in figure 10.16

Choose **O**K   Displays text in the drawing, as shown in figure 10.17

Choose **E**dit, *then the Text Editor tool*

Text Editor Select object: *Click on the*   Opens the Text Editor
text in the drawing

continues

Choose the **S**ettings *button and change the font to* ROMANS, *then choose* **O**K	Changes the font
Click on the Word Wrap *check box*	Activates Word Wrap

Drag the right side of the Text Editor window to the left to narrow the text string (see fig. 10.18), then choose **O**K.

Choose **V**iew, *then the* Zoom Full *tool*	Shows the drawing, as shown in figure 10.19

Save the drawing.

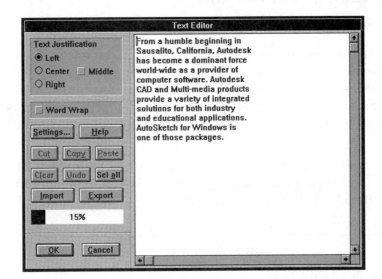

Figure 10.16:

Importing text into the Text Editor.

Once text has been imported into a drawing, many features of the Text Editor are useful for changing the appearance of the text. The *word-wrap function*, used in the last exercise, enables you to adjust the width of the text string by resizing the Text Editor's window size.

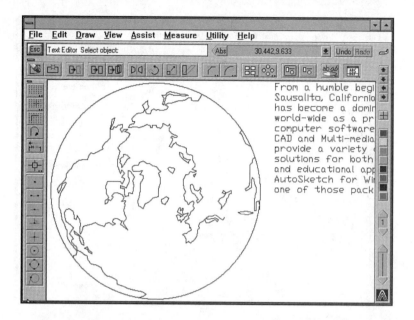

Figure 10.17:

The text is imported into the drawing.

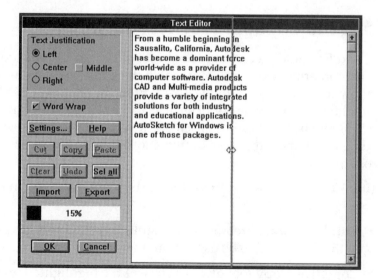

Figure 10.18:

Changing the width of the text string.

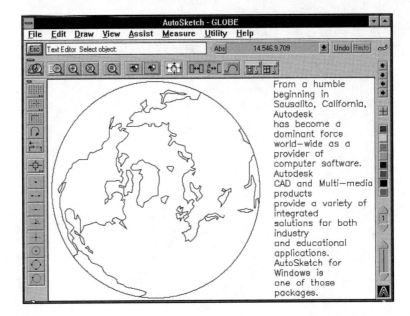

Figure 10.19:
The completed GLOBE drawing.

Using the Clipboard for Text Manipulation

The Text Editor also contains its own set of Windows-type tools for manipulating text. The Copy tool in the Utility toolbox uses a window to select objects. In the Text Editor, the text must be highlighted before using a tool such as Cut or Copy. You can *highlight* text by positioning the cursor in front of the text, then holding down the left mouse button and dragging the cursor across the text.

Figure 10.18 shows the set of buttons, which are described in the following list:

- **Cut.** The Cut tool removes the highlighted text and places it in the Clipboard to be used in another location.

- **Copy.** The Copy tool places a copy of the highlighted text in the Clipboard.

- **Paste.** The Paste tool inserts the contents of the Clipboard at the current cursor location.

- **Clear.** The Clear tool erases all highlighted text.

- **Undo.** The Undo tool undoes the last action taken, such as Clear or Cut.

- **Sel all.** The Select All tool highlights all the text in the Text Editor.

Some of these buttons are dimmed until the conditions are right for the button to be used. Paste does not work unless something is in the Clipboard. Cut is not activated without highlighted text.

These tools can be used within the AutoSketch Text Editor, or they can be used with other external Windows applications.

Dynamic Graphics Exchange: Object Linking and Embedding

OLE capabilities are not included with the training edition of AutoSketch.

The Copy and Paste tools enable you to move text and graphics data from one application to another. Suppose, for example, that you are working on a technical document that used graphics data from a product drawing. Because software such as Windows Write has little graphics-editing capability, any necessary graphics editing must be done in AutoSketch, and the new drawing must be pasted back into the document. Whenever the original product drawing is updated, the technical report document becomes obsolete.

Some exciting capabilities of Windows make it possible for you to overcome these difficulties by using embedding and linking to help update related documents.

Two important features of Windows application software that support object linking and embedding are the following:

- **Server.** An application package is a *server* if its objects can be linked or embedded in other applications. AutoSketch is a server, as is Windows Paintbrush.

- **Client.** Software applications that can accept linked or embedded objects are called *clients*. AutoSketch is not a client; Windows Write is a client.

Embedding an AutoSketch Drawing in Write

The process of embedding an AutoSketch drawing is similar to the copying and pasting procedures already discussed in this chapter. Once the drawing has been embedded into a document, you can edit the drawing by double-clicking on the graphic area while running the client application. This process causes AutoSketch to run and open a drawing containing the graphic on which you double-clicked. You can then edit the embedded objects. This process does not change the original drawing; it only updates the client file.

 Be sure to use the Copy Objects tool in AutoSketch to place the objects into the Clipboard. If you use the Copy Bitmap or Copy Metafile tools, you cannot edit the objects in AutoSketch as an embedded file.

In the next exercise, you copy the GLOBE.SKD entities to the Clipboard, then embed the picture of the globe in a Windows Write document. Double-clicking on the globe document opens a window of AutoSketch, in which you can make changes to the graphics embedded in that document.

Embedding AutoSketch Objects

Begin AutoSketch, and open the GLOBE drawing.

Choose **U**tility, *then the Copy Objects tool*

`Copy Objects: Select object:` *Pick two diagonal points to window the globe (see fig. 10.20)*

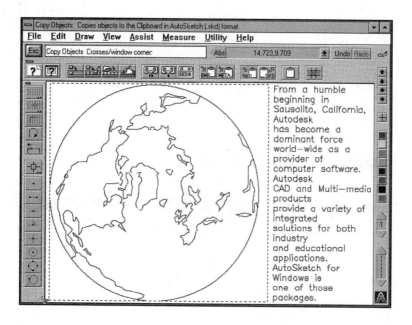

Figure 10.20:

Copying the objects from AutoSketch to the Clipboard.

Exit AutoSketch, and open the Windows Write program. Enter a title, as shown in figure 10.21.

Choose **E**dit, *then* **P**aste	Pastes objects, as shown in figure 10.22
Double-click on the globe entities	Opens the AutoSketch window

Use the Leader tool from the Measure toolbox to place a leader, similar to the one shown in figure 10.23.

Choose **F**ile, *then* **U**pdate, *then* E**x**it *and* Return to (Untitled) — Returns to the Write document with updates, as shown in figure 10.24

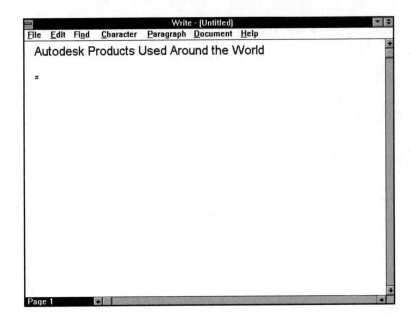

Figure 10.21:

Typing the title in the Write document.

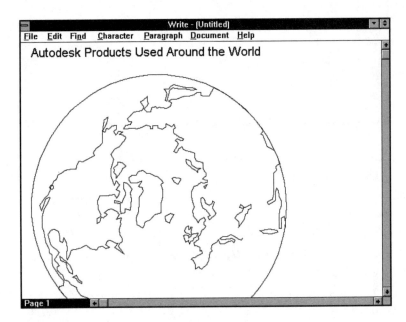

Figure 10.22:

Pasting the objects into the Write document.

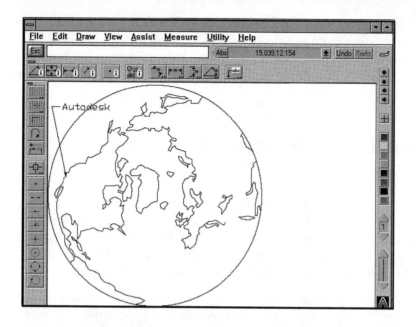

Figure 10.23:
Editing an embedded drawing.

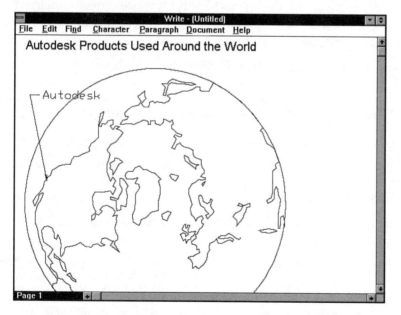

Figure 10.24:
The final result of editing the embedded graphics.

The original drawing file, GLOBE.SKD, has not been changed. The embedding capability is powerful because merely double-clicking on the embedded objects brings up those objects in the server application. After editing, the Update tool automatically updates the client document.

Linking AutoSketch Objects into a Write Document

Linking is more of a dynamic link between applications. It works much like embedding, except that when the objects in the client application are updated, the original file from the server application is also updated. When the original drawing file is updated, the client document is updated the next time it is opened.

You can edit linked objects in two ways. Double-clicking on them from the client application opens a server-application window, but the editing process works slowly. A more efficient method of updating objects is to open the original server file, make the changes, and then open the client file so it can be updated.

The following exercise uses both of these methods.

Creating an Object Link between AutoSketch and Write

Begin a new file using Write. Type in a title, as shown in figure 10.25.

Choose Edit, then Paste Link	Pastes the globe objects shown in figure 10.26
Double-click on the globe entities	Opens the AutoSketch window

Change to a dashed linetype, and draw several concentric circles, as seen in figure 10.27.

Choose File, then Exit, *and* Yes	Saves the changes, and exits to the Write document seen in figure 10.28

Note that some of the circles were not linked because they were drawn outside the area chosen with the Copy Objects tool.

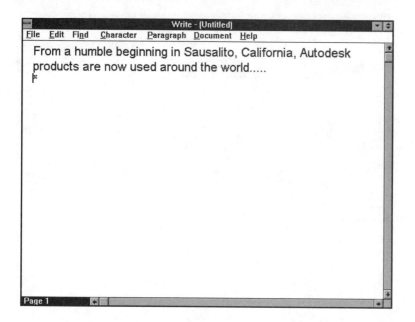

Figure 10.25:
Typing a title in the Write document.

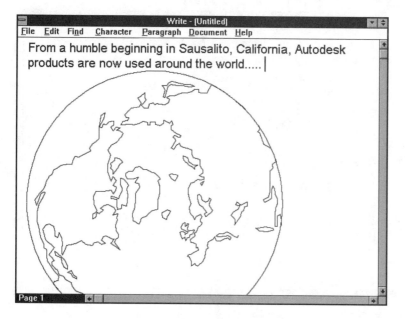

Figure 10.26:
Linking the objects with Paste Link.

continues

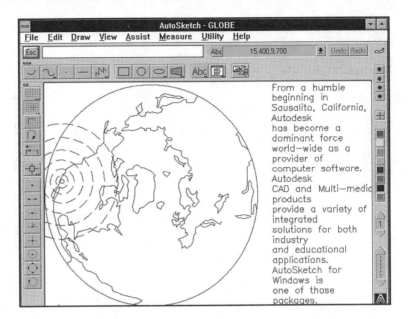

Figure 10.27:

Editing the
linked objects.

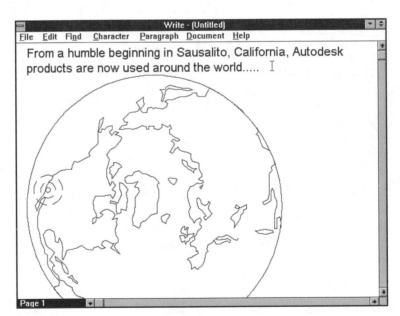

Figure 10.28:

Updating the
document with
the linked
objects.

Choose **F**ile, *then* **Ex**it, *and save the file as* GLOBE-L

Open the GLOBE drawing in AutoSketch, and add the lines shown in figure 10.29. Exit AutoSketch, saving your changes, and open the GLOBE-L document in Write.

Choose **Y**es *in the dialog box shown in*   Updates the links
figure 10.30

Both methods of updating linked objects were used in this exercise. You may have noticed that AutoSketch ran rather slowly when it was run from the client document, but the updating was automatic. When the server application (the AutoSketch drawing) was separately modified, you were notified by the dialog box shown in figure 10.30 that an update had taken place.

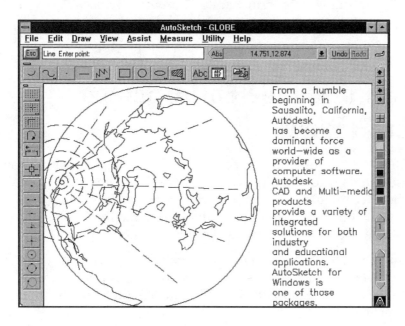

Figure 10.29:

Modifying the original AutoSketch drawing.

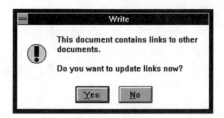

Figure 10.30:

The link update dialog box in Write.

 For more information on linking and embedding, consult the Windows Resource Kit from Microsoft and the documentation of other Windows applications that act as a server or client.

New Riders Publishing has several books that cover this topic, including *Maximizing Windows 3.1* and *Ultimate Windows 3.1*.

Capturing the Entire Screen in Windows

All the techniques for moving graphic images in this chapter have used methods of highlighting or windowing to specify the objects. These techniques select only specific items in the drawing window. If you want to copy the entire screen into the Clipboard (not just the drawing area), use the Print Screen key.

This key places a bit-map image of the current screen into Clipboard. Figure 10.31 shows the contents of the Clipboard that resulted from opening the GLOBE drawing, then pressing the Print Screen key.

 You can press the Alt and Print Screen keys together to copy the contents of the active window into the Clipboard.

334

On some systems, you must hold down the Shift key while you press the Print Screen key. Many other software packages are available that give you a wide variety of tools for performing screen captures.

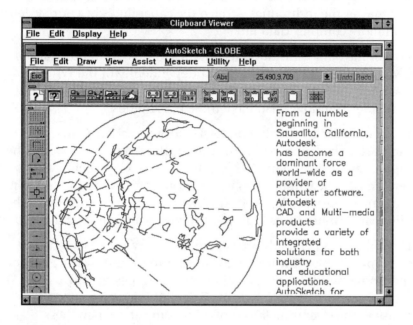

Figure 10.31:

The entire screen copied to the Clipboard by pressing the Print Screen key.

Summary

The data-sharing capabilities of Windows application software are almost unlimited. The exercises in this chapter covered only a few of the possible combinations of software applications and data-sharing capabilities. Refer to the documentation of your other Windows applications for more information on this topic (or to various books available from New Riders Publishing). Once you become comfortable with your first Windows application, the other applications become easy to learn.

The exercises in this chapter did not emphasize running several windows concurrently because you may have memory or graphics limitations on your system. Try opening several of your Windows applications at once, and try some of the techniques shown in this chapter. Remember to start out with small, simple files. As you master the techniques, stretch the capabilities of your system with more complex data links.

Two of the data-translation techniques discussed in this chapter—DXF files and text files—are run independently of the Windows operating system. Many other software applications that do not run under Windows also have these capabilities.

The special tools available under Windows include Cut, Copy, and Paste. The Clipboard is the buffer that temporarily stores the entities, and it is updated whenever a Cut or Copy command is performed. The Clipboard Viewer, a program found in the Main program group, can be used to view or save Clipboard files if the Clipboard cannot be called up from within another application.

The linking and embedding capabilities of Windows opens up many possibilities for interactively running Windows applications and updating files that use data from other files. Again, as you explore more complex levels of object linking, you notice a decrease in the operating speed of your computer when these files are open.

Chapter 11 includes two drawing tutorials you can use to sharpen your drawing skills and see how AutoSketch can be used to complete some production drawings.

Practicing with AutoSketch

All AutoSketch drawing and editing tools have been explained and demonstrated in the first eight chapters of this book. These tools are similar to those found in many other CAD software packages. Perhaps you are still unsure of how to create a certain type of drawing by using these tools. The best way to improve your CAD drafting techniques is to work through a few more complete production drawings.

Chapter 11 contains two drawing tutorials. The first drawing is a three-view mechanical drawing of a Harley-Davidson transmission cover. The second tutorial is an architectural application. Try both of these, or choose the one that best fits your applications.

Creating a Three-View Mechanical Drawing

The level of detail in the tutorials in this chapter is less than that found in the earlier parts of this book. You can use a different technique than what is shown to complete a certain part of the drawing. The same drawing may be approached quite differently by separate individuals. The important thing is that the end results be technically accurate and conform to relevant drawing standards.

Planning and Developing the Drawing

Before beginning a CAD drawing, it is important to develop a plan for the way you want the drawing to look and what information will be needed to create it. You waste time and lose concentration if you must backtrack in your drawing to correct areas that were not properly planned. The more experience you have in CAD drafting, the easier the planning process will be. After you develop the same type of drawing several times, it becomes much easier to plan your steps.

You must consider the following factors when planning and developing the drawing:

- **Number of views required.** Although some mechanical components can be shown as one view with a note describing the thickness, other components may require five or more views to fully show the details of the part.

- **Purpose of the drawing.** A production drawing intended as a complete shop drawing includes every dimension and every detail required to make the part.

- **Scale and sheet size.** The final plotting-sheet size must be determined, along with the plotting-scale factor of the part. The plotting-scale factor may affect text heights and linetype scales used in the drawing.

- **Drawing standards.** Any drawing standards that affect text height, dimensioning, title blocks, or view layout should be understood and integrated into the drawing.

The transmission cover shown in the three-view drawing is an aluminum casting that was made from a special casting drawing. The drawing you will create is the drawing used to machine the casting.

Several of the drawing exercises in this book began with a title block and border. The drawing limits were also set at the beginning of the drawing. This time, you begin by drawing the views in proper alignment to each other. Near the end of the drawing, you insert a border and place the views into final position in that border.

Several views are required to show the part. It is important that these views are drawn in *orthographic position*, meaning that the views are properly aligned with each other.

One of the views is a *section view*, showing the cross-sectional shape of the part at the cutting-plane line.

The *datum position*, instead of being at the lower left corner of the drawing screen, will be located at the datum point of the part. It is the 0, 0 reference point for defining absolute coordinates. This arrangement helps when using absolute coordinates, and it also enables you to create a DXF file for CAM machining with the datum point at the proper place on the part.

Drawing the Transmission Cover

The most efficient method of drawing a three-view drawing is to draw the front (or central) view, and then project the other views from that view. Table 11.1 shows the layers and linetypes used in the drawing. You can choose your own color scheme.

Table 11.1   Layer and Linetype Specifications

Entity Type	Layer	Linetype
Object lines	1	Continuous
Center lines	2	Center
Hidden lines	3	Hidden
Section lines	4	Phantom
Notes and dimensions	5	Continuous
Title block and border	10	Continuous

In the following exercise, you begin the drawing by creating several construction circles at the 0,0 point. Use the Zoom and Pan tools often to size and locate your working area so that you maximize your drawing screen area. Whenever you are asked to pick a point, type coordinates or use the attach modes to maintain accuracy in your drawing.

Beginning the Drawing

Begin a new drawing in AutoSketch, and name it COVER.

Choose **D**raw, *then the Circle tool*

Circle Center point: **0,0** ⏎   Locates the center point

Point on circle: **r(.5,0)** ⏎   Specifies .5 radius

Draw four more circles at 0,0 with radii of: .7, 1.3, 1.5, 2. Pan and zoom to the view shown in figure 11.1.

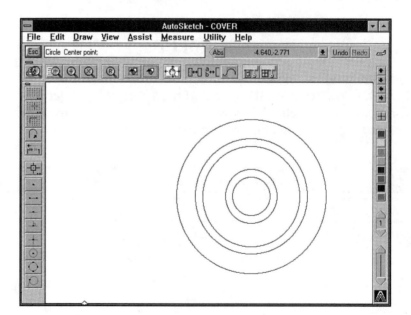

Figure 11.1:

Drawing the first circles.

Now you can use a series of editing commands to continue with this view. The three larger circles will be broken at the top and bottom quadrant points because only the right half is used.

When drawing arcs, you must decide whether it is easier to draw a full circle, and then break it; or draw a three-point arc with the Arc tool.

The fastest way to draw arcs often is to use the Fillet tool. To use this technique, construct the outline of the object feature, and use the Fillet tool set to the radius of your desired arc.

In the following exercise, you use the Ring Array tool to create copies of the bolt holes. Then you use the Mirror tool to create the left side of the cover.

Drawing the Bolt Hole Circles

Use the Break tool to break the three largest circles at the top and bottom quadrant points, as shown in figure 11.3.

Choose **D**raw, *then the Circle tool*

`Circle Center point:` **0,2** ↵

`Point on circle:` **r(.17,0)** ↵

`Center point:` **0,2** ↵

`Point on circle:` **r(.35,0)** ↵

Choose **E**dit, *then double-click on the*   Opens the Ring Array
Ring Array tool   Settings dialog box

Change your settings to match those in the Ring Array Settings dialog box, shown in figure 11.2.

`Ring Array Select object:` *Window the*   Creates the array
last two circles drawn   (see fig. 11.3)

continues

Break the large arc at ① and ②, as shown in figure 11.3. Draw a line from 0,2 to -1,2 and from 0,-2 to -1,-2.

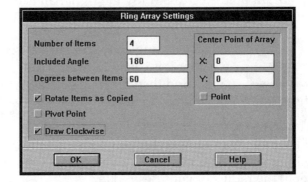

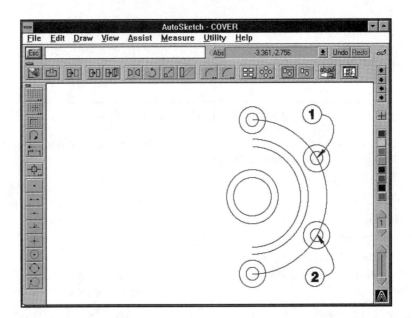

Figure 11.3:

Break points in the arc.

Choose **E**dit, *then double-click on the Fillet tool*

Opens the Fillet Settings dialog box

Set the fillet radius to .5.

```
Fillet Select object(s):
```
Pick the line at ① *(see fig. 11.4)*

```
Select second object:
```
Pick the circle at ①

Continue to fillet until your drawing looks like figure 11.4.

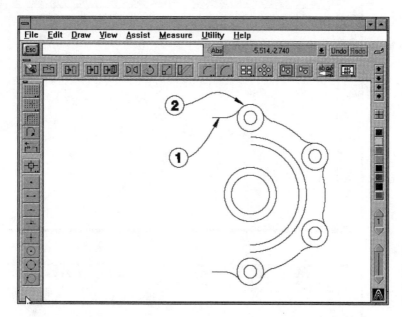

Figure 11.4:

Picking the entities for a fillet.

Choose the Break tool

`Break Select object:` *Pick the circle near* ① *(see fig. 11.5)*

`First point:` *Using the End Point attach mode, pick the end of the arc near* ①

`Second point:` *Pick the end of the arc near* ①

Continue to break the circles in a counterclockwise direction until your drawing looks like figure 11.6.

The large arc was broken in two places so that the Fillet tool could trim the end of the arc without removing too much of it. It is important to use attach modes when breaking circles so the circles break at the precise endpoint of the arc.

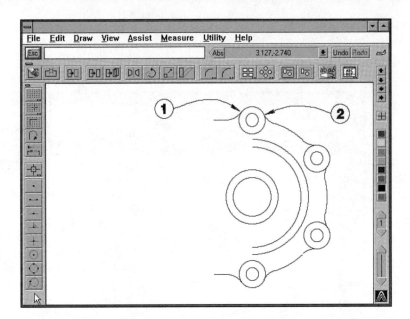

Figure 11.5:
Picking the
break points.

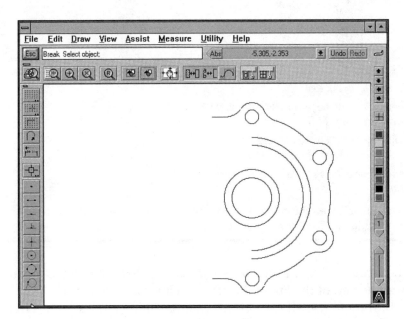

Figure 11.6:
The completed
half of the
cover.

The following exercise completes the front view of the transmission cover. The rest of the front view of the cover can be easily generated with the Mirror tool. A bushing boss needs to be drawn near the top. The Properties tool from the Edit toolbox gives the hidden lines the correct layer and linetype. Remember to change colors when you change layers.

Finishing the Front View of the Cover

*Choose **E**dit, then the Mirror tool*

`Mirror Select object:` *Window all of the entities*

`Base point:` **-1,2** ↵

`Second point:` **-1,-2** ↵   Objects are mirrored

Erase the two small circles on the left side, and connect the two arcs with lines, as shown in figure 11.7.

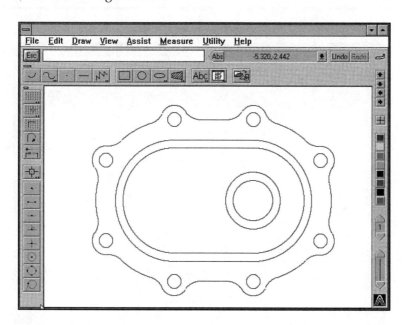

Figure 11.7:
The cover after using the Mirror tool.

Draw a vertical line from -.5,1.3 to -.5,2.3.

*Choose **E**dit, then the Multi-copy tool*

continues

```
Multiple Copy Select object:
```
Pick the vertical line
```
From point: /LPOINT ↵
To point: r(-.25,0) ↵
To point: r(-.25,0) ↵
To point: r(-.25,0) ↵
To point: r(-.25,0) ↵
```

Draw a line across the top of these lines, and break the horizontal line at ① in figure 11.8.

Add the two .25 fillets shown in figure 11.9.

Change the current layer to 3 and the linetype to Hidden.

*Choose **E**dit, then the Property(Change) tool*

```
Change Property Select object:
```
Pick two arcs and six lines (see fig. 11.9)

Save the drawing.

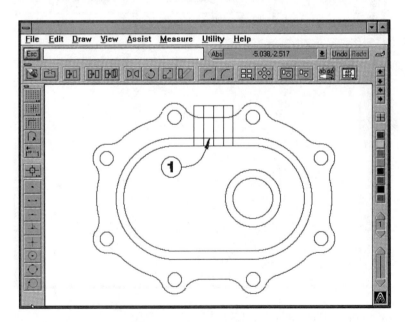

Figure 11.8:

Drawing the lines for the bushing boss.

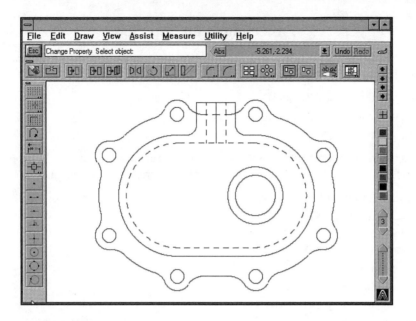

Figure 11.9:
The completed front view.

 It is often easier to change the properties of entities after they are created than to always remember to create the entities with the correct properties. The middle vertical line in the bushing boss will be changed to a center line.

Next, you draw the top view. Imagine holding the cover so that you are looking at the front view, then rotating the bottom of the cover 90 degrees away from you. That is how the top view should appear. In a manual drawing, a series of vertical construction lines are projected up from the front view. You use this technique in AutoSketch so that you do not have to calculate all the coordinates needed.

The following exercise shows you how to project from the front view to begin developing the geometry for the top view.

Projecting to the Top View

Zoom to the view shown in figure 11.10. Change back to layer 1 with a Continuous linetype.

Choose **D**raw, *then the Line tool*

```
Line Enter point: -5,5 ↵
To point: 2.5,5 ↵
```

Activate the Ortho mode, and also the Quadrant, End Point, and Perpendicular attach modes. Draw the vertical lines shown in figure 11.10.

Choose **E**dit, *then the Multi-copy tool*

```
Multiple Copy Select object:
```
Pick the top horizontal line

```
From point: /LPOINT ↵
To point: r(0,-.25) ↵
To point: r(0,-1.3) ↵
To point: r(0,-.2) ↵
To point: r(0,-.38) ↵
```

Using the Break tool with the Intersect attach mode active, break all the lines showing the screw holes in the top view, as seen in figure 11.11.

By projecting up from all the critical points on the front view, the construction geometry is created without entering coordinates. The horizontal line forms the upper edge of the top view. It is important to use the proper attach modes for accurate breaks.

In a really complicated drawing, you may not want to project all of the geometry up at the same time.

Continue using the Break and Fillet tools to trim the rest of the top view to proper size.

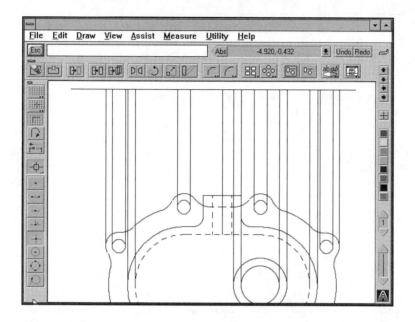

Figure 11.10:

Projecting from the front to the top view.

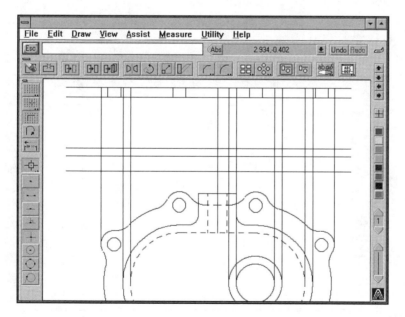

Figure 11.11:

Breaking the lines for the screw holes.

Finishing the Top View

Use the Break tool to trim the outside of the top view, as shown in figure 11.12.

Use the Fillet tool to trim the rest of the lines, as shown in figure 11.13. Break the horizontal line at the .1 radius fillet before performing the fillet.

Finally, break the horizontal line at ① and ② in figure 11.14. Add two more .1 radius fillets in those same corners. Finish breaking the lines, and change the appropriate lines and arcs to a hidden linetype, as shown in figure 11.14.

*Choose **D**raw, then the Circle tool*

Circle Center point: **-1,4** ↵

Point on circle: **r(.5,0)** ↵

Center point: **-1,4** ↵

Point on circle: **r(.25,0)** ↵

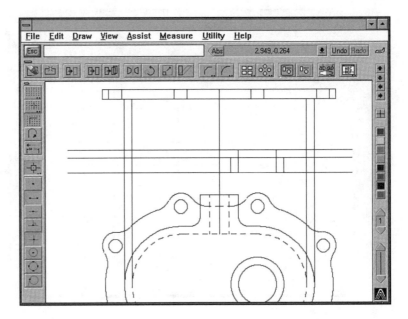

Figure 11.12:

Breaking more lines around the flange base.

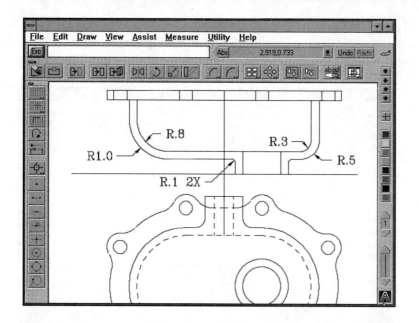

Figure 11.13:

Using the Fillet tool to trim the lines.

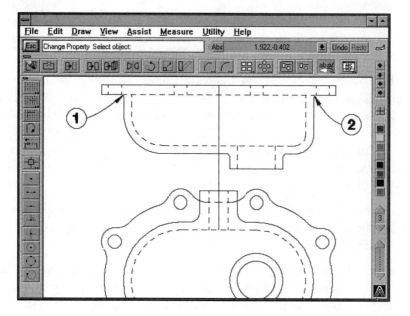

Figure 11.14:

Breaking and filleting two corners and changing the linetype.

351

If everything went well, your finished top view should appear similar to figure 11.15. Later on, you may want to move the views farther apart for dimensioning.

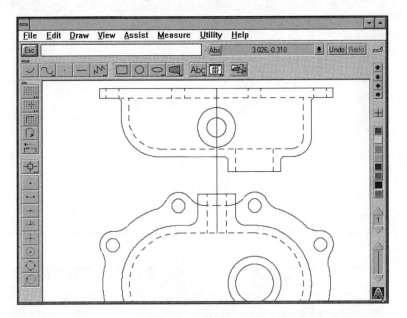

Figure 11.15:
The completed
top view.

When the three views have been completed, center lines and dimension lines will be added. Another special type of line, called a *cutting-plane line,* is added to see where the section for the third view will be taken. Looking at the cutting-plane line in figure 11.16, imagine how the cover would appear if you sawed through the cover at the cutting-plane line and then viewed the cut section in the direction of the cutting-plane arrows.

You draw the cutting plane as a double line to help it stand out from the other entities. A wide polyline with breaks added can also be used for this type of entity.

Because the side view is a section view, there is not as much detail to add. Hidden lines are never shown in a section view. The parts of the section view that have been cut through, however, will be filled with a pattern.

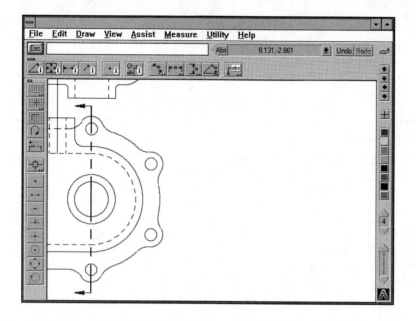

Figure 11.16:
The cutting-plane line in the front view.

Beginning the Section View

Zoom to the view shown in figure 11.16, and change to layer 4 with a linetype of Phantom.

Choose **D**raw, *then the Line tool*

Line Enter point: **.01,2.65** ↵

To point: **.01,-2.65** ↵

Enter point: **-.01,2.65** ↵

To point: **-.01,-2.65** ↵

Choose **M**easure, *then double-click on*   Opens the Dimension
the Leader tool   Settings dialog box

Change settings for a solid leader arrow with an arrow size of .3.

Leader Start point: **-.5,2.65** ↵

To point: **0,2.65** ↵

Choose **C**ancel

Leader Start point: **-.5,-2.65** ↵

To point: **0,-2.65** ↵

Choose **C**ancel

continues

Change back to layer 1 with a Continuous linetype.

*Choose **D**raw, then the Line tool*

Line Enter Point: **7,3** ↵

To point: **7,-2.5** ↵

Activate the Ortho mode and the End Point, Intersect, and Quadrant attach modes. Project the horizontal lines from the front view, as shown in figure 11.17.

*Choose **E**dit, then the Multi-copy tool*

Multiple Copy Select object:
Pick the right vertical line

From point: **/LPOINT** ↵

To point: **r(-.25,0)** ↵

To point: **r(-1.3,0)** ↵

To point: **r(-.2,0)** ↵

To point: **r(-.38,0)** ↵

Save the drawing.

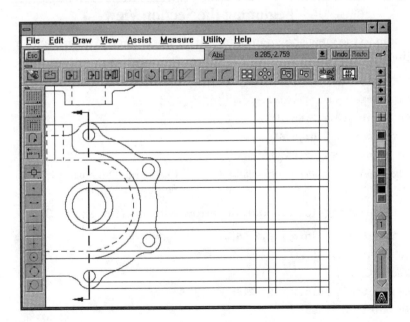

Figure 11.17:

Projecting from the front view to the section view.

Notice that constructing the section view is much like constructing the top view. The same offsets were used with the Multiple Copy tool in the top view because both of these views show the same depth dimensions on the cover.

Continue now with the next exercise to trim the geometry in the section view. Remember that when you want to fillet more than once to the same line, you should break the line first so the whole line is not trimmed back by the Fillet tool.

Finishing the Side View

Use the Break tool to break the lines at the flange, as shown in figure 11.18. Then break the two vertical lines near ① and ②.

Use the Fillet tool to trim the remaining lines. Use two .5 radii, two .3 radii, and two .1 radii (see fig. 11.19).

Finally, use the Break tool to clean up the remaining lines, as seen in figure 11.20.

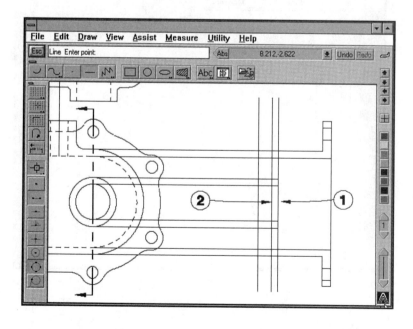

Figure 11.18:

Breaking the lines for the side view.

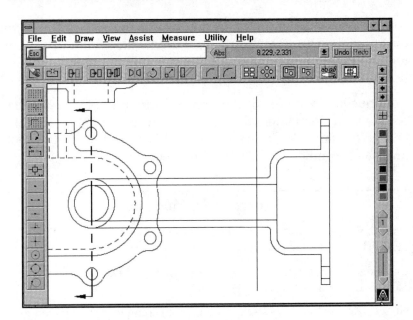

Figure 11.19:
Using the Fillet tool to trim the lines.

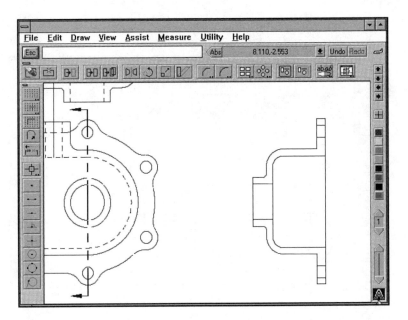

Figure 11.20:
The section view after breaking and filleting.

Notice that this cross-section is symmetrical. You can save some time by creating only one half of it, and then mirroring the image for the other half. The Pattern Fill tool places the hatch pattern on the cut sections.

After the top two parts are filled, it may be easier to mirror down to the bottom. Instead of risking double entities on the bottom, the bottom half should first be erased, then everything can be mirrored. Remember to use the Arc mode for specifying the boundary of the large hatch pattern.

Using Pattern Fill on the Section View

Choose **D***raw, then double-click on the*   Opens the Pattern
Pattern Fill tool   Settings dialog box

Set the pattern to ANSI31, with a .5 scale and no boundary.

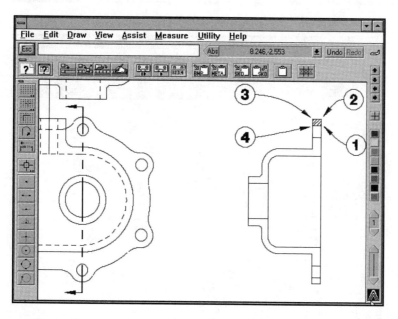

Figure 11.21:

Creating the first pattern fill.

continues

```
Pattern Fill First point:
```
Pick the corner near ① *(see fig. 11.21)*

`To point:` *Pick the corner near* ②

`To point:` *Pick the corner near* ③

`To point:` *Pick the corner near* ④

`To point:` *Pick the corner near* ①   Fills with the pattern

Perform the same technique, using Arc mode when needed, to fill the other area, as shown in figure 11.22.

Erase the lower half of the view, as shown in figure 11.22.

Choose **E***dit, then the Mirror tool*

```
Mirror Select objects:
```
Window in the two filled areas

`Base point:` **0,0** ↵

`Second point:` **1,0** ↵   Mirrors the pattern fill, as seen in figure 11.23

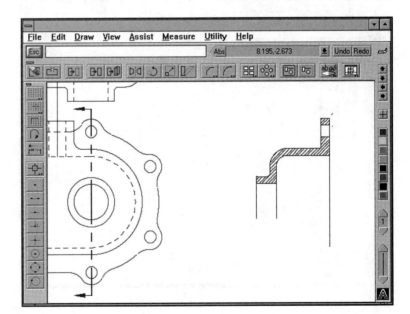

Figure 11.22:

Creating the second pattern fill.

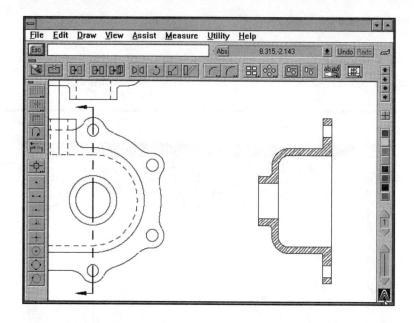

Figure 11.23:
The completed pattern fills after mirroring.

To finish this drawing, the following tasks should be completed:

- The views should be positioned to each other at a proper distance for dimensioning.
- Center lines should be added as needed.
- Dimensions and notes should be added.
- A title block and border should be placed around the views.
- The title block should be filled in with the appropriate text.

The following exercise includes several of these steps. You may finish up the rest of the drawing as much as you want.

Completing the Drawing

Move the top view up about 1". Change the layer to 2, and the linetype to Center. Change the property of the vertical line between the two views, and stretch the length, as shown in figure 11.24. Draw the other center lines by using the Line tool.

continues

*Choose **D**raw, then the Part tool*   Opens the Select Part File
                                                         dialog box

Enter CHAP11 in the Active Filename text box.

Part To point: **-5.5,-5** ↵   Inserts the title block
                                                         (see fig. 11.25)

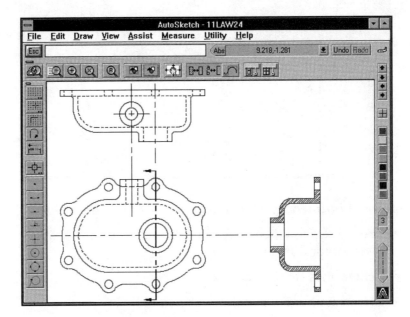

Figure 11.24:

Positioning the
views and
adding the
center lines.

The drawing is now finished. Complete annotating and dimensioning will make the drawing of the Harley-Davidson transmission cover a full production drawing, which can be used to
machine the casting. If the drawing is accurate, a DXF file of the
entities can be sent directly to a CAM programming system for
Computer Numerical Machining code.

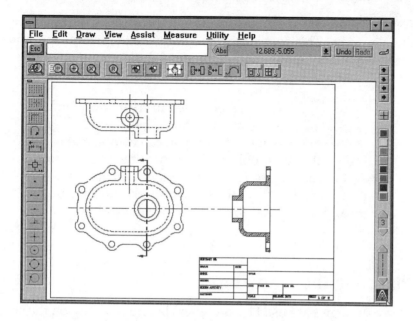

Figure 11.25:
Adding the border and title block.

Creating an Architectural Plan View and Elevation

The second half of this chapter is divided into two sections, each with an exercise. The first exercise develops a plan of a simple garden gazebo. During the second exercise, you will create an elevation by using the plan that was developed.

Creating plans and elevations for architectural applications is similar to producing orthographic drawings for mechanical applications. An architectural plan view shows the top view, or floor plan, of a building. The elevation view shows a building from the front or side, displaying the heights and roof lines. Although mechanical drawings often show several views in relationship to each other, architectural drawings show the various views on separate drawing sheets.

Generally, architects and builders begin projects by designing in the plan view. This enables them to organize the size, shape, and planning that ultimately directs the final design.

The methods used to create the plan of the gazebo should be viewed as suggestions. If you can complete the tasks with other tools, you are encouraged to do so. As long as the final drawing contains the information needed to build the structure, let your ingenuity and newly developed skills be your guide.

Planning the Drawing

Many strategies are used by designers before deciding on the size and shape of a structure. The setting and use of this structure dictated that wood should be used. The whole gazebo is constructed entirely of wood.

Although wood has natural beauty, there are limitations to its use. A wood beam can span only so far before it becomes bulky and expensive, so the size of the building is restricted to a total span of 12'. A 12' octagon fits nicely alongside the elevation on an 8 1/2-by-11-inch paper.

Architectural plans are conventionally drawn at the scale of 1/4"=1'-0". This scale may change, depending on the size and complexity of the project. For the purposes of this drawing, the conventional scale is fine. The drawing itself should be divided into different layers to separate the information. Use the information in table 11.2 to organize the layers in the plan drawing.

Table 11.2	Layer and Linetype Specifications	
Entity Type	Layer	Linetype
Object lines	1	Continuous
Construction lines	2	Center
Roof-overhang lines	3	Hidden
Patterns	4	Continuous
Notes and dimensions	5	Continuous
Title block and border	10	Continuous

Drawing the Plan

The octagonal plan is divided into eight "wedges." Each wedge is defined by the structure that supports the floor. The easiest way to develop the plan is to complete one of the wedges, and perform a ring array to create the other seven pieces. Begin the exercise by making the columns that support the roof structure.

Drawing the Columns

Open the CHAP 11-2 drawing, and save it as MY-11.

Double-click on the Current Layer button, and disable the visible button on layer 10, then choose OK

Choose **Draw***, then select the Box tool*

`Box First corner:` *Pick a point in the drawing area near the coordinates 22',22'*

`To point: r(7.5,7.5)` ↵

Choose **View***, then select the Zoom Box tool to zoom into a view similar to figure 11.26*

continues

363

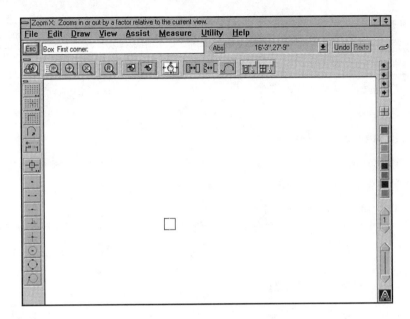

Figure 11.26:

The initial position of the first column.

Double-click on the Midpoint attach tool

*Choose **D**raw, then select the Line tool*

Line From point: *Select the midpoint of the bottom edge of the square*

To point: **p(6'6,90)** ↵

*Choose **E**dit, then select the Move tool*

Move Select objects: *Pick the square*

From point: *Choose any location in the drawing area*

To point: **p(6,90)** ↵

Choose the Group tool

Group Select object: *Form a crosses selection box on the entities*

Choose the Copy tool

Copy Select objects: *Pick the square*

Double-click on the End Point attach tool

`From point:` *Pick a corner on the square*

`To point:` *Pick the same corner*

Choose the Rotate tool

`Rotate Select objects:` *Pick the square*

`Center of rotation:` *Pick at the highest point on the centerline*

`Second point or angle:` **45** ↵

Perform a redraw to see the original and the rotated group.

`Rotate Select objects:` *Choose both groups with a crossing window*

`Center of rotation:` *Pick at the highest point on the center lines*

`Second point or angle:` **-22.5** ↵

Choose **D**raw, *then select the Line tool*

Create the lines at ① and ②. Then use the Copy tool to copy ① at 5.5 inches in the 90-degree direction and 3 inches in the direction of 270 degrees (see fig.11.27).

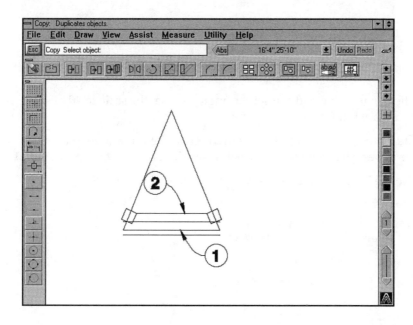

Figure 11.27:

Copying the lines.

Finishing the First Part of the Gazebo

Use the Erase and Break tools to edit your drawing (see fig. 11.28).

Use the scroll buttons in the Current Layer display box to set the layer to 3.

*Choose **D**raw, then double-click on the*
Pattern Fill tool

Figure 11.28:

The cleaned-up drawing, after using Erase and Brake.

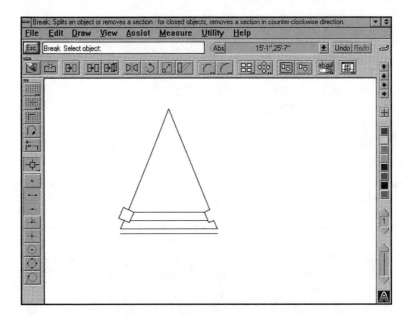

Click on the Line pattern, set the angle to 0, set the scale to 40, disable the Boundary button, and choose OK.

Create the pattern boundary from the center of the wedge to the inside of the rail and back to the center point (see fig. 11.29), then choose **A**ccept.

Use the Edit tools on the drawing to emulate figure 11.30.

Choose the Ring Array tool

```
Ring Array Select object:
```
Use a crosses selection box to select all
entities in the view

`Center point of array:` *Pick the center point on the plan*

Choose **M**odify, *and set the Number of Items to 8, then choose* OK

Choose **A**ccept

Choose View, select the Zoom X tool at .75 Magnification, then use the Pan tool to center the drawing (see fig. 11.31).

Press F12

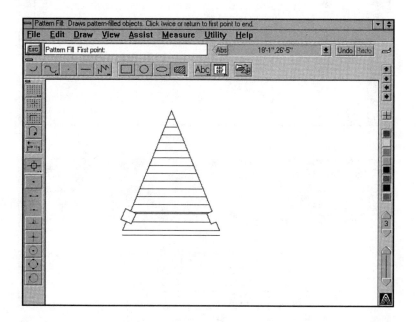

Figure 11.29:
Inserting the pattern fill.

Notice that the pattern fill maintained its orientation in all the wedges. Because you created each wedge with its own pattern fill, changing the orientation of the pattern is easy. In the next exercise, you complete the plan of the gazebo with several drawing and editing tools.

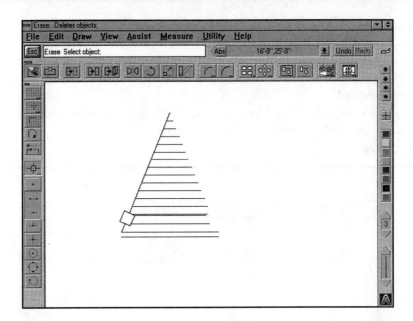

Figure 11.30:
Erasing the
right edge.

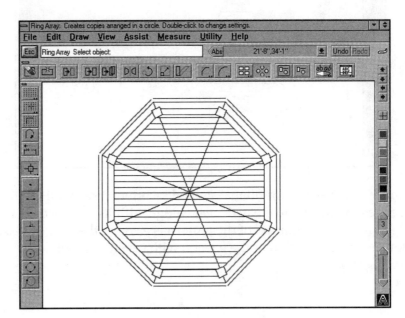

Figure 11.31:
The ring array.

Completing the Plan

Change the current layer to 4

*Choose **D**raw, then double-click on the
Pattern Fill tool*

*Change the angle of the pattern to
90, and then choose OK*

*Choose **E**dit, then select the Property(Change) tool*

`Change Property Select object:` *Pick at
① (see fig. 11.32)*

`Change Property Select object:` *Pick at ①*

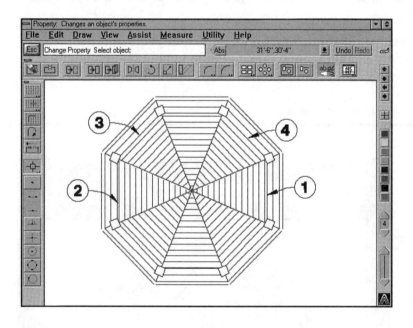

Figure 11.32:
Rotating the
pattern.

Repeat the preceding process by changing the pattern angle to 45 and
changing the property at ③ and its opposite. Change the pattern angle to
-45, and change the properties at ④ and its opposite to create the patterns shown in figure 11.32.

Change the current layer to 3, and the current linetype to hidden with a
scale factor of 24.

continues

Change the properties of the roof overhang around the outside of the gazebo.

Double-click on the Fillet tool, and set the radius to 0.

Fillet the roof overhang around the outside of the gazebo to clean up the edges, as shown in figure 11.34.

Create a zoom box that mimics the view shown in figure 11.34.

*Choose **Edit**, then select the Erase tool*

`Erase Select object:` *Pick at* ①
(see fig. 11.34)

Change the current layer to 1 and the linetype to continuous.

*Choose **Draw**, then select the Box tool*

`Box First corner:` *Pick at* ②

`Second corner:` **r(-5'4,-12)** ↵

*Choose **View**, then select the Zoom Full tool*

Press F12 to save the drawing

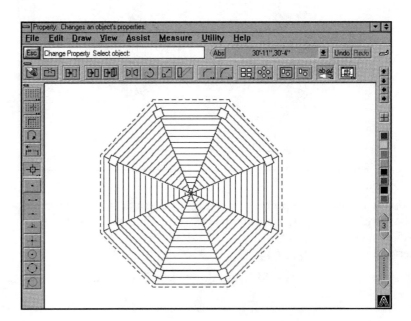

Figure 11.33:

Changing properties.

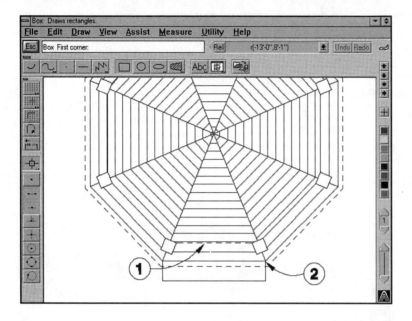

You can complete this drawing by adding dimensions and notes. Layer 5 has been reserved to contain this information.

Now that the plan is drawn, the elevation can be created. The second part of the architectural exercise generates the entry elevation of the gazebo.

Creating the Elevation

To complete the gazebo, an elevation view will be constructed. An *elevation view* illustrates the materials, sizes, and shapes of the exterior elements, as well as the heights of the floor and ceiling planes.

The elevation you will be creating has been broken down into stages. The first stage involves transferring the major lines from the plan view.

Beginning the Elevation

Continue with the MY-11 drawing. Turn on layer 10, and use the Zoom Full tool.

*Choose **E**dit, then select the Move tool*

`Move Select object:` *Use a crosses selection box to pick the whole plan*

`From point:` *Choose anywhere in the drawing area near the plan*

`To point:` *Pick a point in the upper center of the drawing (see fig. 11.35)*

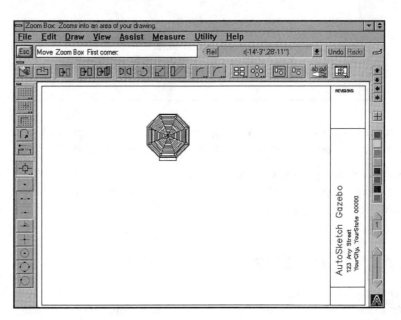

Figure 11.35:

Moving the plan view.

Change the current layer to 2, and turn off the visibility of layer 4

*Choose **V**iew, then use the zoom tools to create a view similar to figure 11.36*

Click on Ortho to make it active

*Choose **D**raw, then select the Line tool*

Draw a horizontal line to represent the ground line similar to ①, as shown in 11.38.

*Choose **E**dit, then select the Multi-copy tool*

`Multi-copy Select object:` *Pick at* ① *(see fig. 11.36)*

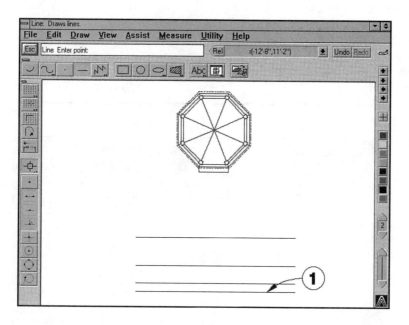

Figure 11.36:
The magnified view.

`From point:` *Pick anywhere in the drawing area*

`To point:` **p(18,90)** ↵   Creates the floor-height line

`To point:` **p(36,90)** ↵   Creates the railing-height line

`To point:` **p(5',90)** ↵   Creates the 8' ceiling-height line

`To point:` *Press Esc*

Choose the Line tool

Click on the End Point and Perpendicular attach tools

*Choose **V**iew, then use the Zoom box tool to create a view similar to figure 11.37*

continues

Use the Line tool and the F9 key (Last View) to drop the lines from the plan, perpendicular to the ground line.

*Choose **E**dit, then select the Mirror tool*

`Mirror Select objects:` *Use a crosses selection box to pick all the dropped vertical lines*

`Base point:` *Pick the middle of the stair and drag the cursor down*

Pick the second point anywhere in the drawing area, straight down from the first point (see fig. 11.38)

Press F12

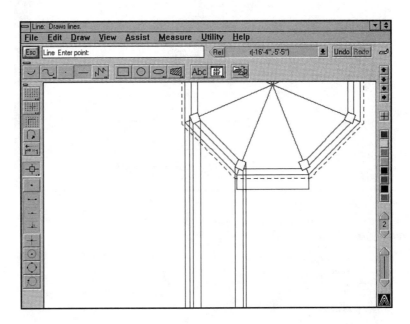

Figure 11.37:

A closer view of the plan.

The second stage of the elevation drawing focuses on editing the drawing by cleaning up with the Break, Erase, and Fillet tools.

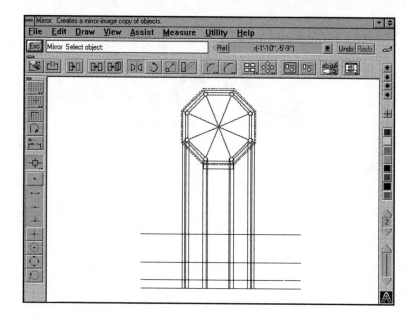

Figure 11.38:
Completing the setup.

Continuing the Elevation

*Choose **V**iew, then select the Zoom box tool*

Zoom into the drawing, as shown in figure 11.39.

Click on the Intersect attach tool

Use the Edit tools to remove the hidden lines shown in figure 11.39 and remove the railing line from between the columns shown in figure 11.40.

*Choose **E**dit, then select the Multi-copy tool*

`Multiple Copy Select object:` *Form a window selection box around the top of the railing*

`From point:` *Pick anywhere in the drawing area*

`To point:` **p(1.5,270)** ↵

`To point:` **p(2'3,270)** ↵

continues

375

To point: **p(1.5,270)** ↵

To point: *Press Esc (see fig. 11.40)*

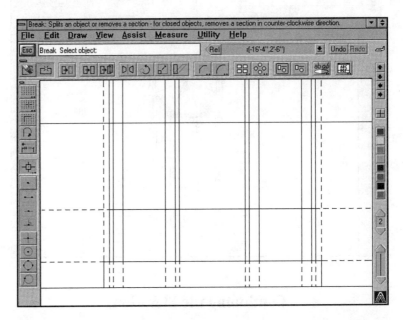

Figure 11.39:

Magnified view.

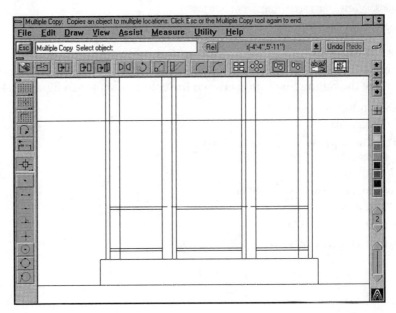

Figure 11.40:

Creating the rail.

Repeat the same series of steps to copy the 8' line down 12" in the
270-degree direction (see fig. 11.41).

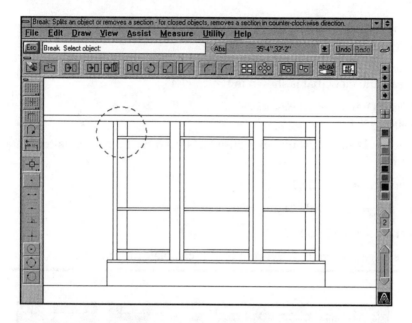

Figure 11.41:

Creating the
lattice trim.

Use the Edit tools to clean up the intersections at which the columns
meet the rails (see the hidden circle in figure 11.41).

Copy the 8' line up 4" and the platform base height line down 1.5" (see
fig. 11.41).

Choose **V**iew, *then select the Zoom X tool*

Choose OK *to accept the* Magnification *of .75*

Use the Pan tool to create a view that is similar to that in figure 11.42.

Choose **E**dit, *then select the Copy tool*

Copy the 4" offset line 4' in the 90-degree direction to form the highest
point of the roof.

Choose **D**raw, *then select the Line tool*

Construct lines from the corners of the overhang in the plan view to the
8' height line in elevation (see fig. 11.42).

continues

Choose **Edit**, then use the Break tool to trim off the line that represents the highest roof point. This forms a line that can be used as a midpoint for the roof planes.

Draw the four lines at which the roof planes intersect, as shown in figure 11.42.

Use the Edit tools to clean up the drawing, and use the Zoom tools to create the view that is shown in figure 11.43.

*Choose **D**raw, then double-click on the
Pattern Fill tool*

The final drawing shown in figure 11.44 used the following patterns and scales:

Roof = **ar-roof** scale:**5**

Railing = **plast** scale:**24** angle:**90**

Lattice = **ansi37** scale:**24**

Use these patterns or select your own to complete the drawing.

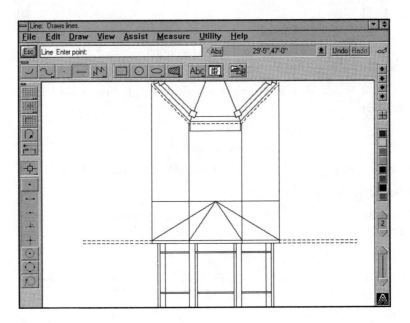

Figure 11.42:

Constructing the roof.

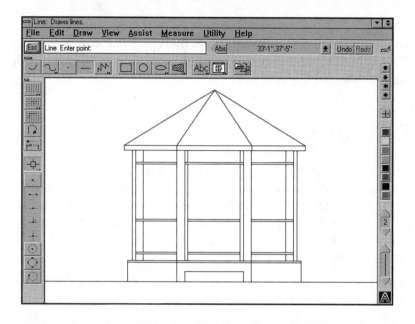

Figure 11.43:
The elevation view.

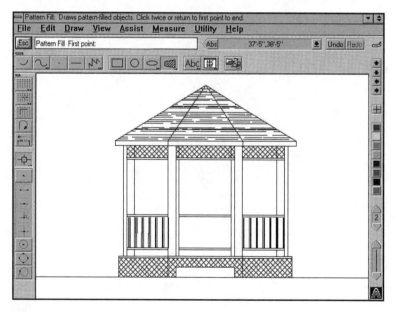

Figure 11.44:
The completed drawing.

Now you have completed the architectural plan and elevation. You can use the methods that were incorporated into producing these drawings on many different projects, from a 20-story building to a backyard birdhouse.

Summary

This chapter has shown you some of the advanced uses of AutoSketch. The ability to efficiently create production drawings may take some time for you to achieve while making the transition from the drafting board to the computer. The time you spend will pay off in the long run as you become more accustomed to the CAD environment.

In the next chapter, you will explore the methods used to customize the way you use AutoSketch.

Using Macros To Enhance AutoSketch Performance

A *macro* is a series of instructions that performs specific activities within a software package. AutoSketch automatically creates a macro by recording a series of actions you perform, or you can create and edit a macro as an ASCII text file.

Many different software applications have the capability to record and run macros. For example, a word processing program may contain a macro to format and begin a memorandum. A spreadsheet program may use a macro to read a data file and graph the results. Similarly, a CAD program, such as AutoSketch, has many good applications for macros.

The following list shows the advantages of using macros in AutoSketch:

- **Avoid repetitive operations.** As you become more familiar with applying AutoSketch to your specific needs, you perform repetitive sequences of operations. You can record these operations in a macro to be used whenever that sequence of operations is needed. This concept is similar to that of saving entities as parts.

- **Encourage uniformity.** If several people are working on similar projects in a company, macros ensure that all the CAD drawings are created uniformly.

- **Create complex operations.** After you have performed a complex operation in AutoSketch, you can save it as a macro (you do not have to remember how to repeat that operation in the future).

  Macros also are useful for providing productivity tools for less experienced users who need to perform special operations.

Recording and Playing a Macro

In AutoSketch, a macro is an ASCII text file that contains the sequence of commands to be executed when the macro is run. Several tools to control macros are found in the Utility toolbox.

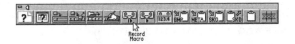

The Record Macro tool activates the recorder. Each tool, setting, or dialog box used while the recorder is turned on is automatically written to the macro file. When you choose the Record Macro tool, the Record Macro File dialog box, shown in figure 12.1, is activated. You can name your macro file in this dialog box.

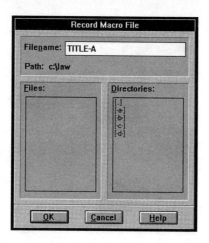

Figure 12.1:
Record Macro File dialog box.

 Following regular DOS conventions, the macro file name can contain up to eight characters. Remember also to specify the proper drive and directory for the macro file. AutoSketch automatically adds an MCR extension.

As soon as the Record Macro tool is activated, the tool icon changes and becomes the End Macro tool. The End Macro tool terminates the recording for the macro.

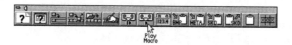

The Play Macro tool runs an existing macro. When you choose the Play Macro tool, the Play Macro File dialog box displays (see fig. 12.2), in which you select the macro you want to play.

In Chapter 8, you used an existing border drawing to begin a new drawing. The following exercise creates a macro to automatically draw a border and title block. You can use this same sequence to create macros for a variety of tasks. The Run Macro tool is then used in a new drawing file to run the macro.

Figure 12.2:

Play Macro File
dialog box.

Recording and Running a Macro

Begin a new drawing in AutoSketch.

Choose **U***tility, then the* Record Macro *tool*	Activates the Record Macro File dialog box
Type **TITLE-A** *in the* File**n**ame *text box (see fig. 12.1), and choose* **O**K	Names the macro file

Notice that the Record Macro tool is now the End Macro tool.

Choose **D***raw, then double-click on the* Polyline *tool*	Activates the Polyline Settings dialog box

Type **.05** *in the* Polyline Width *text box, choose the* Solid Fill *setting, and click on* **O**K

```
Polyline First point: 0,0 ↵
To point: r(10,0) ↵
To point: r(0,8) ↵
To point: r(-10,0) ↵
To point: r(0,-8) ↵
First point: r(6,0) ↵
To point: r(0,2) ↵
```

```
To point: r(4,0) ↵
To point: /LPOINT ↵
```

*Choose **U**tility, then the* End Macro tool   Terminates the recording of the macro

*Choose **F**ile, then **N**ew (do not save existing file)*

*Choose **U**tility, then the* Play Macro tool   Activates the Play Macro File dialog box, as shown in figure 12.2

Double-click on TITLE-A.MCR   Runs the macro

Running the macro draws the border and title block, as shown in figure 12.3.

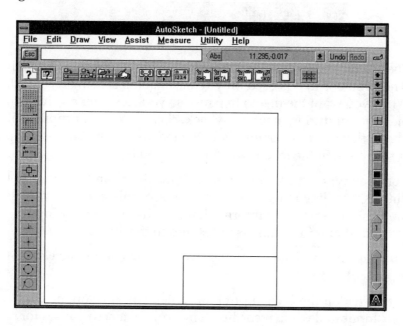

Figure 12.3:
The results of the TITLE-A macro.

Recording a macro is easy. First, plan your steps, and make sure the sequence is correct. Next, activate the Record Macro tool, name the macro, perform the sequence, and then choose the End Macro tool.

Playing a macro also is easy. Use the Play Macro tool to access the Play Macro File dialog box, and select the macro you want to execute.

Including User Input in a Macro

You can make macros more flexible and powerful by making the macro pause for user input. In the previous macro, you may have wanted to specify the width of the polyline while running the macro, for example. Perhaps you may not have wanted to place the lower left corner of the border at the 0,0 datum point. You can use the User Input tool to make the macro pause for user input.

The User Input tool is a little tricky—nothing appears to happen when you use it. It is used only while a macro is being recorded. When you want the macro to pause so you can enter a value or pick a point during macro playback, click on the User Input tool. This action places a command in the macro that enables user input at that point in the macro when it is played back.

Common types of user input include picking points, typing coordinates, or filling in text boxes. While recording a macro, you also must input the specific information after using the User Input tool, but that information is not stored in the macro.

AutoSketch offers the following two ways to choose the User Input tool:

- **Click on the User Input tool.** When you click on the User Input tool while recording a macro, the macro pauses for input at that same point when the macro is played back.

- **Press Ctrl+F10.** When you press and hold the Ctrl key and press the F10 key, the User Input tool is activated. This method is especially helpful when open dialog boxes do not allow toolboxes to be accessed.

The following exercise creates a drawing border macro that is much like the first one, except that user input specifies the polyline width and the lower left corner of the border.

Including User Input in a Macro

Begin a new drawing in AutoSketch.

Choose **U**tility, *then the* Record Macro *tool*	
Enter **TITLE-B** *in the* File**n**ame *text box*	
Choose **D**raw, *then double-click on the* Polyline *tool*	Activates the Polyline Settings dialog box
Press Ctrl+F10	Inserts a user input
Enter **.1** *in the* Polyline Width *text box*	
`Polyline First point:` *Choose* **U**tility, *then the* User Input *tool*	Specifies a user input
`Polyline First point: -3,-3` ↵	Specifies a tentative location
`To point: r(16,0)` ↵	
`To point: r(0,10)` ↵	
`To point: r(-16,0)` ↵	
`To point: r(0,-10)` ↵	Completes the border
Choose **V**iew, *then the* Zoom Full *tool*	Shows the entire border
Choose the Zoom X *tool, and enter* **.9** *in the* Magnification *text box*	Shows more area around the border
Choose **U**tility, *then the* End Macro *tool*	Ends the recording of the macro
Choose **F**ile, *then* **N**ew *(disregard the changes to the existing drawing)*	Opens a new drawing
Choose **U**tility, *then the* Play Macro *tool*	Activates the Play Macro File dialog box
Double-click on TITLE-B. MCR	Begins playing the macro
Enter **.1** *in the* Polyline Width *text box*	

continues

```
Polyline First point: -5,-5 ↵
```
Specifies the lower left corner of the border

The macro draws the border and then zooms the border, as shown in figure 12.4.

Figure 12.4:
The results of the TITLE-B macro.

Remember that when user inputs are called out while recording macros, tentative values also must be given to complete the macro.

In the last step of the macro—zooming to a .9x magnification—you must enter the **.9** scale factor, even if the dialog box already contains that value. That setting may be different the next time the macro is run, and the wrong magnification results if the scale has not been changed.

Writing and Editing Macros

The Record Macro, Run Macro, and User Input tools are simple to use, and they provide all the capability many users require. Similar to creating parts or generating DXF files, AutoSketch handles all the details of generating the macro file itself. The macro file is really a standard ASCII text file, however, which you can create or view on most word processors.

The best way to learn about macro files is to edit them with a text editor. Use a simple macro file that has been generated by AutoSketch, and then make some basic changes or additions to the text file. When you use the Record Macro tool, a complete macro must be recorded again if there are any changes. When you edit the ASCII text macro file itself, you can easily make only the changes you want.

 As with any type of batch file or subroutine, proper spelling and punctuation are important for good results. Pay special attention to spaces (or the lack of them) between words in a macro.

Figure 12.5 shows the TITLE-B.MCR file in Windows Write.

Even without understanding macro programming, you can follow through this text file because you know what the macro is supposed to do.

Beginning a Macro

Each macro file should begin with a heading that identifies the version of AutoSketch with which it was created. If the macro was written with the Record Macro tool, this line is automatically created, as in the first line of the macro in figure 12.5. The word at the beginning of that line—REM—indicates that the line is a *remark*; it is intended for information purposes only.

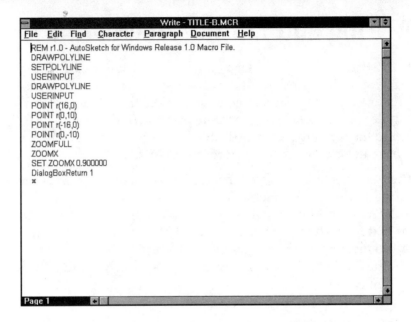

Figure 12.5:
The TITLE-B
macro.

 Macros may not be completely compatible in different versions of
AutoSketch because the tools and
commands may be different.

Understanding Macro Commands

To understand a macro file, you must know the special commands
used in the macro. AutoSketch uses the following special macro
commands to run the software from a text file (notice some of
these commands in the macro file in figure 12.5):

- **DialogBoxReturn.** Many AutoSketch tools activate dialog
  boxes, which must be closed before continuing with an
  operation. Notice that the last line of the macro in figure 12.5
  contains the DialogBoxReturn command, followed by a result
  of 1. The command has no spaces, but a space separates the
  command from the result or the required action. A result of 1

indicates Yes or OK, a result of 0 means Cancel, and a result of -1 indicates No or Modify.

- **Point.** The Point command often is used when drawing entities in a macro. Whenever a tool requires an X,Y point to be entered, such as the points needed for a polyline, the Point command is used—followed by the X and Y coordinates.

- **REM.** Remarks are useful for documenting the actions of a macro or for other information to be used by another person reading the macro. The REM command (or an apostrophe) causes AutoSketch to ignore any further text in that line while running the macro.

- **Set.** An important part of creating macros is controlling the system variables. Even though it may seem tedious, a well-written macro always addresses the system variables that are critical to the performance of the macro.

The TITLE-B macro sets the polyline width and the zoom-magnification factor. The proper format for the Set command is SET *variable-name value*. Notice the space between each of the three parts of the command. The value must be appropriate for the variable being addressed. AutoSketch has 140 variables that can be addressed in a macro. Table 12.1 is a partial list of these variables. (The *AutoSketch Reference Manual* has a complete list.)

Table 12.1   AutoSketch Variables for Macros

Variable Name	Data Type	Description
ARROWSIZE	Real	Dimension arrow size
ATTACH	Boolean	Attach mode on/off
ATTACHCENTER	Boolean	Attach to center on/off

continues

391

Table 12.1		continued
Variable Name	Data Type	Description
ATTACHEND	Boolean	Attach to endpoints on/off
ATTACHINTERSECTION	Boolean	Attach to intersection on/off
ATTACHMIDPOINT	Boolean	Attach to midpoint on/off
ATTACHNODE	Boolean	Attach to node point on/off
ATTACHPERPENDICULAR	Boolean	Attach to perpendicular on/off
ATTACHQUADRANT	Boolean	Attach to quadrant points on/off
ATTACHTANGENT	Boolean	Attach to tangent on/off
CHAMFERA	Real	Chamfer radius A
CHAMFERB	Real	Chamfer radius B
CHPCOLOR	Boolean	Change properties: change color
CHPDIMARROW	Boolean	Change properties: change dimension arrow
CHPDIMUNITS	Boolean	Change properties: change dimension units
CHPDIMTXTPT	Boolean	Change properties: change dimension-text placement
CHPFONT	Boolean	Change properties: change text font

Variable Name	Data Type	Description
CHPLAYER	Boolean	Change properties: change layer
CHPLINETYPE	Boolean	Change properties: change linetype
CHPPATFILL	Boolean	Change properties: change fill pattern
CHPPOLYWIDTH	Boolean	Change properties: change polyline width
CHPTEXT	Boolean	Change properties: change text size, alignment, and so on
COLOR	Integer	Color Number
CREATECLIPBOX	Boolean	Create a clip box during Print Settings command on/off
CREATEPRINTBOX	Boolean	Create a print box during Print Settings command on/off
CROSSHAIRS	Boolean	Crosshairs on/off
DECIPREC	Integer	Decimal precision
DIMARROW	Integer	Dimension arrow style: 0 = Standard 1 = Solid 2 = Tick 3 = Dot 4 = None
DIMTEXT	String	Dimension text
DIMNUMBER	Boolean	Numerical dimension on/off

continues

393

	Table 12.1 continued	
Variable Name	**Data Type**	**Description**
DIMTXTHEIGHT	Real	Dimension text height
DIMTXTALIGN	Boolean	Align dimension text with dimension line on/off
DIMTXTHORIZ	Boolean	Align dimension text horizontally on/off
DIMTXTABOVE	Boolean	Align dimension text above dimension line on/off
DIMTXTWITHIN	Boolean	Align dimension text within the dimension line on/off
DIMTXTLEADER	Boolean	Place dimension text on a leader line on/off
DRAWINGDIR	String	Drawing-directory name
DRAWINGFILENAME	String	Drawing-file name

- **Stop.** The Stop command terminates the macro. This command is useful for troubleshooting long macros or for using only the first part of a long macro.

- **String.** A *string* is alphanumeric data entered from the keyboard. When the String command is used, text is entered from the keyboard as a response to an AutoSketch tool, such as Quick Text.

Nonprintable characters are recorded as a backslash and their corresponding ASCII numerical values. A keyboard Enter, for example, is shown as \013. Consult your *DOS Reference Manual* for a complete list of ASCII codes.

- **UserInput.** A *user input pause* can be written into a macro or placed there with the User Input tool while recording a macro. The UserInput command enables the user to enter a point location or a value in a dialog box as the macro is running. (This command was used twice in the TITLE-B macro.)

Using AutoSketch Commands in Macros

As you draw in AutoSketch, all the tools are chosen from the toolboxes and menus. (You may even recognize a tool by its icon instead of by name.) When AutoSketch is being run from a macro, all the tools must be accessible as commands.

Table 12.2 contains all the AutoSketch commands that can be addressed from a macro. You probably recognize many of these commands because they are similar to the tool names. Notice that all the commands are one word, and that the prefix often indicates the toolbox or function of the tool.

Table 12.2	AutoSketch Commands
Command Name	*Function*
BoxArray	Activates the Box Array (Edit) tool
Break	Activates the Break (Edit) tool
Chamfer	Activates the Chamfer (Edit) tool

continues

Table 12.2   continued

Command Name	Function
ChangeProperty	Activates the Property (Edit) tool
Copy	Activates the Copy (Edit) tool
CopyBitmap	Activates the Copy Bitmap to Clipboard (Utility) tool
CopyMetafile	Activates the Copy to Metafile to Clipboard (Utility) tool
CopyObject	Activates the Copy to AutoSketch format (SKD) to Clipboard (Utility) tool
DrawAlignedDimension	Activates the Aligned Dimension (Measure) tool
DrawAngularDimension	Activates the Angular Dimension (Measure) tool
DrawArc	Activates the Arc (Draw) tool
DrawBox	Activates the Box (Draw) tool
DrawCircle	Activates the Circle (Draw) tool
DrawCurve	Activates the Curve (Draw) tool
DrawEllipse	Activates the Ellipse (Draw) tool
DrawHorizontalDimension	Activates the Horizontal Dimension (Measure) tool
DrawLeader	Activates the Leader Line (Measure) tool
DrawLine	Activates the Line (Draw) tool

Command Name	Function
DrawPart	Activates the Part (Draw) tool
DrawPatternFill	Activates the Pattern Fill (Draw) tool
DrawPoint	Activates the Point (Draw) tool
DrawPolyline	Activates the Polyline (Draw) tool
DrawQuickText	Activates the Quick Text (Draw) tool
DrawTextEditor	Activates the Text Editor (Draw) tool
DrawVerticalDimension	Activates the Vertical Dimension (Measure) tool
EditText	Activates the Text Editor (Edit) tool
Erase	Activates the Erase (Edit) tool
ExportDXF	Creates a DXF file of the current drawing
ExportSlide	Creates a Slide file of the current view
Fillet	Activates the Fillet (Edit) tool
Group	Activates the Group (Edit) tool
MeasureAngle	Activates the Angle (Measure) tool
MeasureArea	Activates the Area (Measure) tool
MeasureBearing	Activates the Bearing (Measure) tool
MeasureDistance	Activates the Distance (Measure) tool
MeasurePoint	Activates the Point (Measure) tool

continues

Table 12.2 continued	
Command Name	*Function*
Mirror	Activates the Mirror (Edit) tool
Move	Activates the Move (Edit) tool
MultipleCopy	Activates the Multiple Copy (Edit) tool
NewFile	Activates the New (File) command
OpenFile	Activates the Open (File) command
PartClip	Activates the Part Clip (File) tool
PasteClipboard	Activates the Paste from Clipboard (Utility) tool
Print	Prints the drawing
Quit	Exits AutoSketch
ReadDXF	Activates the Read DXF (File) command
Redo	Reverses the effect of the last Undo command
Redraw	Redraws the screen
RingArray	Activates the Ring Array (Edit) tool
Rotate	Activates the Rotate (Edit) tool
SaveFile	Saves the current drawing
SaveFileAs	Saves the current drawing as a new file name
Scale	Activates the Scale (Edit) tool

Command Name	Function
ScrollDown	Activates the Scroll Down button
ScrollLeft	Activates the Scroll Left button
ScrollRight	Activates the Scroll Right button
ScrollUp	Activates the Scroll Up button
SetAttach	Opens the Attachment Settings dialog box
SetBoxArray	Opens the Box Array Settings dialog box
SetChamfer	Opens the Chamfer Settings dialog box
SetColor	Opens the Color Settings dialog box
SetCurve	Opens the Curve Settings dialog box
SetDimension	Opens the Dimension Settings dialog box
SetDwgSettings	Opens the Drawing Settings dialog box
SetEllipse	Opens the Ellipse Settings dialog box
SetFillet	Opens the Fillet Settings dialog box
SetGrid	Opens the Grid/Snap/Limits Settings dialog box
SetLayer	Opens the Layer Settings dialog box
SetLimits	Opens the Grid/Snap/Limits Settings dialog box

continues

Table 12.2	continued
Command Name	**Function**
SetLineType	Opens the Line Type Settings dialog box
SetPartBase	Opens the Part Base Settings dialog box
SetPattern	Opens the Pattern Settings dialog box
SetPrintArea	Opens the Print Settings dialog box
SetPolyline	Opens the Polyline Settings dialog box
SetProperty	Opens the Property Settings dialog box
SetRingArray	Opens the Ring Array Settings dialog box
SetSelectionArea	Opens the Selection Area Settings dialog box
SetSnap	Opens the Grid/Snap/Limits Settings dialog box
SetText	Opens the Text Settings dialog box
SetUnits	Opens the Units Display Settings dialog box
ShowProperties	Opens the Show Properties dialog box
Stretch	Activates the Stretch (Edit) tool
ToggleArcMode	Toggles Arc mode
ToggleAttachMode	Toggles Attach mode

Command Name	Function
ToggleCrosshairs	Toggles the crosshairs cursor
ToggleDimSlide	Toggles Dimension Slide mode
ToggleFillMode	Toggles Fill mode
ToggleFrame	Toggles Curve Frame display
ToggleGrid	Toggles Grid display
ToggleOrthoMode	Toggles Ortho mode
ToggleSnap	Toggles Snap mode
Undo	Undoes the last operation
Ungroup	Activates the Ungroup (Edit) tool
ViewLastPrintBox	Activates the Last Print Box (View) tool
ViewLastView	Activates the Last View (View) tool
ViewPan	Activates the Pan (View) tool
ViewSlide	Displays a slide file
ZoomBox	Activates the Zoom Box (View) tool
ZoomFull	Activates the Zoom Full (View) tool
ZoomLimits	Activates the Zoom Limits (View) tool
ZoomX	Activates the Zoom X (View) tool

In some cases, either an AutoSketch command or a set variable can be used in a macro to change a setting. Some of these commands and variables are used in macros in the remaining part of this chapter.

Editing Macros

Existing macros can be modified by bringing up the macro file in a text editor and making the appropriate changes. Even the AutoSketch Text Editor is sufficient to write and modify macros.

The following exercise shows you how to modify the TITLE-B macro you created earlier in the chapter. The instructions to draw a title block are added, and a change block is inserted as a part.

A file called CHGBLK.SKD has been included in your \LAW directory for this exercise. A user-input command is used to locate the change block in the drawing. Figure 12.6 shows the additional lines that are added to the macro to perform these steps.

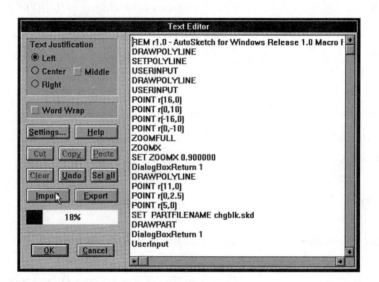

Figure 12.6:

Adding to the TITLE-B macro.

Editing a Macro

Open a new drawing in AutoSketch.

*Choose **D**raw, then the* Text Editor *tool*

`Text Editor Enter Point:` *Pick a point*   Activates the Text Editor

*Click on the **I**mport button*   Opens the Import Text File
dialog box

Enter \LAW\TITLE-B.MCR *in the* Filename *text box*	Imports the file into the Text Editor

Add the new lines of text, as shown in figure 12.6.

Choose Export	Opens the Export Text File dialog box
Enter \LAW\TITLE-B.MCR *in the* Filename *text box*	Exports the file with the same name
Choose Cancel *to leave the Text Editor*	
Choose No *so the changes are not saved in the drawing*	
Choose Utility, *then the* Play Macro tool	Opens the Play Macro File dialog box
Double-click on TITLE-B.MCR	Begins running the macro
Enter .1 *in the* Polyline Width *text box*	
Polyline First point: **0,0** ↵	Locates the lower left corner of border
Part To point: *Using the* End Point *attach tool, pick near* ① *(see fig. 12.7)*	Locates the change block in the corner

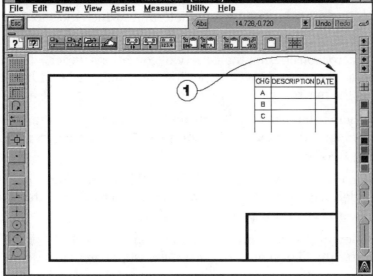

Figure 12.7:

Running the modified TITLE-B macro.

Using a familiar word processor, you soon will be editing, cutting, pasting, and combining macro files to perform many useful tasks. Plan ahead so that the names of the macros will be helpful in describing what the macro does.

A common practice is to experiment with a macro file in a window running concurrently with AutoSketch. Save the macro file before running it in AutoSketch, or the latest changes will not be read when the macro is played back.

Writing a Complete Macro

To avoid extensive editing and troubleshooting of new macro files, follow these steps when you write a macro:

- Assign a name for the macro that is consistent with your other macros and that shows what the macro will do.

- Write an outline, or flowchart, describing the sequence of the macro. This outline helps to determine which tools to use.

- Think about the settings that are critical to the success of the macro, considering the variety of conditions under which the macro may be run. These settings may have to be addressed in the macro.

- Try the steps in AutoSketch, and document each required tool (and the input that it requires). Determine where user inputs are needed.

- Finally, begin writing the macro. If the macro is long, consider playing it after each part is finished to be sure that the macro is working properly.

The following exercise involves writing a macro to add balloon labels to a detail drawing. A *balloon label* is a circle with a detail number inside it. The balloon is connected to the appropriate detail on the drawing with a curved line.

The three main components of the macro are created with the Circle, Quick Text, and Curve tools. User input is required for the balloon location, the detail number, and the curve location. In this macro, it is assumed that the user has the appropriate attach modes active.

The macro addresses the layer, color, linetype settings, and all the text settings in the beginning. Then the circle is drawn and the detail number added. Finally, the curve is drawn. Figure 12.8 shows the macro as it is typed into the AutoSketch Text Editor.

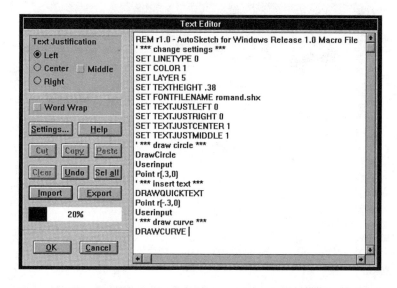

Figure 12.8:
The BALLOON macro in the Text Editor.

Writing the Balloon Macro

Open a new drawing in AutoSketch, and type the macro shown in figure 12.8 in the Text Editor.

Click on the **E***xport button* dialog box	Opens the Export Text File
Enter \LAW\BALLOON.MCR	Saves the file
Click on the **C***ancel button*	Exits the Text Editor

continues

*Choose **N**o when asked to save changes*	Does not update the existing drawing
*Choose **U**tility, then the* Play Macro *tool*	Opens the Play Macro File dialog box
Double-click on BALLOON.MCR	Runs the macro

`Circle center point:` *Pick a point near the center of the screen*

`Quick Text Enter text:` **5** ↵

`Curve First point:`

Pick several points to draw a curve similar to that shown in figure 12.9.

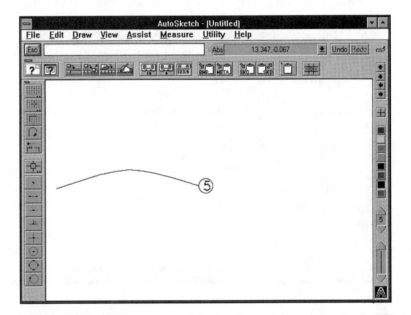

Figure 12.9:

The results of the BALLOON macro.

Several additional *comments* (lines starting with apostrophes) were added to the macro to make it easier to read. If you have any errors in your macro, the line number containing the error is shown in the error box to help find the problem. Watch for spelling or punctuation errors. If you want to change the macro, bring it up in any text editor, and make the changes. Then save the file, and try to run the macro again.

Using Macros Creatively

Macros help to automate AutoSketch operations in many ways. For special applications, macros can be run from DOS. This procedure requires a command that first runs Windows, then runs AutoSketch, and finally calls up a macro.

The format for this command is WIN sketch -Mfilename. The WIN statement runs Windows; the sketch statement runs AutoSketch; and the -M statement is a command to run a macro. The macro file name, without the extension, should immediately follow the -M (without a space).

 Running a macro from a DOS prompt works only if the proper path names and directories have been established. Otherwise, the Windows and AutoSketch files cannot be accessed with this command.

Another capability that makes AutoSketch ideal for extensive customization is the Button Editor tool. Custom tool buttons can be drawn or imported as captured images, and then assigned as existing toolboxes; or new toolboxes can be created with these buttons. Instead of using the Play Macro tool to run a macro, you can choose a macro's tool icon just like any other standard tool.

Complete instruction for using the Button Editor and editing toolboxes is beyond the scope of this book. These tools are documented in the AutoSketch Help utility.

Summary

To many users, learning an existing software application seems quite a challenge. Customizing that software package may seem out of reach to the average user. Remember that the software is written by programmers who probably do not know your business as well as you do; therefore, they have provided you with the tools to improve the software. You are probably the best candidate to modify AutoSketch to really meet your needs. If you talk to others who feel that a particular software package has significantly increased their productivity, there is a good chance that they have customized it.

If you have had experience in programming, or have customized other software, AutoSketch macros will be easy for you to learn. Remember to start with simple macros, and then to build upon them as your confidence increases. Plan your steps and document your results so that the project truly will be useful when it is completed.

After you have experimented with customizing CAD software, you may decide that it is more economical to purchase a third-party package for your software instead of creating it yourself.

Command
Reference

Command Reference

The following list defines the AutoSketch commands in alphabetical order. In this reference, you find the tool or command name, followed by the item's menu or toolbox location in parentheses. The items are listed as they appear when the SmartCursor passes over them.

 You can invoke many of these items by using *shortcut keys*. If a shortcut key is available, it is listed at the end of the description.

About AutoSketch... (Help)

Displays the AutoSketch release number, release date, registration number, name and company of the registered user, and copyright information. The information appears in a moveable window.

Align Dimension (Measure)

Provides a dimension between two points at any angle. AutoSketch draws the dimension string parallel to the line between the two points.

Angle (Measure)

Measures angles in the drawing. Pick a base point, then specify two different directions from that point. AutoSketch then displays the angle in an information box.

Angle Dimension (Measure)

Provides the angle between two nonparallel lines. The angle dimension consists of an arc, broken by the angle text in degrees. If the angle is small and the text does not fit inside the arc, AutoSketch places the dimension text outside the angle lines.

Arc (Draw)

Section of a circle specified by selecting a start point, a point on the arc, and an endpoint. Shortcut: Alt-F4.

Arc Mode (Assist)

Enables you to switch between selecting line points or arc points while you create polylines or pattern-fill boundaries. When Arc Mode is highlighted, you are creating arc points. Shortcut: Ctrl-F1.

Area (Measure)

Enables you to measure the area within a specified perimeter. You define the perimeter with a series of points. When you define the area, the first and last points must be the same. AutoSketch calculates the information, and displays the length of the perimeter and its enclosed area in an information box. When architectural units are active, the area is shown in square feet and square inches.

Attach (Assist)

Controls the way entities are selected while you draw and edit. The Icon button is highlighted when one or more of the Attach tools (Endpoint, Midpoint, Center, and so on) are active.

Double-click on the Icon button to display the Attachment Settings dialog box, which enables you to define the type of attachments you want to have active. Shortcut: Alt-F8.

Bearing (Measure)

Measures the bearing angle between two points. Two selected points that have the same Y coordinate have a bearing angle of 0 or 180 degrees, depending on which point is picked first. The angle appears in an information box.

Box (Draw)

Creates rectangles by defining opposite diagonal corners. You can define points by picking them on the screen with the cursor or by entering their coordinates from the keyboard. Shortcut: Ctrl-F7.

Box Array (Edit)

Creates multiple copies of objects in a rectangular pattern. Double-click on the Icon box to display the Box Array Settings dialog box. This dialog box enables you to set the number of rows, number of columns, and distances between each. The Fit option creates the array within a specified rectangle; you also can create arrays at any angle.

Break (Edit)

Erases part of an object, or breaks entities into two separate objects. Polylines, boxes, circles, and ellipses must have break points specified in a counterclockwise direction. Break does not work on pattern fills. Shortcut: F4.

Button Editor (Utility)

Enables you to create custom icon buttons. Buttons are saved as bit-map (BMP) files that are 27 pixels wide by 20 pixels high. The

Button Editor has its own limited drawing tools and color palette. After you create a button, it can be linked to a macro with the Toolbox Editor to create a new tool.

Center (Assist)

Picks the center point of a circle, ellipse, or arc. The Center tool cannot be used with the Quadrant tool. When picking the center of an arc, Center is the only Attach tool that can be active. When the tool is active, both the Attach tool icon and the Center icon are highlighted.

Chamfer (Edit)

Creates a beveled edge at the intersection of two lines. Double-click on the tool to bring up the Chamfer Settings dialog box, which enables you to specify how far from the intersection the chamfer should start. The line created by a chamfer is like any other line; you can modify it unless it is a polyline, box, or pattern-fill border. A chamfer line on a polyline or pattern-fill boundary becomes part of the polyline. If a box is chamfered, it turns the whole entity into a polyline.

Circle (Draw)

Enables you to create a circle by picking a center point, then specifying a radius (the distance between the center point and a point on the circle). You can use the mouse or the keyboard to define the two points.

Contents (Help)

Displays an alphabetical list of AutoSketch topics for easy reference. Each menu, toolbox, tool, dialog box, button, and feature is listed as a topic. Double-click on any topic to display information in a scrollable text window.

Copy (Edit)

Enables you to copy entities from one position on the screen to another. The copied objects have the same properties as the original objects. Shortcut: F6.

 Use the Attach tools for more precision when specifying From and To points.

Copy Bitmap (Utility)

Enables you to specify an area of the graphics window to copy to the Clipboard as a BMP file. Although you cannot paste a bit map into an AutoSketch drawing, most popular Windows programs accept files in a BMP format.

Copy Metafile (Utility)

Enables you to copy objects in your drawing area to the Clipboard in a metafile format. Although you cannot paste a metafile into an AutoSketch drawing, many Windows programs accept files in a metafile format.

Copy Objects (Utility)

Enables you to copy objects in your drawing area to the Clipboard in an AutoSketch format. You can paste these objects from the Clipboard into an AutoSketch drawing.

Create Toolbox (Utility)

Creates a custom toolbox and SketchTools. When you pick the icon, the Toolbox Editor dialog box appears. You can fill the empty toolbox with existing tools or with custom tools you create using the Button Editor. The dialog box explains the way to create a new toolbox. You can create many toolboxes, save them on the hard drive as TBX files, then use them in later drawing sessions. After you create and save a new toolbox, its name appears in the menu bar next to <u>H</u>elp.

Curve (Draw)

Creates smooth curves. After you pick control points that define a frame, AutoSketch fits a curve into the frame. A *frame point* works like a magnet that pulls on the curve: the more control points in an area, the more the curve is stretched toward the points. The curve connects to the first and last point of the frame, which remains invisible unless you turn on the Frame tool. Edit the curve by editing the frame. Double-click on the icon to display the Curve Settings dialog box. It controls the way in which all curves appear in the drawing area. Drawing Segments specifies the number of segments used to display the curve; more segments make smoother curves, but increase the time needed to redraw the screen.

Dim Slide (Assist)

Enables you to reposition the dimension text parallel to the dimension string line. When Dim Slide is turned off, you can move the dimension text in any direction. The tool must be activated before you can select the text you want to edit.

Distance (Measure)

Displays the distance between two points in current units. The calculated distance appears in an information box, but is not added to the drawing.

Drawing Settings (Utility)

Displays a list of settings in a dialog box. These settings control the way many of the tools work. You can control these settings through other tools, but Drawing Settings enables you to define many settings in one place.

Edit Toolbox (Utility)

Enables you to edit or customize existing toolboxes by adding, deleting, or rearranging tools. When you pick this tool, a dialog box explains the editing procedure. When you save a modified toolbox, the changes take effect immediately. A newly created toolbox appears on the menu bar next to <u>H</u>elp. If you want to change a toolbox back to its original state, go to its control menu, and choose <u>R</u>eset Toolbox from <u>E</u>dit options.

Ellipse (Draw)

Enables you to draw ellipses by using one of three methods. Double-click on the icon to display a dialog box that includes the following three options:

- **Center and Both Axes.** Enables you to specify the center point and the horizontal axis, followed by the vertical axis. The *axis distance* is one-half the axis length. This method is the default.

- **Axis and Planar Rotation.** Prompts you for the center point, then the horizontal axis, followed by the rotation around the major axis. The last point does not have to lie on the ellipse.

- **Two Foci and Point.** Enables you to specify the two foci points and a point on the ellipse.

End Macro (Utility)

Tells AutoSketch that you are finished defining the macro. This tool appears in place of Record Macro in the toolbox while you are creating a macro.

End Point (Assist)

Enables you to select the endpoints of any entity. When the tool is active, both the Attach tool icon and the End Point icon are highlighted.

417

When two entities meet, there is always an endpoint (except with circles and ellipses), but there is not always an intersection.

Erase (Edit)

Removes entities from a drawing. You can use a selection box to select more than one entity, and use the Undo button (or F2) if you make a mistake. If entities are directly on top of one another, AutoSketch removes the entity created last. Shortcut: F3.

Exit (File)

Enables you to quit your drawing session. If you have made changes since the last save, a dialog box asks if you want to save them. Choose Yes to save the changes. If you are working on a new file that has never been saved, the Save dialog box appears. Select No to close AutoSketch. Choose Cancel to quit the exiting process. Shortcut: Alt-F4.

Export DXF (File)

Saves the current drawing to the hard drive in AutoDesk DXF format. The current drawing's file name appears in the Filename text box in the Export DXF dialog box. To accept the file name, choose OK. Depending on the complexity, saving the DXF file can take some time.

When exporting DXF files, turn off the Fill tool if your drawing contains complex pattern fills. Pattern fills explode into individual entities during the exporting process, and can create particularly large data files.

Export Slide (File)

Creates a slide file of the current drawing area. Making a slide file is similar to taking a snapshot of the screen. You cannot modify or edit a slide file. The slide file is saved to the hard drive with an SLD extension. *See also* View Slide.

Fill (View)

Enables you to turn off a pattern fill or solid color inside a pattern-fill boundary or a thick polyline. Turning off the fill only hides the information, it does not remove it. (The pattern-fill boundary remains visible on the screen.) Drawings with fills turned off regenerate and print faster. When you turn the fill back on, the patterns and solid colors return.

Fillet (Edit)

Creates an arc between two intersecting lines, arcs, circles, or any combination of the three. You can select the two objects to fillet individually or by using a selection box. If any of the objects is a circle, the fillet arc is created through tangent points on the circles using the current radius setting. AutoSketch warns you if it cannot create the fillet because the radius is too large for the selected objects. If you fillet a polygon, box, or pattern-fill border, the fillet radius takes on the properties of the selected object.

Like a chamfered entity, a filleted box becomes a polyline. If you fillet a thickened polyline, the thickness information is not transferred to the fillet arc. The Property(Change) tool thickens the fillet arc to match the polyline. Double-click on the Fillet icon to display the Fillet Setting dialog box, which enables you to specify the fillet radius.

Frame (View)

Enables you to show or hide the frame that defines a curve or specifies the boundary of a pattern fill. *Curve frames* are line segments and control points that define the curve. To modify a curve, you must edit its control points. You do not need to display the frame to reshape the curve. By default, the frame is off. Even if the frame appears in the drawing area, however, it does not print.

Game (Utility)

Enables you to play a game similar to Tic-Tac-Toe. The object of the game is to place four Xs in a horizontal, vertical, or diagonal line while preventing AutoSketch from placing four Os in a similar fashion. You also can win by placing the last mark at the top of a column. If you quit in the middle of a game, the current state of the game is saved until you exit the program or return to play again.

Grid (Assist)

Graphic equivalent to graph paper. The grid intersections are represented by a series of dots, which appear only on the screen. You cannot select or print them because they are not entities. Double-click on the Icon button to display the Grid/Snap/Limits dialog box, which enables you to adjust the grid spacing. When the Icon button is highlighted, the grid is on and is displayed to the current drawing limits. Shortcut: Alt-F6. *See also* Snap.

Group (Edit)

Enables you to group objects together so that AutoSketch treats them as one entity. You can add up to 1000 entities to a single group. You then can group groups together to form a *nested group*. You can nest a group up to eight levels deep. When objects are grouped, the entities retain their own individual properties, even though the group is treated as one object. Objects in a group cannot be chamfered, filleted, or broken until they are ungrouped. Entities in a group have their own control points, so the Attach tools affect each entity in a group. Shortcut: Alt-F9.

Hide Pop-ups (View)

Enables you to hide or show toolboxes and windows that are floating in the drawing area. Does not hide the current toolbox that is located in the main toolbox area or to the right and left sides of the screen. When Hide Pop-ups is selected, the tool name is switched to Show Pop-ups.

Hide Toolboxes (View)

Hides or displays all currently open toolboxes and pop-up windows. When you pick the Hide Toolboxes tool, it switches to Show Toolboxes. Use this tool to temporarily expand the size of the drawing area. Choose any toolbox in the menu bar to make it reappear.

Horiz. Dimension (Measure)

Creates a dimension that calculates the horizontal distance between two points. After you select the two points, AutoSketch prompts you for a dimension line parallel to the horizontal. The dimension measures the horizontal length only. If the dimension text does not fit between the extension lines, AutoSketch moves the arrowheads and text outside the lines. If the text is too small to read, use the Property(Change) tool to increase the text size.

 Do not attempt to dimension a vertical line with a horizontal dimension—the result is zero.

Import DXF... (File)

Enables you to insert a DXF file into the current drawing. *DXF* is a popular drawing exchange format that enables CAD users of different packages to pass files to one another. Any imported file becomes part of the current drawing.

If you want to use the DXF file as a drawing, start a new drawing, then import the DXF file. After you select the file to import, another dialog box asks: Explode Large Blocks and/or Import Visible Attributes? Because AutoSketch is limited to eight nested groups and groups are limited to 1000 objects, the capability to control the imported DXF is crucial. Depending on the complexity of the DXF file to be imported, the importing process can take some time.

 If AutoSketch encounters objects in the DXF file that it does not recognize, it ignores them. DXF files from programs other than AutoDesk can be unpredictable, so be prepared for possible surprises (large arcs, missing text or entities, unreadable files, and so on).

Intersect (Assist)

Grabs the point at which two entities meet or cross. Like the other Attach tools, the icon box is highlighted when the Intersect tool is active.

Last Print Box (View)

Displays the portion of the drawing contained within the print box. If the drawing has more than one print box, AutoSketch displays the last print box you defined. Like other entities, you can erase print boxes or place them on an invisible layer. If you erase the last print box, AutoSketch uses the one you created prior to the last one.

Last View (View)

Displays the last view defined by the Pan or Zoom tools. You can click on the tool repeatedly to switch between the current and previous views. Shortcut: F9.

Leader (Measure)

Points to an object in the drawing, and enables you to include notation describing the object. The arrowhead at the beginning and the text string at the end of the leader are optional. The current dimension settings define the arrow type and the text style. The leader, arrowhead, and text string are three separate, editable entities. Double-click on Leader to display the Dimension Settings dialog box.

Line (Draw)

Enables you to create line segments by defining the two endpoints of the line. If you want to create a series of connected lines, use the Polyline tool. You can define endpoints by using the cursor or by entering coordinates from the keyboard. All current properties are applied to the line (linetype, color, layer). Shortcut: Alt-F1.

Midpoint (Assist)

Selects the middle point of an entity. Like the other Attach tools, the icon box is highlighted when the Midpoint tool is active. Circles, ellipses, and text do not have any recognizable midpoints.

Mirror (Edit)

Enables you to create a mirror-image copy of an object. AutoSketch creates a copy of the original on either side of an invisible mirror line. AutoSketch asks you to specify the mirror line's endpoints. The angle at which the two points are picked determines the orientation of the mirror-image copy. Shortcut: Ctrl-F3.

 Text is not affected by the Mirror tool. It always reads from left to right. Blocks of multiple text lines can be affected, however. Depending on the way you select the mirror line, for instance, the first line in a text block may be the last in the mirrored copy. A left-justified text block may become right-justified in the mirrored copy.

Move (Edit)

Changes the location of an entity or group of objects in the drawing. You are prompted to provide a From point and a To point, which serve as reference points for AutoSketch as it moves the objects. You can specify points by using the cursor or by entering coordinates from the keyboard.

Multi-copy (Edit)

Copies one or more objects to several points on the screen. The copied objects have the same properties as the original objects. After you establish the original From and To points, AutoSketch uses the last point specified as the new From point. If you make a mistake and click on the Undo button, AutoSketch deletes all copies created during the multicopy operation but leaves the original objects intact.

New (File)

Starts a new drawing. AutoSketch calls the drawing Untitled until you save the file and assign a name to it. If you are working on a drawing that you have not saved, and you select the New command, AutoSketch prompts you to save your work.

Node Point (Assist)

Snaps to points on text objects or to entities created by using the Point tool. For single-line text, it locates endpoints at the bottom of the string of text. For multiple-line text blocks, Node Point locates the endpoints of the first line of text in the block. Like the other Attach tools, the icon box is highlighted when the Node Point tool is active.

Open... (File)

Opens existing SKD files on any drive in any directory. When you select the Open command, an Open Drawing File dialog box appears with small drawings of each file in an icon box. To open the files, you can do the following:

- Double-click on the drawing icon box.

- Click on the drawing icon box, then choose OK.

- Select the file name from the Active Filename list box, then choose OK.

If you are in the middle of an unsaved drawing session and select Open, AutoSketch prompts you to save your work.

Open Toolbox (Utility)

Enables you to open an existing custom toolbox. Click on this tool to display the Open Toolbox dialog box, which shows you the TBX files saved to disk.

Ortho (Assist)

Restricts the cursor movement to horizontal and vertical directions from the last point specified. In other words, you can draw or modify objects only in 0-, 90-, 180-, and 270-degree directions. When Ortho is active, the icon box is highlighted. Shortcut: Alt-F5.

Pan (View)

Retains the current magnification as you move around the drawing area. By picking a reference point and the new destination point, you can alter the view of the drawing to the two points specified. You also can pan by using the scroll buttons in the vertical status bar on the right side of the graphics window. Shortcut: F8.

Part (Draw)

Inserts parts into the current drawing. A *part* is any SKD drawing or portion of a drawing that has been saved. When you choose the Part tool, a dialog box appears, showing icon boxes for all available parts. You can change directories or drives to locate needed parts.

To open a file, double-click on the part icon box; click on it, and choose OK; or select it from the Active Filename list box, and choose OK. The Insertion Options in the lower right corner of the dialog box enable you to rotate the part when you insert it. If this option is not checked, the part is inserted in the orientation in which it was created.

Part Clip... (File)

Enables you to create parts that contain one or more objects from the current drawing. Parts are saved to the hard drive as SKD files, and can be opened and modified like any other drawing. When you define a part, AutoSketch prompts you to select the objects you want to include in the part and the part-base location. If you do not specify the part-base location, the default is 0,0. You can change the part-base location by using the Drawing Settings tool.

Paste Objects (Utility)

Pastes the contents of the Clipboard into the current drawing. The Clipboard must contain SKD-formatted information. If the Clipboard contains metafiles or bit-mapped graphics, you cannot paste them into an AutoSketch drawing. *See also* Copy Object.

Pattern Fill (Draw)

Creates closed polygons and circles filled with user-specified patterns. The default pattern is a crosshatch with horizontal and vertical lines. You create a pattern-filled object by defining its boundary using arcs and line segments. The Arc Mode tool enables you to switch between arcs and straight-line segments while creating the boundary line. After you define the pattern style and boundary, AutoSketch displays a dialog box with three buttons:

- **Accept**. Uses the current information, and inserts the pattern fill.

- **Modify**. Enables you to adjust the pattern style (type, scale, rotation, and alignment point).

- **Cancel.** Quits the pattern-fill process without creating the fill.

A *pattern-fill boundary* can have up to 200 control points. Arcs only use two points (endpoints) instead of three, toward the total of 200. If a pattern fill has already been created, you can edit the boundary by using any Edit tool. You must, however, edit the pattern style by using the Property tool. The complexity of pattern fills within a drawing can affect the time it takes for AutoSketch to regenerate the screen or print the file.

The Fill tool switches between displaying the pattern fills or just the boundary. When you double-click on the Icon button, the

Pattern Settings dialog box appears. All available patterns are shown as icon boxes. Directly below the icons is the Pattern Options box. Pattern Options affects the following settings:

- **Angle**. Changes the angle of the pattern. The default angle appears in the Pattern icon box.

- **Scale.** Changes the scale of the pattern. You almost always need to adjust the pattern, based on the scale of the drawing.

- **Boundary.** Determines whether or not a boundary is drawn on the screen. If this option is not checked, the boundary still exists, but it is not visible.

- **Double Hatch Area**. Applies only to the default crosshatch pattern.

- **Pattern Alignment Point**. The location at which AutoSketch begins drawing the pattern. The default is 0,0.

Perpendicular (Assist)

Enables you to draw a normal from a point to an object. A *normal* is created by a line that forms a 90-degree angle between an object and another point at the attachment point. This tool draws a perpendicular line to or from an object. All other Attach tools (except Tangent) take precedence over Perpendicular.

Perpendicular requires you to pick two points before you form the attachment because AutoSketch needs a second point to calculate the normal. Like the other Attach tools, the icon box is highlighted when the Perpendicular tool is active.

Play Macro (Utility)

Plays back a macro that is saved to the hard drive. *Macros* are a series of prerecorded actions you can create to increase productivity. Macros are saved with an MCR extension; you can edit them in DOS.

Point (Draw)

Creates points. *Points* are entities; they have a position but no size. A point prints on your drawing by using the smallest dot that your printer can print. You can select points by using the Node Point Attach tool.

Point (Measure)

Enables you to display the exact coordinates of any point in your drawing. If you want to know the position of the endpoint of a certain line, highlight the Endpoint tool, and choose Point. After you pick the line, an information box displays the exact X,Y coordinates of the endpoint on the line.

Polyline (Draw)

Creates a series of connected arcs and line segments as one entity. Unlike some other entities, polylines can have width. You can fill that width with a solid or any available pattern. The Fill tool controls whether or not the width fill is visible. If the width is zero, a polyline looks like any other entity on the screen.

If a polyline has width, it cannot have a linetype other than solid. If a wide polyline is chamfered or filleted, the new line or arc does not have the same width information until you utilize the Property tool in the Edit toolbox. You cannot fillet polylines to other entities, but the intersections within the polyline are automatically mitered to produce a smooth corner. Double-click on the icon box to display the Polyline Settings dialog box. From this dialog box, you can specify the width and fill type.

Preferences (Utility)

Tells AutoSketch in which directory to store the Undo file. The Undo file stores all the changes in the drawing since the last save. It also controls whether or not selection sets are highlighted. When you are editing, large selection sets take time to highlight; by removing the check mark in the dialog box, selection sets do not highlight.

Although this option saves time, novice users should leave the highlights turned on because selected entities are easier to control when you can see the objects that have been selected. This dialog box also enables you to disable the Undo button on the horizontal status bar.

Print (File)

Enables you to quickly print a drawing to a printer or a file. If you are printing to a printer, AutoSketch creates one copy at a scale that fits on the paper, by default. Shortcut: F11.

Detailed printer settings are fully explained in Chapter 6.

Print Settings (File)

Displays a dialog box that enables you to specify the way the drawing is printed. All the options are related, so you must take care when determining the print method.

The printing discussion in Chapter 6 provides you with more information on printing options.

Property(Change) (Edit)

Enables you to change the properties of existing objects. Double-click on this command to open a dialog box, which you can use to modify any desired property. If a check mark appears next to the item in the list, that item reflects the current property settings. If, for example, you do not want to change the linetype, but you need to adjust the color, deselect the line type. Click on any of the property buttons to examine the current setting of that particular property.

Quadrant (Assist)

Selects an arc or circle at the four points corresponding to 0, 90, 180, or 270 degrees. Like the other Attach tools, the icon box is highlighted when the Quadrant tool is active.

Quick Help (Help)

Displays a short description of the item in the title bar at the top of the screen when you move the cursor over a tool or a button in the graphics window. By default, Quick Help is turned on. An invaluable tool for the novice user.

Quick Text (Draw)

Creates a single line of text, up to 256 characters long, with the current text settings. Each additional line of text is its own entity. The Text Editor in the Draw toolbox enables you to select the text and edit it within a separate window. After you create the text, you also can change the font, width, rotation, and so on by using the Property(Change) tool.

Read Me (Help)

Explains the latest developments that might not have been included in the manuals at the time of its release. You should read this file.

Record Macro (Utility)

Records the actions that create a macro file. Macros help you to increase your productivity by recording a series of often-used command strings.

The macro records the movement of the cursor, so be careful when you construct it. If you create a macro that turns on the the Snap tool, for example, the macro might actually turn off the tool if it currently is turned on.

Redraw (View)

Refreshes the screen. When editing a drawing, overlapping entities that are moved leave temporary gaps in the objects. Redraw assures you that the entities are indeed intact. You also can re-draw the screen by clicking on the Autodesk logo in the lower right corner. You can perform a redraw at any time—even in the midst of using a tool.

Ring Array (Edit)

Creates multiple copies of an object around a center point. You can specify whether the copied objects stay in the same orientation as the original or are rotated perpendicular to the center point. Each of the copied objects is an individual object. Double-click on the Icon button to display the Ring Array Settings dialog box. This dialog box enables you to specify the numbers of objects to create, the angle to cover, the center point of the array, and the objects' rotation (if any).

Rotate (Edit)

Enables you to change the orientation of an object, relative to the horizontal and vertical axes. If you use the keyboard to specify the center point and rotation angle, no restrictions apply. If you use the cursor to pick the points, however, the Ortho and Snap tools limit the angles and center-point definition. If associative dimen-sioning is turned on, the horizontal and vertical dimensions might change. Shortcut: Ctrl-F5.

Save (File)

Copies the file to your hard or floppy drive. If the current drawing has a file name, AutoSketch quickly updates the file and creates a backup (BAK) file. You can rename backup files as SKD files if you want to use them in AutoSketch.

If you are saving the drawing for the first time, you must supply AutoSketch with a file name before it can save the drawing. The drawing is saved as an SKD file with all the current settings activated. A save clears the Undo file buffer, because you cannot Undo immediately after a save. Shortcut: F12.

For best results, learn to save your work often. If your system crashes or you make a mistake, you can easily retrieve most of your work without losing much time.

Save As (File)

Enables you to save the current drawing under a new file name. By using this strategy, AutoSketch creates a new file based on the original while leaving the original intact. The check box at the bottom of the dialog box enables you to save to the DOS version of AutoSketch.

Scale (Edit)

Enables you to reduce or enlarge an object to any size. *Scaling* uniformly changes the object's vertical and horizontal directions. The specified base point affects the direction of the scale. If the base point is selected on the left side of the object, for example, the object's size increases to the right. Shortcut: Ctrl-F6.

Search (Help)

Provides you with a reference tool for information on AutoSketch tools and topics. By specifying a key word, or highlighting one in the list and clicking on Show Topics, topics related to the search criteria specified appear. If you want to read more about a topic, double-click on the topic. AutoSketch then displays a text file on the selected topic. The user can edit or print this text file. *See also* Contents.

Show Clipboard (Utility)

Displays the contents of the Clipboard. If the objects are SKD parts, you can paste them directly into the drawing. Bit maps and metafiles cannot be pasted back into AutoSketch. The Clipboard appears on top of all windows that might be open in the graphics window.

Show Properties (Measure)

All entities created in AutoSketch have *properties*, which include color, linetype, and layer. Polylines also can have width. When you draw an object, that object takes on the current default property settings of the drawing. You can modify object properties using the Property(Change) tool.

SmartCursor (Help)

Displays the name of the tool or button the cursor is touching in the graphics window. By default, the SmartCursor is on. *See also* Quick Help.

Snap (Assist)

Restricts the cursor's movements to an invisible grid that you define. When Snap is active, the cursor jumps from point to point on the snap interval, and displays a small + next to the cursor. The Grid tool helps to define the points of the snap interval, particularly if the grid and snap intervals are equal. The grid, however, does not have to be turned on to use the snap, and vice versa.

Double-clicking on the icon box opens the Grid/Snap/Limits dialog box. The default sets the grid equal to the snap, so if you change either spacing, they both change accordingly. If you deselect Grid=Snap, you can adjust these options independently, and they do not have to be based on a square grid size.

 Snap sometimes interferes with entity selection. If the snap is set larger than the current view, the cursor disappears because it is jumping from interval points outside the drawing area.

Stretch (Edit)

Enables you to grab control points on an object and distort its shape. If you cross one-half of a rectangle using the Stretch tool, you can drag the two control points from inside the selection box to a new point on the screen. The selection box always operates as a crosses box during a stretch operation. If unwanted entities are included in the crosses box, those entities do not change, as long as you do not select their control points. You might find the Ortho tool useful as you perform stretch operations. Shortcut: F7.

 You cannot stretch circles, ellipses, or points.

Tangent (Assist)

Locates tangent points on arcs, ellipses, circles, polylines, and pattern-fill boundaries. An object tangent to a circle touches the circle at exactly one point. Like the other Attach tools, the icon box is highlighted when the Tangent tool is active.

Text (View)

Increases redraw speed. When Text is turned off, AutoSketch replaces the text string with a rectangle that approximates the size of the text. Remember, the text is not replaced—it is temporarily hidden, and a rectangle takes its place.

Text Editor (Draw and Edit)

Creates or edits text in a drawing. The text editor in the Draw toolbox enables you to create blocks, or multiple lines of text, and import ASCII text files; the text editor in the Edit toolbox enables you to modify the text and text settings. When the tool is selected in either toolbox, a scrollable editing screen appears.

The text editor in the Draw toolbox imports only ASCII text files fewer than 2,048 characters; any additional characters are truncated. Similarly, you can export text to an ASCII text file. The capability to import or export text is useful for notes and specifications.

See Chapter 6 for a detailed description of the text options.

Ungroup (Edit)

Reverses the effects of the Group tool. You can group objects together as one entity; at some point, however, you might want to edit the group. Perform an ungroup, do the modifications, then regroup the objects.

User Input (Utility)

Pauses the macro recording for user input. You can pause the macro, for example, to enable the user to pick a center point of a circle before the macro proceeds.

Using Help (Help)

Provides general information about the Windows help commands. It does not contain any information specific to AutoSketch.

Vert. Dimension (Measure)

Creates a dimension that calculates the vertical distance between two points. After you select the two points, AutoSketch prompts you for a dimension line parallel to the vertical edge of the screen. The dimension measures only the vertical dimension. If the dimension text does not fit between the extension lines, AutoSketch moves the arrowheads and text outside the lines. If the text is too small to read, use the Property(Change) tool to increase the text size. Do not attempt to dimension a horizontal line with a vertical dimension—the result is always zero.

View Slide (File)

Enables you to display SLD files created by using the Export Slide command. The slide appears over the current drawing, but it does not alter the drawing beneath it. To remove the slide from the drawing area, perform a redraw or use any zoom tool that refreshes the screen. The slide is just a temporary display and cannot be edited in AutoSketch.

Zoom Box (View)

Enables you to zoom in or magnify a drawing by enclosing an area in a zoom box. By selecting the opposite diagonal corners of a box, AutoSketch zooms into the specified area. To return to the previous view, select the Last View tool. Shortcut: F10.

Zoom Full (View)

Zooms out to the extents of the drawing. The *extents* are defined by the outermost edges of all the entities in the drawing, whether or not they are contained within the drawing limits.

Zoom Limits (View)

Zooms to the current limits of the drawing. If objects are outside the limits, they are not included. The *limits* is the area that the grid covers when it is active.

Zoom X (View)

Enables you to zoom by a magnification factor relative to the current view. If the magnification factor is .75, for example, the current view is reduced 75%. If the magnification factor is 2, the current view is two times larger. Numbers fewer than one zoom in; numbers greater than one zoom out.

Index

Symbols

[..] dots in brackets, 89
30/60/90-degree triangle, 282

A

About AutoSketch... command (Help menu), 411
absolute coordinates, 98, 144-146
accessing, tools, 24-25
Accessories program group, 73
Active Filename text box, 228
Aerial View, 91, 158-160
Align Dimension tool, 195-196, 412
alphabet of lines, 44-45
Alt (Alternate) key, 60
Alt-F1 key combination (Line), 423
Alt-F4 key combination (Exit), 418
Alt-F5 key combination (Ortho), 425
Alt-F6 key combination (Grid), 420
Alt-F8 key combination (Attach), 413
Alt-F9 key combination (Group), 420
Alternate (Alt) key, 60
AM/FM cassette recorder, drawing, 245-279
American National Standards Institute, *see* ANSI
Angle Dimension tool, 197-198, 412
Angle tool, 412
angles
    baseline, box array, 269
    determining, 265

pattern, 256
polar-coordinate, 149
ANSI (American National Standards Institute), drawing-format requirements, 40
application software, 83
applications
    architectural
        elevations, creating, 371-380
        layer/linetype specifications, 362-363
        octagonal plan, drawing, 363-371
        plans/elevations, designing, 361-363
    drawing, features, 41-44
    multiple, running, 81-83
Arc mode, 357
Arc Mode tool, 251-254, 258, 412, 426
Arc tool, 32-33, 100-101, 341, 412
architectural applications
    elevations, creating, 371-380
    layer/linetype specifications, 362-363
    octagonal plan, drawing, 363-371
    plans/elevations, designing, 361-363
architectural drawings, 41, 134
architectural units format, 129-130
arcs
    creating, 419
    drawing, 100-101, 111-112, 177-178, 341
        isometric, 287-288
    in polylines, 251-254

U

WANT MORE INFORMATION?

CHECK OUT THESE RELATED TITLES:

	QTY	PRICE	TOTAL

Inside AutoCAD, Release 12. Completely revised for AutoCAD 12, this book-and-disk set is your complete guide to understanding AutoCAD. You won't find another book about AutoCAD this comprehensive, detailed, and easy to use. That is why *Inside AutoCAD Release 12* is the world's #1 selling AutoCAD title—successfully teaching more people to use AutoCAD than any other AutoCAD title! ISBN: 1-56205-055-9.
(Also available for **Inside AutoCAD Release 12 for Windows**, ISBN: 1-56205-146-6, $37.95)

_____ $37.95 _____

Maximizing AutoCAD Release 12. Filled with expert techniques for customizing AutoCAD, including demonstrations of ways to create a complete, customized AutoCAD system. Extensive coverage of menu and macro creation, including DIESEL is included. Also includes information on ways to customize support files. ISBN: 1-56205-086-9.

_____ $39.95 _____

Maximizing AutoLISP. Learn ways to take advantage of AutoLISP, AutoCAD's built-in programming language. This comprehensive reference and tutorial explains every AutoLISP function. The text carefully introduces and explains programming concepts, and demonstrates those concepts with annotated sample programs. If you want to learn AutoLISP, you need this book. ISBN: 1-56205-085-0.

_____ $39.95 _____

AutoCAD Release 12: The Professional Reference, 2nd Edition. This reference offers detailed examples of how each command works, and its effect on other drawing entities. *AutoCAD: The Professional Reference* takes you beyond menus and commands to learn the inner workings of essential features used every day for drawing, editing, dimensioning, and plotting. Covers releases 11 and 12. ISBN: 1-56205-059-1.

_____ $42.95 _____

Name _____

Company _____

Address _____

City _____ State ____ ZIP _____

Phone _____ Fax _____

☐ Check Enclosed ☐ VISA ☐ MasterCard

Card #_____Exp. Date _____

Signature _____

Prices are subject to change. Call for availability and pricing information on latest editions.

Subtotal _____

Shipping _____

$4.00 for the first book and $1.75 for each additional book.

Total _____
Indiana residents add 5% sales tax.

New Riders Publishing 201 West 103rd Street • Indianapolis, Indiana 46290 USA

Orders/Customer Service: 1-800-541-6789
Fax: 1-800-448-3804